多複變會議

1984

SEVERAL COMPLEX VARIABLES

Proceedings of the 1981 Hangzhou Conference

J. J. Kohn
Q.-k. Lu
R. Remmert
Y.-T. Siu, editors

Editors:

J. J. Kohn
Department of Mathematics
Princeton University
Princeton, NJ 08544

R. Remmert
Mathematisches Institüt
der Universität
Einstein-strasse 64
D-4400 Münster, F.R.G.

Q.-k. Lu
Acadima Sinica
Beijing
China

Y.-T. Siu
Department of Mathematics
Harvard University
Cambridge, MA 02138

Library of Congress Cataloging in Publication Data

Several complex variables.

1. Functions of several complex variables— Congresses.
I. Kohn, Joseph John, 1932- .
QA331.S45 1984 515.9'4 84-6210
ISBN 0-8176-3189-5

CIP-Kurztitelaufnahme der Deutschen Bibliothek

Several complex variables : proceedings of the
1981 Hangzhou conference / J. J. Kohn ..., ed. -
Boston ; Basel ; Stuttgart : Birkhäuser, 1984.
ISBN 3-7643-3189-5 (Basel ...)
ISBN 0-8176-3189-5 (Boston)

NE: Kohn, Joseph J. [Hrsg.]

ISBN 0-8176-3189-5
ISBN 3-7643-3189-5
Printed in USA
9 8 7 6 5 4 3 2 1

TABLE OF CONTENTS

LIST OF SPEAKERS

Steven R. Bell Boundary behavior of holomorphic mappings

David Catlin Invariant metrics on pseudoconvex domains

Guang-xiao Chen Harmonic analysis on compact groups

Shu-jin Chen The integral representation of the domain of polyhedron in the space C^n

John P. D'Angelo Local bounds for orders of contact and a conjecture about subellipticity

Otto Forster Holomorphic vector bundles on tori

Paul Gerardin Geometrie des compactifications des espaces Hermitiens localement symetriques

I. R. Graham Removable singularities for holomorphic functions which satisfy the area-BMO condition

L. K. Hua On an ideal of ring of differential operators

Shoshichi Kobayashi Holomorphic projective structures and invariant distances

J. J. Kohn Microlocalization of CR structures

Ingo Lieb Integral formulae in complex analysis

Qi-keng Lu On the representative domain

Hing-Sun Luk A note on the boundary Laplace operator

Shigeo Nakano Some aspects of pseudoconvexity theory in several complex variables

Junjiro Noguchi A higher-dimensional analogue of Mordell's conjecture over function fields

John C. Polking The $\bar{\partial}$ Neumann kernel on the ball in C^n

Reinhold Remmert From domains in C^n to general complex spaces

Halsey Royden The Schwarz lemma in several complex variables

Michael Schneider Submanifolds of projective space with semi-stable normal bundles

Yum-Tong Siu Complex-analyticity of harmonic maps and vanishing theorems

Ji-huai Shi (joint work with Sheng Kung) Singular integrals in several complex variables

K. Stein Rank-complete function fields

Wilhelm Stoll The characterization of strictly parabolic spaces

Günther Trautmann Parameters for instanton bundles and smoothness of M(0,2)

Qi-ming Wang On real hypersurfaces in CP^n

Wen-tsün Wu Chern classes on algebraic varieties with arbitrary singularities

Y. L. Xin The characteristic numbers of 4-dimensional Kaehler manifolds

Yi-Chao Xu The invariant differential operators on N-Siegel domains

Hong-cang Yang (joint work with Zhi-hua Chen) On the Schwarz lemma for complete Hermitian manifolds

Lo Yang A general criterion

Stephen S.-T. Yau Complete invariants for isolated hypersurface singularities

Weiping Yin A remark on Poisson kernels

Qi-huang Yu Holomorphic maps and conformal transformation on Hermitian manifolds

Guang-hou Zhang Deficient values and asymptotic values of entire and meromorphic functions

Jia-qing Zhong The degree of strong nondegeneracy of the bisectional curvature of exceptional bounded symmetric domains

Tong-de Zhong Some applications of Bochner-Martinelli integral representation

LIST OF PARTICIPANTS

*Steven R. Bell, Department of Mathematics, Princeton University, Princeton, New Jersey 08544, U.S.A.

*David Catlin, Department of Mathematics, Princeton University, Princeton, New Jersey 08544, U.S.A.

Guang-xiao Chen, Institute of Applied Mathematics, Academia Sinica, Beijing, China.

Huaihui Chen,Institute of Mathematics, Academia Sinica, Beijing, China.

Jionxin Chen, Department of Mathematics, Xiamen University, Xiamen, China.

*Shujin Chen, Department of Mathematics, Xiamen Univerity, Xiamen, China.

Wanxi Chen, Department of Mathematics, University of Science and Technology of China, Hefei, Anhuei, China.

*Zhihua Chen,Institute of Mathematics, Academia Sinica, Beijing, China.

*John P. D'Angelo, Department of Mathematics, University of Illinois, Urbana, Illinois 61801, U.S.A.

*Otto Forster, Mathematisches Institut der Universität, Roxeler Strasse 64, D-4400 Münster, West Germany.

*Paul Gerardin, Universite Paris VII, U.E.R. de Mathematiques, Tour 45-55, 5me Etage, 2 Place Jussieu, 75221 Paris Cedex 05, France.

Sheng Gong, Department of Mathematics, University of Science and Technology of China, Hefei, Anhuei, China.

*Ian R. Graham, Department of Mathematics, University of Toronto, Toronto, Canada M5S 1A1.

Wenhua He, Department of Mathematics, Xiamen University, Xiamen, China.

Zu-qi He, Institute of Applied Mathematics, Academia Sinica, Beijing, China.

*L. K. Hua, Institute of Mathematics, Academia Sinica, Beijing, China.

*J. J. Kohn, Department of Mathematics, Princeton University, Princeton, New Jersey 08544, U.S.A.

*Ingo Lieb, Mathematisches Institut der Universität, Wegelerstrasse 10, D-5300 Bonn, West Germany..

Ruili Long,Institute of Mathematics, Academia Sinica, Beijing, China.

*Qi-keng Lu, Institute of Mathematics, Academia Sinica, Beijing, China.

Ruquian Lu,Institute of Mathematics, Academia Sinica, Beijing, China.

*Hing-Sun Luk, Department of Mathematics, Chinese University of Hong Kong, Shatin, Hong Kong

*S. Nakano, Research Institute for Mathematical Sciences, Kyoto University, Kitashirakawa, Sakyo-ku, Kyoto 606, Japan.

*J. Noguchi, Department of Mathematics, Tokyo Institute of Technology, Ookayama, Meguro, Tokyo 152, Japan

John C. Polking, Departement of Mathematics, Rice University, Houston, Texas 77001, U.S.A.

Reinhold Remmert, Mathematisches Institut der Universität, Roxeler Strasse 64, D-4400 Münster, West Germany.

Halsey L. Royden, Department of Mathematics, Stanford University, Stanford, California 94305, U.S.A.

*Michael Schneider, Mathematisches Institut der Universität Bayreuth, Universitätsstrasse 30, Postfach 3008, D-8580 Bayreuth, West Germany.

He Shi, Institute of System Science, Academia Sinica, Beijing, China.

*Jihuai Shi, Department of Mathematics, University of Science and Technology of China, Hefei, Anhuei, China.

*Yum-Tong Siu, Department of Mathematics, Stanford University, Stanford, California 94305, U.S.A.

Elias M. Stein, Department of Mathematics, Princeton University, Princeton, New Jersey 08544, U.S.A.

*Karl Stein, Mathematisches Institut der Universität, Theresienstrasse 39, D-8000 Müchen 2, West Germany.

*Wilhelm Stoll, Department of Mathematics, University of Notre Dame, Notre Dame, Indiana 46556, U.S.A.

*Günther Trautmann, Fachbereich Mathematik, Erwin-Schrödinger-Strasse, D-6750 Kaiserslautern, West Germany.

Qi-ming Wang,Institute of Mathematics, Academia Sinica, Beijing, China.

Shi-kun Wang, Institute of Applied Mathematics, Academia Sinica, Beijing, China.

Tao Wen, Department of Mathematics, Shandong University, Shandong, China.

Ke Wu, Institute of Theoretical Physics, Academia Sinica, Beijing, China.

*Wen-tsün Wu, Institute of System Science, Academia Sinica, Beijing, China.

*Y. L. Xin, Department of Mathematics, Fudan University, Shanghai, China.

Yi-chao Xu,Institute of Mathematics, Academia Sinica, Beijing, China.

*Hong-cong Yang,Institute of Mathematics, Academia Sinica, Beijing, China.

*Lo Yang, Institute of Mathematics, Academia Sinica, Beijing, China.

*Stephen S.-T. Yau, Department of Mathematics, University of Illinois at Chicago Circle, Chicago, Illinois 60680, U.S.A.

*Weiping Yin, Department of Mathematics, University of Science and Technology of China, Hefei, Anhuei, China.

*Qi-huang Yu, Institute of Applied Mathematics, Academia Sinica, Beijing, China.

Guanghou Zhang, Institute of Mathematics, Academia Sinica, Beijing, China.

Jinghao Zhang, Department of Mathematics, Fudan University, Shanghai, China.

*Jia-qing Zhong, Institute of Mathematics, Academia Sinica, Beijing, China.

*Tong-de Zhong, Department of Mathematics, Xiamen University, Xiamen, China.

---

*Contributors to this volume.

PREFACE

In recent years there has been increasing interaction among various branches of mathematics. This is especially evident in the theory of several complex variables where fruitful interplays of the methods of algebraic geometry, differential geometry, and partial differential equations have led to unexpected insights and new directions of research.

In China there has been a long tradition of study in complex analysis, differential geometry and differential equations as interrelated subjects due to the influence of Professors S. S. Chern and L. K. Hua. After a long period of isolation, in recent years there is a resurgence of scientific activity and a resumption of scientific exchange with other countries. The Hangzhou conference is the first international conference in several complex variables held in China. It offered a good opportunity for mathematicians from China, U.S., Germany, Japan, Canada, and France to meet and to discuss their work.

The papers presented in the conference encompass all major aspects of several complex variables, in particular, in such areas as complex differential geometry, integral representation, boundary behavior of holomorphic functions, invariant metrics, holomorphic vector bundles, and pseudoconvexity. Most of the participants wrote up their talks for these proceedings. Some of the papers are surveys and the others present original results. This volume constitutes an overview of the current trends of research in several complex variables.

We would like to thank Professors S. S. Chern and L. K. Hua and the Academia Sinica for their support of the conference and the officials of the City of Hangzhou and the Province of Zhejiang for their hospitality.

J. J. Kohn

Q.-k. Lu

R. Remmert

Y.-T. Siu

Section One

Methods of Partial Differential Equations

Several Complex Variables
Proceedings of the 1981 Hangzhou Conference

Boundary behavior of holomorphic mappings

Steven R. Bell
Princeton University
Princeton, New Jersey

Suppose that $f : D_1 \longrightarrow D_2$ is a proper holomorphic mapping between smooth bounded domains D_1 and D_2 contained in $\mathbb{C}^n$. There are two fundamental problems in the theory of functions of several complex variables concerning the boundary behavior of f.

Problem I : Does f extend smoothly to the boundary of D_1?

Problem II : Does f extend holomorphically past the boundary of D_1?

Problems I and II can be answered in the affirmative only in certain special cases in which the domains D_1 and D_2 have a particularly simple form. Before describing some of these cases, it is necessary to introduce some definitions and notations.

Boundary behavior of mappings between bounded domains is intimately connected to regularity properties of the Bergman projections of these domains. The Bergman projection P associated to a bounded domain D contained in $\mathbb{C}^n$ is the orthogonal projection of $L^2(D)$ onto its closed subspace $H(D)$ consisting of L^2 holomorphic functions on D. A smooth bounded domain D is said to satisfy *condition R* if the Bergman projection P associated to D maps $C^\infty(\bar{D})$ into $C^\infty(\bar{D})$. A bounded domain D is said to satisfy *condition Q1* if P maps $C_0^\infty(D)$ into $H(\bar{D})$, the space of holomorphic functions on D which extend to be holomorphic in a neighborhood of $\bar{D}$. The domain D is said to satisfy *condition Q2* if $H(\bar{D})$ is contained in $P(C_0^\infty(D))$.

We are now in a position to describe some of the known partial solutions to problems I and II. The results are stated in terms of conditions R, Q1, and Q2. Later in this note, we shall be more specific about what types of domains

Received 25 November, 1981

satisfy these conditions.

Theorem I : Suppose D_1 and D_2 are smooth bounded domains contained in $\mathbb{C}^n$, and suppose f is a proper holomorphic mapping of D_1 onto D_2. Then f extends smoothly to the boundary of D_1 whenever:

A) D_1 and D_2 both satisfy condition R and f is one to one ([1]), or

B) D_1 and D_2 are pseudoconvex and one of D_1 or D_2 satisfy condition R and f is one to one ([3]), or

C) D_1 and D_2 are pseudoconvex and one of D_1 or D_2 satisfy condition R and f is unbranched ([7]), or

D) the conditions of Theorem II below are met.

Theorem II : ([4]) If $f : D_1 \longrightarrow D_2$ is a proper holomorphic mapping between bounded domains in $\mathbb{C}^n$, and if D_1 satisfies condition Q1 and D_2 satisfies condition Q2, then f extends holomorphically to a neighborhood of $\overline{D}_1$

The remainder of this note will be devoted to describing certain classes of domains which satisfy conditions R, Q1, or Q2.

Condition R is known to hold for a wide variety of domains. For example, smooth bounded strictly pseudoconvex domains satisfy condition R (Kohn [9]). When this fact is combined with Theorem I, part (A), the original theorem of Fefferman [8] is obtained on boundary regularity of biholomorphic mappings between strictly pseudoconvex domains. Another important class of domains for which condition R is known to hold is the class of smooth bounded pseudoconvex domains with real analytic boundaries (Kohn [10], Diederich and Fornaess [6]). Smooth bounded Reinhardt domains which contain the origin are also known to satisfy condition R (Bell and Boas [2]).

Condition Q2 holds in any smooth bounded domain with real analytic boundary ([4]), and in any bounded complete Reinhardt domain.

Condition Q1 holds in bounded complete Reinhardt domains and in any smooth bounded pseudoconvex domain with real analytic boundary for which the $\bar{\partial}$-Neumann problem is globally analytic hypoelliptic. The $\bar{\partial}$-Neumann problem is known to be globally analytic hypoelliptic in smooth bounded strictly pseudoconvex domains with real analytic boundaries (Derridj and Tartakoff [5], Komatsu [11], Tartakoff [4], Trèves [13]).

There is not an adequate proof in [4] of the fact that global analytic hypoellipticity of the $\bar{\partial}$-Neumann problem implies that condition Q1 holds. Therefore, we conclude this note by proving this result in detail.

Assume that the $\bar{\partial}$-Neumann problem associated to a smooth bounded domain D with real analytic boundary is globally analytic hypoelliptic. This means that for every $\bar{\partial}$-closed (0,1) form α which is real analytic in a neighborhood of $\bar{D}$, the solution $\Lambda\alpha$ to the problem

$$\begin{cases} \bar{\partial}\Lambda\alpha = \alpha \\ \Lambda\alpha \quad \text{orthogonal to} \quad H(D) \end{cases}$$

is also real analytic in a neighborhood of $\bar{D}$. The Bergman projection P associated to D can be written $P = I - \Lambda\bar{\partial}$. In the language of the $\bar{\partial}$-Neumann theory ([9,10]), $\Lambda = \bar{\partial}^* N$ where N is the $\bar{\partial}$-Neumann operator. The formula $P = I - \Lambda\bar{\partial}$ is the familiar Kohn formula for the Bergman projection.

Suppose that ϕ is a function in $C_0^\infty(D)$. We wish to show that $P\phi$ extends to be holomorphic in a neighborhood of $\bar{D}$. Let Π denote the orthogonal projection of $L^2(D)$ onto its subspace consisting of L^2 harmonic functions. The projection Π can be written $\Pi = I - \Delta G\Delta$ where G is the solution operator to the problem:

$$\begin{cases} \Delta^2 Gv = v \\ Gv = 0 \quad \text{and} \quad \nabla Gv = 0 \quad \text{on} \quad bD. \end{cases}$$

It is not hard to verify that $P\Pi = P$. Now $\Pi\phi$ is harmonic in a neighborhood of $\bar{D}$ because G is locally analytic hypoelliptic. Finally, $P\phi = P\Pi\phi$ is holomorphic in a neighborhood of $\bar{D}$ because Λ is globally analtic hypoelliptic.

REFERENCES

(1) S. Bell and E. Ligocka, *A simplification and extension of Fefferman's theorem on biholomorphic mappings*, Invent. Math. 57 (1980), 283-289.

(2) S. Bell and H. Boas, *Regularity of the Bergman projection in weakly pseudoconvex domains*, Math. Ann. 257 (1981), 23-30.

(3) S. Bell, *Biholomorphic mappings and the $\bar{\partial}$-problem*, Ann. of Math. 114 (1981), 103-113.

(4) _______, *Analytic hypoellipticity of the $\bar{\partial}$-Neumann problem and extendability of holomorphic mappings*, Acta Math. 147 (1981), 109-116.

(5) M. Derridj and D. Tartakoff, *On the global real analyticity of solutions to the $\bar{\partial}$-Neumann problem*, Comm. Partial Diff. Eqns. 1 (1976), 401-435.

(6) K. Diederich and J. E. Fornaess, *Pseudoconvex domains with real analytic boundary*, Ann. of Math. 107 (1978), 371-384.

(7) ___________, *A remark on a paper of S. R. Bell*, Manuscripta Math. 34 (1981), 31-44.

(8) C. Fefferman, *The Bergman kernel and biholomorphic mappings of pseudoconvex domains*, Invent. Math. 26 (1974), 1-65.

(9) J. J. Kohn, *Harmonic integrals on strongly pseudoconvex manifolds, I and II*, Ann. of Math. 78 (1963), 112-148 and 79 (1964), 450-472.

(10) _________, *Subellipticity of the $\bar{\partial}$-Neumann problem on pseudoconvex domains: sufficient conditions*, Acta Math. 142 (1979), 79-122.

(11) G. Komatsu, *Global analytic hypoellipticity of the $\bar{\partial}$-Neumann problem*, Tôhoku Math. J. Ser. 2, 28 (1976), 145-156.

(12) D. Tartakoff, *The local real analyticity of solutions to $\square_b$ and the $\bar{\partial}$-Neumann problem*, Acta Math. 145 (1980), 177-204.

(13) F. Trèves, *Analytic hypo-ellipticity of a class of pseudodifferential operators with double characteristics and applications to the $\bar{\partial}$-Neumann problem*, Comm. Partial Diff. Eqns. 3 (1978), 475-642.

Mathematics Department
Princeton University
Princeton, New Jersey 08544
U. S. A.

Several Complex Variables
Proceedings of the 1981 Hangzhou Conference

Invariant metrics on pseudoconvex domains

by

David W. Catlin

Let Ω be a bounded domain in $\mathbb{C}^n$. Each of the metrics of Bergman, Caratheodory, and Kobayashi assigns a positive number to a given non-zero tangent vector X above a point z in Ω. This assignment is invariant in the sense that if f is a biholomorphism of Ω onto another bounded domain Ω', then the metric applied to X equals the value of the metric on Ω' applied to the tangent vector $df(X)$ at the point $f(z)$. Although it is very difficult to calculate the precise value of the above metrics in all but a few special cases, it is sometimes possible to compute a formula for the asymptotic behavior of the metric as the point z approaches the boundary of Ω. When Ω is a smoothly bounded strongly pseudoconvex domain, asymptotic formulas for the Bergman metric were obtained by Diederich [3] and later in much more precise form by Fefferman [4]. Formulas for the asymptotic behavior of the Caratheodory and Kobayashi metric on the same domains were obtained by Graham [5]. In this note we shall consider the case of pseudoconvex domains of finite type in $\mathbb{C}^2$. Instead of determining an asymptotic formula for the above metrics, we obtain only a formula that expresses the approximate size of the metrics. In a sense which we shall make precise, these metrics are all equivalent for the given class of domains. We also obtain a formula for the approximate size of the Bergman kernel $K(z,\bar{z})$ of the domain Ω.

Received 14 November, 1982

First we give the definition of each of the above metrics. Let z be a point of a bounded domain Ω in $\mathbb{C}^n$ and let X be a tangent vector of type $(1,0)$ at the point z. Denote the set of holomorphic functions on Ω by $A(\Omega)$. The Caratheodory metric [7] $F_C(z;X)$ is defined by

$$F_C(z;X) = \sup\{|Xf|;\ f \in A(\Omega) \text{ and } \|f\|_{L^\infty(\Omega)} \le 1\}$$

The Bergman kernel $K(z,\bar{z})$ and the Bergman metric $ds(z;x)$ [1] are defined by

$$K(z,\bar{z}) = \sup\{|f(z)|^2;\ f \in A(\Omega) \text{ and } \|f\|_{L^2(\Omega)} \le 1\}$$

$$b(z;X) = \sup\{|X(f)|;\ f \in A(\Omega),\ f(z) = 0, \text{ and } \|f\|_{L^2(\Omega)} \le 1\}$$

$$ds(z,X) = b(z;X)/(K(z,z))^{1/2}.$$

Let D_r denote the disc of radius r in $\mathbb{C}$. The Kobayashi metric is given by

$$F_K(z;X) = \inf\{\tfrac{1}{r};\ \text{there exists holomorphic map } f:D_r \longrightarrow \Omega.$$
$$\text{with } f(0) = z \text{ and } df(\tfrac{\partial}{\partial z}\big|_0) = X\}.$$

We now briefly describe the definition of finite type [2,8] in $\mathbb{C}^2$. Let Ω be a smoothly bounded domain in $\mathbb{C}^2$. Thus there is a smooth real-valued function r defined in $\mathbb{C}^2$ such that $\Omega = \{z;r(z)<0\}$ and $dr(z) \neq 0$ whenever $r(z) = 0$. We define two vector fields L_1 and L_2 by

$L_1 = \frac{\partial r}{\partial z_2}\frac{\partial}{\partial z_1} - \frac{\partial r}{\partial z_1}\frac{\partial}{\partial z_2}$ and $L_2 = \frac{\partial r}{\partial \bar{z}_1}\frac{\partial}{\partial z_1} + \frac{\partial r}{\partial \bar{z}_2}\frac{\partial}{\partial z_2}$. Thus the vector fields L_1 and L_2 are respectively tangent and transverse to the boundary of Ω . For all $z \in \bar{\Omega}$, we define the Levi function $\lambda(z)$ by $\lambda(z) = \partial r([L_1,\bar{L}_1])(z)$. A point z in the boundary of Ω is said to be of type m $(m \geq 2)$ if

(1) there exist vector fields $L^1,\ldots,L^{m-2}$, with $L^i = L_1$ or $\bar{L}_1$, such that $L^1 \ldots L^{m-2}\lambda(z) \neq 0$; and

(2) for all k , $2 \leq k < m$, if $L^i = L_1$ or $\bar{L}_1$, then $L^1 \ldots L^{k-2}\lambda(z) = 0$.

Thus the boundary of Ω is strongly pseudoconvex at z if and only if $\lambda(z) > 0$. It is easy to see that the type of a given point z must be an even integer if the boundary of Ω is pseudoconvex near z . An example of a point of type $2m$ $(m \geq 1)$ is given by the origin in the domain $\Omega' = \{z = (z_1,z_2);\ \mathrm{Re}\ z_2 + |z_1|^{2m} < 0\}$

We can now define the formula for the approximate size of the above metrics. Define functions $C_k(z)$ by $C_k(z) = (L_1\bar{L}_1)^{k-1}\lambda(z)$. It is not difficult to show that when Ω is pseudoconvex near a point z in the boundary, then z is of type $2m$ if and only if $C_m(z) \neq 0$ and $C_k(z) = 0$ for all $k, 1 \leq k < m$. Now let $X = a_1L_1 + a_2L_2$ be a tangent vector of type $(1,0)$ at a point z in Ω . Define $M_m(z;X)$ by

$$M_m(z;X) = |a_2|\ |r(z)|^{-1} + |a_1| \sum_{k=1}^{m} |C_k(z)|^{\frac{1}{2k}} |r(z)|^{-\frac{1}{2k}} .$$

We can state the theorem as follows:

<u>Theorem</u>. Let Ω be a smoothly bounded domain in $\mathbb{C}^2$. Let z_0 be a given point in the boundary of Ω, and assume that z_0 is of type $2m$. Then there exist a neighborhood U about z_0 and positive constants C and c such that for every tangent vector $X = a_1L_1 + a_2L_2$ at a point $z \in U \cap \Omega$,

(1) $cM_m(z;X) \le ds(z;X) \le CM_m(z;X)$

(2) $cM_m(z;X) \le F_C(z;X) \le CM_m(z;X)$

(3) $cM_m(z;X) \le F_K(z;X) \le CM_m(z;X)$.

Also, for all $z \in U \cap \Omega$, the Bergman kernel satisfies

(4) $cK(z,\bar{z}) \le |r(z)|^{-2} \sum_{k=1}^{m} |C_k(z)|^{\frac{1}{k}}\ |r(z)|^{-\frac{1}{k}} \le CK(z,\bar{z})$.

The proof of the above theorem is a careful application of the method of weighted L^2-estimates for $\bar{\partial}$ used in [6] to prove the Oka-Weil approximation theorem. In fact, one can define regions in the domain Ω that are approximately equal to the unit ball of the above metric $M_m(z;X)$. Since each of these regions B is biholomorphic to a polydisc, it is easy to calculate any of the invariant quantities associated with these regions. For the Bergman kernel, for example, there is holomorphic function f with

$\|f\|^2_{L^2(B)} \le 1$ that maximizes the value of $|f(z)|^2$, where z is the point in the region corresponding to the center of the polydisc.

By using the $\bar{\partial}$-estimates, we can apply a precise form of the Oka-Weil theorem and conclude that there is a holomorphic function $\tilde{f}$ on Ω with $\|\tilde{f}\|^2_{L^2(\Omega)} \le C^2$ and $|\tilde{f}(z) - f(z)|^2 \le \frac{1}{4}$. Here C is a universal constant, independent of z and f. This implies that

$$K_\Omega(z,\bar{z}) \ge \frac{1}{C^2} |\tilde{f}|^2 \ge \frac{1}{4C^2} |f(z)|^2 .$$

Finally since z corresponds to the center of the polydisc, it is easy to show that $|f(z)|^2$ equals the inverse of the volume of the polydisc, which in turn is approximately equal to the inverse of the volume of the region B. In this way one obtains a lower found for the Bergman kernel.

Since the corresponding upper bound is trivial, we conclude that the Bergman kernel is approximately equal to the inverse of the volume of the unit ball of the metric M_m, which gives (4). Similar reasoning applies to the other invariant quantities. We should point out that many of the above concepts are closely related to the boundary metric constructed by Nagel, Stein, and Wainger [9].

References

1. S. Bergman, The kernel function and conformal mapping, Math. Surveys, V. 2nd ed., Providence, 1970.

2. T. Bloom and I. Graham, A geometric characterization of points of type m on real submanifolds of $\mathbb{C}^n$, J. of Diff. Geometry 12 (1977), 171-182.

3. K. Diederich, Das Randverhalten der Bergmanschen Kernfunktion und Metrik in Streng pseudo-konvexen Gebieten, Math. Ann. 187 (1970), 9-36.

4. C. Fefferman, The Bergman kernel and biholomorphic mappings of pseudoconvex domains, Inventiones Math. (1974), 1-65.

5. I. Graham, The boundary behavior of the Caratheodory and Kobayashi metrics on strictly pseudoconvex domains in $\mathbb{C}^n$ with smooth boundary, Ph.D. dissertation, Princeton Univ., 1973.

6. L. Hörmander, Introduction to complex analysis in several variables, Van Nostrand, 1966.

7. S. Kobayashi, Hyperbolic manifolds and holomorphic mappings, Marcel Dekker, 1970.

8. J.J. Kohn, Boundary behavior of $\bar\partial$ on weakly pseudoconvex manifolds of dimension two, J. Diff. Geometry 6 (1972), 523-542.

9. A. Nagel, E.M. Stein, and S. Wainger, Proc. Nat'l. Acad. Sci., U.S.A., Vol. 78, pp. 6596-6599, 1981.

LOCAL BOUNDS FOR ORDERS OF CONTACT AND A CONJECTURE ABOUT SUBELLIPTICITY

John P. D'Angelo

University of Illinois
Urbana, Illinois, USA

This work describes the local geometry of a real hypersurface of $\mathbb{C}^n$, and how it relates to subelliptic estimates for the $\bar{\partial}$-Neumann problem. The geometric results appear in (3,5); the results on subellipticity appear in the works of Kohn (7,8) and Catlin (1,2). In this paper we formulate a conjecture about the interplay between these subjects.

Suppose that Ω is an open domain in $\mathbb{C}^n$ with smooth boundary M. The results on order of contact of complex analytic varieties with M do not require pseudoconvexity; the results on the $\bar{\partial}$-Neumann problem assume that Ω is bounded and pseudoconvex. We begin with a summary of results on subellipticity.

1. Definition of subelliptic estimates.

Let Ω be bounded and pseudoconvex. Suppose that p_o is a point in M. We say that the $\bar{\partial}$-Neumann problem is ε-subelliptic on $(0,q)$ forms if there are positive constants C and ε such that

$$*_q \qquad \|u\|_\varepsilon^2 \leq C(\|\bar{\partial}u\|^2 + \|\bar{\partial}^*u\|^2 + \|u\|^2)$$

whenever u is a smooth $(0,q)$ form supported near p_o and in the domain of $\bar{\partial}^*$. The norm $\| \ \|_\varepsilon$ denotes the tangential Sobolev ε-norm; the other norms are L_2 norms.

Received 21 October, 1981

2. Theorem (Kohn). Suppose that M is a real analytic manifold near p_o, and that there is no germ of a complex analytic q dimensional variety at p_o that lies in M. Then $*_q$ holds for some positive epsilon.

3. Theorem (Kohn, Greiner, Rothschild-Stein). Suppose that q equals $n - 1$. The following are equivalent:

3.1. The maximum order of tangency of complex analytic q dimensional manifolds with M at p_o is the number m.

3.2. $*_q$ holds with ε equal to $1/m$, but for no larger ε.

4. Theorem (Catlin). Suppose that r is a local defining function for M near p_o, and that there is a complex analytic variety V, and constants c and β, so that

$$|r(z)| \leq c|z - p_o|^{\beta} \quad \text{for all } z \text{ in } V.$$

Then, if $*_q$ holds, we must have $\varepsilon \leq 1/\beta$.

Theorem 2 above gives sufficient conditions for some subelliptic estimate; Theorems 3 and 4 give necessary conditions for a subelliptic estimate with a particular value of epsilon. By Catlin's theorem, we see that the maximum "order of contact" of q dimensional complex analytic varieties with M at p_o gives a lower bound for the reciprocal of epsilon. D'Angelo showed in (4) that equality fails in general. Examples of this behavior follow immediately from a precise study of the notion of order of contact; we now proceed to outline this theory. For simplicity of exposition, we restrict to the most important case; namely, the maximum order of contact of complex analytic one dimensional varieties with M at p_o.

5. Notations and Definitions.

5.1. $Cur(p)$ denotes the set of all germs of non-constant holomorphic maps z, such that $z : (\mathbb{C},0) \to (\mathbb{C}^n,p)$.

5.2. A_p denotes the ring of germs of holomorphic functions at p.

5.3. C_p^∞ denotes the ring of germs of smooth real valued functions at p.

5.4. Let g be an element of any of the above. $o_p(g) = o(g)$ denotes the order of vanishing of the function $g - g(p)$ at the point p. We usually drop the subscript p.

5.5. Let J be an ideal in A_p or C_p^∞. We define the invariant $T(J)$, called the order of contact of J, by

$$T(J) = \sup \inf o(z^*g)/o(z).$$

Here the sup is taken over all z in $Cur(p)$, the inf is taken over all g in J, and z^*g denotes the pullback, or restriction, of g to the image of z.

5.6. Let J be an ideal as above. We write j_kJ for the ideal generated by the k-th order Taylor polynomials of elements of J.

6. Definition of maximum order of contact of complex analytic curves with M at p.

We write $\Delta(M,p)$ for this number.

$$\Delta(M,p) = T(J_p(M)).$$

Here $J_p(M)$ denotes the ideal in C_p^∞ of germs of functions that vanish on M. In terms of a local defining function r for M, we have $J_p(M) = (r)$. We also consider the hypersurface M_k defined by j_kr; thus $J_p(M_k) = j_k(J_0(M))$.

We now state three theorems about this function $\Delta(M,p)$. All these results appear in (5).

7. Theorem. $\Delta(M,p)$ is finite if and only if there is an integer k so that $\Delta(M_k p) \leq k$. This is also equivalent to $\Delta(M_k,p)$ being eventually constant (and finite) as a function of k.

8. Theorem. Suppose that M is an algebraic real hypersurface, and that r is a polynomial defining function for M. For each p in M, there are holomorphic polynomials (depending on p) $h,f_1,\ldots,f_N,g_1,\ldots,g_N$, all vanishing at p, such that

$$(8.1) \qquad r(z,\bar{z}) = 2\mathrm{Re}(h(z)) + \Sigma|f_k(z)|^2 - \Sigma|g_k(z)|^2.$$

Let $I(U,p)$ denote the ideal in A_p generated by h and the components of $f - Ug$, where U is a unitary matrix of constants. We have the following estimate for $\Delta(M,p)$.

$$\sup_U T(I(U,p)) \leq \Delta(M,p) \leq 2 \sup_U T(I(U,p)).$$

9. Theorem. Let M be any smooth hypersurface, and let p_o lie in M. Suppose that $\Delta(M,p_o)$ is finite. Then there is a neghborhood of p_o on which

$$9.1. \qquad \Delta(M,p) \leq 2(\Delta(M,p_o))^{n-1}.$$

Furthermore, if M is pseudoconvex near p_o, we have

$$9.2. \qquad \Delta(M,p) \leq (\Delta(M,p_o))^{n-1}/2^{n-2}.$$

Remarks on the proof of Theorem 9. Theorems 7 and 8 can be used to reduce the calculation of $\Delta(M,p)$ to that of $\Delta(M_k,p)$ and hence to that of $T(I(U,p))$. Unfortunately the invariant T does not depend on an upper semicontinuous fashion with respect to the parameters involved. To pass to nearby points, we replace $T(I(U,p))$ by $D(I(U,p))$, where $D(J)$ denotes the vector space dimension of A_p/J. D is upper semicontinuous, and we have the estimate

10. $T(J) \leq D(J) \leq (T(J))^{n-q}$ if J contains q independent linear forms.

By using 10 and the upper semicontinuity of D, we obtain the estimates 9.1 and 9.2. Furthermore examples in (3,5) show that the estimate in the pseudoconvex case is sharp.

An analysis of the work of Kohn on subellipticity reveals that his constructions work in full neighborhoods. Therefore it is reasonable to conjecture that any geometric data implying sharp subelliptic estimates must be upper semicontinuous. This observation and Theorems 3, 4, and 9 form the basis for the following conjecture:

11. Conjecture. Let M be a smooth, real hypersurface that bounds a bounded, pseudoconvex domain in $\mathbb{C}^n$. Suppose that p lies in M, and that $\Delta(M,p)$ is finite. Then the $\bar{\partial}$-Neumann problem is ε-subelliptic at p, i.e. *1 holds at p. Also

11.1. $\Delta(M,p) \leq 1/\varepsilon \leq (\Delta(M,p))^{n-1}/2^{n-2}$.

<u>12. Remarks</u>. If n equals two, 11.1 holds by Theorem 3. The first inequality in 11.1 always holds by Catlin's Theorem 4. Also, although this conjecture was first explicitly formulated by the author at the international conference in Hangzhou, it is a natural outgrowth of discussions held with D. Catlin in the summer of 1981. Finally the author believes that analogous results hold for the maximum order of contact of q dimensional varieties with M at p.

References

(1) D. Catlin, "Necessary conditions for subellipticity and hypoellipticity of the $\bar{\partial}$-Neumann problem on pseudoconvex domains," <u>Recent Developments in Several Complex Variables</u>, Princeton Univ. Press, 1981.

(2) ________, "Necessary conditions for subellipticity of the $\bar{\partial}$-Neumann problem," (preprint).

(3) J. D'Angelo, "Sharp local bounds for orders of contact," Proc. Nat. Acad. Sci. USA 78(1981), 3998-3999.

(4) ___________, "Subelliptic estimates and failure of semi continuity for orders of contact," Duke Math. J. 47(1980), 955-957.

(5) ___________, "Real hypersurfaces, orders of contact, and applications," Annals of Math. (to appear).

(6) P. Greiner, "On subelliptic estimates of the $\bar{\partial}$-Neumann problem," J. Differential Geometry 9(1974), 239-250.

(7) J. Kohn, "Boundary behavior of $\bar{\partial}$ on weakly pseudoconvex manifolds of dimension two," J. Differential Geometry 6(1972), 523-542.

(8) _______, "Subellipticity of the $\bar{\partial}$-Neumann problem on pseudoconvex domains: sufficient conditions," Acta Math. 142(1979), 79-122.

(9) L. Rothschild and E. Stein, "Hypoelliptic differential operators and nilpotent Lie groups," Acta Math. 137(1976), 247-320.

Several Complex Variables
Proceedings of the 1981 Hangzhou Conference

ON AN IDEAL OF RING OF DIFFERENTIAL OPERATORS

L.K. Hua

In the study of harmonic analysis of several complex variables in classical domains, we have noted a peculiar phenomenon related to the Laplace-Beltrami operator and a matrix operator, which gives rise to a new result in the theory of rings of differential operators.

Let

$$(1) \qquad \Omega = \sum_{i,j}\sum_{\alpha,\beta}(\delta_{ij}-\sum_{\gamma}\bar{z}_{i\gamma}z_{j\gamma})(\delta_{\alpha\beta}-\sum_{k}\bar{z}_{k}\,z_{k\beta})\frac{\partial^2}{\partial\bar{z}_{i\alpha}\partial z_{j\beta}}$$

be a differential operator, where we omit the limits of summation and subscripts i,j,α,β, run from 1 to n. It can "break" as follows:

$$(2) \qquad \Omega = \sum_{i,j}(\delta_{ij}-\sum_{\gamma}\bar{z}_{i\gamma}z_{j\gamma})A_{ij},$$

where

$$(3) \qquad A_{ij} = \sum_{\alpha,\beta}(\delta_{\alpha\beta}-\sum_{k}\bar{z}_{k\alpha}z_{k\beta})\frac{\partial^2}{\partial\bar{z}_{i\alpha}\partial z_{j\beta}}$$

which are n^2 operators.

It was proved by the author [1],[2] that in the domain $\mathfrak{D}$ formed by all $n\times n$ complex matrices $Z = (z_{ij})_{1\le i,j\le n}$ with $1-Z\bar{Z}' > 0$, every function u satisfying

$$(4) \qquad \Omega u = 0$$

Received 30 April 1983

satisfies also

$$(5) \qquad \mathfrak{A}_{ij}\, u = 0$$

which are n independent equations.

Let us introduce the following

<u>Definition</u>. Let Λ be a linear differential operator in a certain domain D. If Λ can "break" (in the sense above) into a sum of ℓ independent operators and no more, we define ℓ to be the arithmetic invariant of the operator Λ.

The previous consideration asserts that the arithmetic invariant of Ω in $\mathfrak{D}$ is $\geq n^2$. It is easy to prove that for a differential operator with constant coefficients, the arithmetic invariant equals 1, i.e., this "break" phenomenon does not happen to the partial differential operators with constant coefficients.

A step further, we can prove that any differential operator Λ of the second order satisfying $\Lambda u = 0$ for all u with $\Omega u = 0$ is just a linear combination of $\mathfrak{A}_{ij}$ and

$$(6) \qquad \mathfrak{B}_{\alpha\beta} = \sum_{\substack{i,j \\ 1\leq\alpha,\beta\leq n}} (\delta_{ij} - \sum_i \bar{z}_{i\alpha} z_{i\beta}) \frac{\partial^2}{\partial \bar{z}_{i\alpha} \partial z_{j\beta}} ,$$

with functions in z_{ij}, $\bar{z}_{ij}$ as coefficients.

More generally, in 1963 the author suggested the following idea [4].

Let us start with a field of C^∞ functions of m variables in a domain, global or bounded or local. The aggregate of all differential operators forms a non-commutative ring $\mathfrak{O}$ of polynomials in m variables $\partial_i = \frac{\partial}{\partial x_i}$, $1 \leq i \leq m$. The operations of ring are understood as usual, so this ring is neither commutative nor associative.

Let

(7) $$\Omega_1, \Omega_2, \cdots, \Omega_s$$

be a set of operators. The set of functions u satisfying

(8) $$\Omega_1 u = 0, \quad \Omega_2 u = 0, \cdots, \Omega_s u = 0$$

is denoted by $\mathfrak{F}(\Omega_1, \cdots, \Omega_s)$. Analogous to algebraic geometry, we say that all these u's form a functional variety which is a generalization of algebraic variety. Those operators Λ satisfying

(9) $$\Lambda u = 0$$

for all u belonging to $\mathfrak{F}(\Omega_1, \cdots, \Omega_s)$ form a left ideal $\mathfrak{a}$ of the ring $\mathfrak{O}$. If there exist $\Lambda_1, \cdots, \Lambda_r$ in $\mathfrak{a}$ such that every element of $\mathfrak{a}$ can be expressed as

(10) $$M_1\Lambda_1 + M_2\Lambda_2 + \cdots + M_r\Lambda_r, \quad M_i \in \mathfrak{O}, \ 1 \leq i \leq r$$

and r is the smallest integer with this property, then we say that $\Lambda_1, \cdots, \Lambda_r$ form a basis of $\mathfrak{a}$. (The existence can be proved by well-known argument.) In particular, when

$\Omega_1,\cdots,\Omega_s$ itself form a basis of $\mathfrak{a}$, $\mathfrak{a}$ is called the prime (left) ideal.

In this note we state the following result.

Theorem. The ideal $\mathfrak{a}$ derived from Ω $(s = 1)$ given in (1) has a basis A_{ij} of n^2 elements.

This is a phenomenon different from that of algebraic geometry, for in the latter case an ideal generated by a quadratic function

$$f(x) = \sum_{i,j=1}^{n} a_{ij}x_ix_j + \sum b_ix_i + c, \qquad a_{ij} = a_{ji}$$

is always a principal ideal $\mathfrak{a} = (f(x))$, i.e., every element of $\mathfrak{a}$ is divisible by $f(x)$.

Note that the Hilbert Nullstellensatz holds for the ring of operators with constant coefficients [4], but it does not hold for the non-commutative ring which we consider here. A counterexample is this: A_{11}^{ℓ} does not belong to (Ω) for any integer ℓ, where (Ω) means the ideal $\mathfrak{a}$ derived from Ω as before.

For the proof of the Theorem we need an algebraic theorem. First we introduce the following

Definition. Let $W = (w_{ij})_{1\leq i,j\leq n}$ be a complex $n\times n$ matrix and $F(W)$ be a ring of polynomials $f(W)$ in $2n^2$ variables $w_{ij},\bar{w}_{ij}$, $1 \leq i,j \leq n$. By a unitary ideal we mean the ideal consisting of all f satisfying

$$f(U) = 0 \tag{11}$$

for all unitary U.

Then we have

<u>Lemma</u>. The following set of n^2 elements is a basis for the unitary ideal defined above:

$$(12) \qquad \delta_{ij} - \sum_{\gamma} \bar{w}_{i\gamma} w_{j\gamma}, \qquad 1 \leq i,j \leq n.$$

The Lemma is an extension of a result of H. Weyl [3]. In his book, "The classical groups", p. 142, we read that any polynomial of n real variables x_{ij}, $1 \leq i,j \leq n$, which vanishes for x_{ij} forming an orthogonal matrix can be expressed as a linear combination of n(n+1) polynomials

$$(13) \qquad \delta_{ij} - \sum_{\alpha} x_{i\alpha} x_{j\alpha}, \qquad \delta_{\alpha\beta} - \sum_{i} x_{i\alpha} x_{i\beta}$$

with polynomial coefficients (with a restricted degree).

Recently we found a straightforward proof different from his. We established a general theorem, which has as consequence the following: the orthogonal ideal has a basis of $\frac{1}{2}n(n+1)$ elements and the unitary ideal has a basis given in the Lemma above.

Now we explain the proof of the Theorem. We use the matrix notation for operation and list the well-known facts from [1] and [2].

The domain $\mathfrak{D} = \{Z = Z^{(n)} \mid 1 - Z\bar{Z}' > 0\}$ has the following transitive group action:

$$(14) \qquad W = (AZ+B)(CZ+D)^{-1} = (Z\bar{B}'+\bar{A}')^{-1}(Z\bar{D}'+\bar{C}')$$

where A,B,C,D are n-rowed matrices satisfying

$$(15)\qquad \begin{pmatrix} A & B \\ C & D \end{pmatrix}\begin{pmatrix} I & O \\ O & -I \end{pmatrix}\overline{\begin{pmatrix} A & B \\ C & D \end{pmatrix}}' = \begin{pmatrix} I & O \\ O & -I \end{pmatrix}.$$

For this group we have

$$(16)\qquad \begin{aligned} dW &= (Z\overline{B}'+\overline{A}')^{-1} dZ (CZ+D)^{-1}, \\ \partial_Z' &= (CZ+D)^{-1} \partial_W' (Z\overline{B}'+\overline{A}')^{-1}, \\ &(I-W\overline{W}')\overline{\partial}_W (I-\overline{W}'W)\, \partial_W' \\ &\quad = (Z\overline{B}'+\overline{A}')^{-1} (I-Z\overline{Z}')\overline{\partial}_Z (I-\overline{Z}'Z)\, \partial_Z' (Z\overline{B}'+\overline{A}'), \end{aligned}$$

where

$$\partial_Z = \begin{pmatrix} \frac{\partial}{\partial t_{11}} & \cdots & \frac{\partial}{\partial z_{1n}} \\ \cdots & \cdots & \cdots \\ \frac{\partial}{\partial z_{n1}} & \cdots & \frac{\partial}{\partial z_{nn}} \end{pmatrix}, \qquad \overline{\partial}_Z = \partial_{\overline{Z}}.$$

Hence

$$(17)\qquad \Omega = \operatorname{tr}[(I-Z\overline{Z}')\overline{\partial}_Z (I-\overline{Z}'Z)\, \partial_Z']$$

is a differential operator invariant under (14), i.e., the operator given in (1).

The functional variety $\mathfrak{F}(\Omega)$ defined by Ω is given by the Poisson integral

$$(18) \qquad u(Z) = \frac{1}{\omega_n} \int_{\mathfrak{U}} P(Z,U)\varphi(U)\dot{U} ,$$

where

$$(19) \qquad P(Z,U) = \frac{\det(I-Z\overline{Z}')^n}{\det(I-Z\overline{U}')^n \cdot \det(I-U\overline{Z}')^n}$$

is the Poisson kernel annihilated by Ω, $\mathfrak{U}$ is a manifold of unitary group whose volume is ω_n.

Thus $\mathfrak{F}(\Omega)$ has a kernel $P(Z,U)$, i.e. an operator Λ satisfying

$$(20) \qquad \Lambda P(Z,U) = 0 \qquad\qquad (\text{or } \Lambda P(Z,W)\big|_{W\overline{W}'=I} = 0).$$

This implies that

$$(21) \qquad \Lambda u = 0$$

for any u in $\mathfrak{F}(\Omega)$. Thus the (left) ideal $\mathfrak{a}$ consists of those Λ satisfying (20).

Let us write transformation (14) in explicit form

$$(22) \qquad Z = Q(Z_1-T)(I-\overline{T}'Z_1)^{-1}R^{-1}$$

$$(23) \qquad Q(I-T\overline{T}')\overline{Q}' = I, \qquad R(I-\overline{T}'T)\overline{R}' = I$$

which carries (any) point $Z = T$ in $\mathfrak{D}$ into $Z = 0$. Then the corresponding transformation for Poisson function (for any complex matrix W) is

$$(24) \qquad P(Z,W) = P(Z_1,W_1)\det(I-\bar{T}'T)^{-n}\left|\det(I-\bar{T}'W_1)\right|^{2n}$$

where W and W_1 are related in (22).

It is also easy to verify that

$$(25) \qquad \bar{\partial}_{Z_1}(I-\bar{Z}'Z_1)\,\partial'_Z\, P(Z,W)\Big|_{W\bar{W}'=I} = 0$$

and

$$(26) \qquad \bar{\partial}_Z\,\partial'_Z\Big|_{Z=0} = (I-Z\bar{Z}')\bar{\partial}_Z(I-\bar{Z}'Z)\,\partial'_Z\Big|_{Z=0}$$

$$= (Z_1\bar{B}'+\bar{A}')^{-1}(I-Z_1\bar{Z}_1')\bar{\partial}_{Z_1}(I-\bar{Z}_1'Z_1)\,\partial'_{Z_1}(Z_1\bar{B}'+\bar{A}')\Big|_{Z_1=T'}$$

where

$$Z_1\bar{B}'+\bar{A}' = (I-Z_1\bar{T}')\bar{Q}' .$$

Let Λ_{Z_1} be any (linear differential) operator in $\mathfrak{A}$. Then we have

$$(27) \qquad \Lambda_{Z_1}P(Z_1,W_1)\Big|_{W_1\bar{W}_1'=I} = 0 .$$

For any point $Z_1 = T$ in $\mathfrak{D}$, we use transformation (22) bringing $Z = T$ into $Z = 0$. Suppose that $\Lambda_Z\big|_{Z=T}$ is carried to $\Lambda_Z\big|_{Z=0}$

which is an operator with constant coefficients. We have

$$\Lambda_Z P(Z,W)\Big|_{W\overline{W}'=I} = 0 \tag{28}$$

which is equivalent to (27).

Since $\Lambda_Z P(0,W)$ is a polynomial of unitary ideal, from the Lemma it can be expressed as a linear combination of the basis (12). Starting with this expression, by a lengthy but rather elementary calculation of comparing the coefficients we can get the following explicit form of the operator:

$$\Lambda_Z\Big|_{Z=0} = \mathrm{tr}[F(\overline{\partial},\partial)\overline{\partial}_Z \partial_Z']_{Z=0},$$

where $F(\overline{\partial},\partial)$ is a matrix with operator elements. Then transforming back and using (26), we obtain the required expression for $\Lambda_{Z_1}\Big|_{Z_1=T}$. Since T is arbitrary, the theorem is proved.

As an immediate consequence we have the following

<u>Corollary</u>. The arithmetic invariant of the linear differential operator Ω defined by (1) is n^2.

Naturally our theorem suggests a series of similar results for classical domains and classical manifolds. It enriches the theory of differential operator ring which can be regarded as a generalization of algebraic geometry.

References

(1) Hua, L.K., Harmonic analysis of functions of several complex variables in the classical domains, Science Press, Peking, 1958 (English translation published by AMS, 1964).

(2) Hua, L.K., Look, K.H., Theory of harmonic functions in classical domains, Scientia Sinica, 8 (1959), 1031-1094.

(3) Weyl, H., The classical groups, Princeton, New Jersey, 1946.

(4) Zhong, J.Q., On prime ideal of ring of differential operators, Chinese Math. Ann. 1(1980), 359-374.

Several Complex Variables
Proceedings of the 1981 Hangzhou Conference

Microlocalization of CR structures

by

J. J. Kohn

Let M be a compact C^∞ manifold of dimension $2n+1$. A CR structure on M is given by a subbundle, denoted by $T_b^{1,0}(M)$, of the complexified tangent bundle $\mathbb{C}T(M)$, which satisfies the following properties:

(a) The dimension of the fibers of $T_b^{1,0}(M)$ is n.

(b) $T_b^{1,0}(M) \cap \overline{T_b^{1,0}(M)} = \{0\}$.

(c) If L and L' are vector fields defined on an open set $U \subset M$ with values in $T_b^{1,0}(M)$ then $[L,L']$ also has values in $T_b^{1,0}(M)$.

CR structures occur naturally when M is the boundary of a domain in $\mathbb{C}^{n+1}$ and more generally when M is a submanifold of an $(n+1)$-dimensional complex manifold. In those cases $T_b^{1,0}(M)$ consists of those vectors of the form $\Sigma a_j \frac{\partial}{\partial z_j}$, which are tangent to M, where $z_1,\ldots,z_{n+1}$ are holomorphic coordinates in the ambient space. (The problem of embedding a CR manifold into a complex manifold has received a lot of attention, in particular

Received 3 December 1981

very deep results have recently been obtained by M. Kuranishi, see [1]).

We denote by $\Lambda_b(M) = \oplus \Lambda_b^{p,q}(M)$ the bundle of skew-symmetric multilinear functionals on $T_b^{1,0}(M) \oplus T_b^{0,1}(M)$, where $T_b^{0,1}(M) = \overline{T_b^{1,0}(M)}$. Let $\mathcal{B}^{p,q}(M)$ denote the global C^∞ sections of $\mathcal{G}_b^{p,q}(M)$ over M, in particular $\mathcal{B}^{0,0}(M) = C^\infty(M)$. The operator $\bar\partial_b : \mathcal{B}^{p,q} \to \mathcal{B}^{p,q+1}$ is defined by the Cartan formula

$$(1) \quad \langle \bar\partial_b\phi, A_1\wedge\ldots\wedge A_p\wedge B_1\wedge\ldots\wedge B_{q+1}\rangle$$

$$= \sum (-1)^{j+1} B_j \langle \phi, A_1\wedge\ldots\wedge A_p\wedge B_1\wedge\ldots\wedge \hat{B}_j\wedge\ldots\wedge B_{q+1}\rangle$$

$$+ \sum_{i<j} (-1)^{i+j} \langle \phi, A_1\wedge\ldots\wedge A_p\wedge [B_i,B_j]\wedge B_1\wedge\ldots\wedge\hat{B}_j\wedge B_{q+1}\rangle,$$

where the A_j, B_j are vector fields with values in $T_b^{1,0}(M)$, $T_b^{0,1}(M)$ respectively and $\langle\ ,\ \rangle$ denotes contraction.

The problem that we want to discuss here is the following: given $\alpha \in \mathcal{B}^{p,q+1}$ how does the smoothness of the solution of $\bar\partial_b\phi = \alpha$ depend on α. In fact we will be interested in the special ϕ which is "orthogonal" to the null space of $\bar\partial_b$. To define orthogonal we construct on M a riemannian metric which induces a hermitian inner-product of $T_b^{1,0}(M) \oplus T_b^{0,1}(M)$; then, by integration with respect to the volume element defined by the metric, we define an L_2

inner product and norm on $\mathcal{B}^{p,q}$ and we denote by $L_2^{p,q}$ the completion of $\mathcal{B}^{p,q}$ under this norm.

Consider the 1-form γ on M which annihilates $T_b^{1,0}(M) \oplus T_b^{0,1}(M)$. If γ and γ' are two such forms and if $|\gamma| = |\gamma'|$ then $\gamma = \pm \gamma'$. The characteristic cotangent vectors for the operator $\bar{\partial}_b$ are multiples of γ. Thus by standard microlocalization procedure (See [2]) we have

Proposition. Suppose that ν is an element of the cotangent sphere bundle such that ν is not characteristic. Furthermore, suppose that the microlocalization of α at ν is C^∞. If $\bar{\partial}_b \phi = \alpha$ then the micro-localization of ϕ at ν is C^∞.

Definition. Suppose γ is a real 1-form that annihilates $T_b^{1,0}(M) \oplus T_b^{0,1}(M)$ and suppose $x \in M$, then the Levi form associated with γ at x is the hermitian form on $T_{b,x}^{1,0}(M)$, (where $T_{b,x}^{1,0}(M)$ denotes the fiber of $T_b^{1,0}(M)$ at x) defined as follows. If $L, L' \in T_b^{1,0}(M)$ then the value of the Levi form on L, L' is $\sqrt{-1}\langle d\gamma, L \wedge \bar{L}'\rangle$. M is pseudo-convex at γ if the Levi-form associated with γ is positive semi-definite.

Given $x_0 \in M$ and a 1-form $\gamma \neq 0$ defined in a neighborhood U of x_0 such that γ annihilates $T_{b,x}^{1,0}(M) \oplus T_{b,x}^{0,1}(M)$ for each $x \in U$. For each $q \geq 0$ we will define a sequence of ideals $\{I_k^q(x_0, \gamma)\}$ of genus of C^∞ functions. This is a micro-local version of the definition made in [3], the generalization of these concepts to first order systems is outlined in [4].

<u>Definition</u>. Let $T_b^{1,0}(x,0)$ denote the genus of vector fields at x_0 where values lie in $T_b^{1,0}(M)$ and let $\mathcal{F}^m =$ $\{F = A_1\wedge..\wedge A_m\wedge\bar{B}_1\wedge..\wedge\bar{B}_m | A_j, B_j \in T_b^{1,0}(x_0)\}$. Then we define $I_1^q(x_0,\gamma)$ by

$$I_1^q(x_0,\gamma) = \sqrt[\mathbb{R}]{(\{\langle(d\gamma)^{n-q+1},F\rangle | F \in \mathcal{F}^{n-q+1}\})},$$

where (S) denotes the ideal over the germs of C^∞ functions at x_0 generated by S and $\sqrt[\mathbb{R}]{}$ denotes the real radical which is defined as follows. If J is a set of germs of C^∞ functions then $f \in \sqrt[\mathbb{R}]{J}$ if and only if there is an integer m and $g \in J$ such that $|f|^m \leq |g|$. We then define $I_k^q(x_0,\gamma)$ for $k > 1$ inductively as follows

$$I_k^q(x_0,\gamma) = \sqrt[\mathbb{R}]{(I_{k-1}^q(x_0,\gamma), \bigcup_j S_{j,k}^q)}$$

where

$$S_{j,k}^q = \{\langle\partial_b f_1\wedge\bar{\partial}_b g_1\wedge..\wedge\partial_b f_j\wedge\bar{\partial}_b g_j\wedge(d\gamma)^{n-q-j+1},F\rangle | F \in \mathcal{F}^{n-q+1} \text{ and } f_m, g_m \in I_{k-1}^q\}$$

and $\partial_b f = \overline{\bar{\partial}_b \bar{f}}$. We say that (x_0,γ) is of <u>finite q-type</u> if for some k we have $1 \in I_k^q(x_0,\gamma)$.

Remark: $I_k^q(x_0,\gamma) \subset I_{k+1}^q(x_0,\gamma)$, $I_k^q(x_0,\gamma) \subset I_k^{q+1}(x_0,\gamma)$ and $I_k^q(x_0,\gamma) = I_k^q(x_0,-\gamma)$.

The following theorem gives the microlocalization of subelliptic estimates.

Theorem. If M is pseudo-convex with respect to γ in a neighborhood of x_0 and if $1 \in I_k^{q+1}(x_0,\gamma)$ for some k then there exists $\varepsilon > 0$ such that if $\phi \in L_2^{p,q}$ and $\bar{\partial}_b\phi \in L_2^{p,q+1}$ then the microlocalization of ϕ at γ has finite Sobolev ε-norm. Furthermore, if the microlocalization of $\bar{\partial}_b\phi$ at γ is C^∞ then the microlocalization of ϕ at γ is also C^∞. Dually, if $1 \in I_k^{n-q}(x_0,\gamma)$ then if $\psi \in L_2^{p,q+1}$ and $\bar{\partial}_b^*\psi \in L_2^{p,q}$, where $\bar{\partial}_b^*$ denotes the L^2 adjoint of $\bar{\partial}_b$, then the microlocalization of ψ at $-\gamma$ has finite Sobolev ε-norm and is C^∞ if the microlocalization of $\partial_b^*\psi$ at $-\gamma$ is C^∞.

If the range of $\bar{\partial}_b$ is closed then the range of $\bar{\partial}_b^*$ is also closed and hence equal to the orthogonal complement of the null space of $\bar{\partial}_b$. This condition then enables us to combine the above facts to obtain the following.

Corollary. If the range of $\bar{\partial}_b$ is closed and if $1 \in I_k^m(x_0,\gamma)$ where $m = \min(q+1,n-q)$, if $\phi \in L_2^{p,q}$ is orthogonal to the null space of $\bar{\partial}_b$ and if $\bar{\partial}_b\phi \in L_2^{p,q+1}$ then there exists a neighborhood of x_0 in which ϕ has a finite ε-norm. Further if $\bar\partial_b\phi$ is C^∞ in some neighborhood of x_0 then so is ϕ.

The above results are obtained by analyzing the operator $\Box_b = \bar\partial_b\bar\partial_b^* + \bar\partial_b^*\bar\partial_b$ whose range in $L_2^{p,q}$ is closed whenever $1 \in I_k^t$ for some k, with $t = \min(q,n-q)$. This then implies that the range of $\bar\partial_b$ in $L_2^{p,q}$ is closed under the same condition. Thus the range of $\bar\partial_b$ with domain in $L_2^{p,q}$ (whose range then lies in $L_2^{p,q+1}$) is closed provided $1 \in I_k^s$ where $s = \min(q+1,n-q-1)$. Hence in the above Corollary the assumption that the range of $\bar\partial_b$ is closed follows automatically unless $s < m$, this can happen only if $n \leq 2q+1$.

The most interesting case of this situation is when $q = 0$. Then the null space of $\bar\partial_b$ in $L_2^{0,0}$ consists of the square-integrable CR functions, denoted by $\mathcal{H}_b$. We define the Szego projection operator $S : L_2^{0,0} \to \mathcal{H}_b$ to be the orthogonal projection. Clearly if $u = f - Sf$ then $\bar\partial_b u = \bar\partial_b f$, thus $Sf = f - u$, where u is the unique solution of $\bar\partial_b u = \bar\partial_b f$ which is orthogonal to $\mathcal{H}_b$. The above thus gives the following result concerning the regularity of the operator S.

Theorem. Let M be a pseudo convex CR manifold. Suppose that $\dim M \geq 5$, then if $1 \in I_k^1(x_0,\gamma)$ the operator S preserves regularity in a neighborhood of x_0. That is, there is some neighborhood U of x_0 such that if $V = \{x \in U | f$ is C^∞ in a neighborhood of x} then Sf is C^∞ on V. In case dim M = 3 the same conclusion holds under the additional hypothesis that the range of $\bar{\partial}_b$ is closed.

In [5] D. Burns (using Boutet de Monvel's method in [7]) shows if M is a strongly-pseudo convex CR manifold and if S preserves local regularity (i.e., if Sf is C^∞ wherever f is C^∞) then M is embeddable in $\mathbb{C}^N$ for some N. On the other hand H. Rossi in [6] shows that there are strongly pseudo-convex CR structures on S^3 which are not embeddable (see [5] for a simple proof of this fact). Since strongly-convex implies that $1 \in I_1^1$, the above theorem combined with Burn's result shows that: if M is strongly pseudo-convex, of dimension 3 and if the range of $\bar{\partial}_b$ is closed then M is embeddable. Strongly pseudo-convex M of higher dimension are always embeddable (see [7]).

References

[1] KURANISHI, M.: "Strongly pseudoconvex CR structures over small balls", Annals of Math. (to appear).

[2] TREVES, F.: "Pseudo differential and Fourier Integral Operators", vol. I and II, Plenum Press, New York, 1980.

[3] KOHN, J.J.: "Subellipticity of the $\bar{\partial}$-Neumann problem on pseudo-convex domains: sufficient conditions", Acta Math. 142, 79-122 (1979).

[4] _________: "Subelliptic estimates", Proc. Conf. on Linear PDE, Saint Jean des Monts, 1981.

[5] BURNS, D.: "Global behavior of some tangential Cauchy-Riemann equations", P.D.E. and Geometry (Proc. Conf. Park City, Utah, 1977), p. 51-56, Lecture Notes in Pure and Appl. Math. 48, Dekker, New York, 1979.

[6] ROSSI, H.: "Attaching analytic spaces to a space along a pseudoconvex boundary", Proc. Conf. on Complex Manifolds, (Minneapolis), Springer-Verlag, New York, 1965.

[7] BOUTET DE MONVEL, L.: "Integration des equations de Cauchy-Riemann induites formelles", Seminaire Goulaouic Lions-Schwartz, Exposé IX, 1974 1975.

Several Complex Variables
Proceedings of the 1981 Hangzhou Conference

A Note on the Boundary Laplacian Operator

Hing-Sun Luk

The Chinese University of Hong Kong

§1 Introduction

Let $\tilde{M}$ be a complex manifold of dimension n. Let M be a real hypersurface in $\tilde{M}$ defined by the equation $h = 0$, where h is a C^∞ strictly plurisubharmonic function on a neighborhood U of M with $dh \neq 0$ everywhere. In this note, we study the $\bar{\partial}_b$ complex of M. We first set up a geometric framework by taking the Kähler metric $\langle,\rangle$ on U defined by the Hessian of h. Then we derive a formula for the boundary Laplacian $\Box_b$ in terms of the induced geometry on M. The curvature terms in the formula are given in terms of h alone and are related to the invariants of Chern-Moser in [1]. Finally we give two examples to illustrate the practicality of our formula. A fundamental differential geometric study on the $\bar{\partial}_b$ complex of a strongly pseudoconvex CR manifold has been carried out by N. Tanaka [4]. The theory of harmonic integrals on strongly pseudoconvex structures over small balls has recently been established by M. Kuranishi. It is hoped that this note would stimulate further work in this direction. I should like to thank Professor Kuranishi for his advice and encouragement.

Received 1 Dec. 1981.

§2 Induced geometry on M

Using the notation in §1, let $(z^1, \ldots, z^n)$ be a coordinate system on some open subset V of U. The metric we consider is $\frac{\partial^2 h}{\partial z^i \partial \bar{z}^j} dz^i \otimes d\bar{z}^j$. We shall use subscripts to denote partial derivatives of h; summation over repeated indices will be understood. Let $(h^{\bar{j}k})$ be the inverse matrix of $(h_{i\bar{j}})$. Since $dh \neq 0$, we have

(1) $H := \langle \partial h, \partial h \rangle^{\frac{1}{2}} > 0$.

Shrinking V if necessary, let $\{\zeta^1, \ldots, \zeta^n\}$ be an orthonormal frame of $(1, 0)$ forms on V, where we require that

(2) $\zeta^n = H^{-1} \partial h$.

Let $\{X_1, \ldots, X_n\}$ be the dual frame of $(1, 0)$ vectors on V. Observe that each $X_\alpha (\alpha = 1, \ldots, n-1)$ is tangent to the real hypersurface $h = \text{constant}$ while

(3) $X_n = H^{-1} h_{\bar{j}} h^{\bar{j}k} \frac{\partial}{\partial z^k}$

and X_n is globally defined on U, independent of coordinates. Writing

(3)' $p^k = H^{-2} h_{\bar{j}} h^{\bar{j}k}$ and $P' = p^k \frac{\partial}{\partial z^k}$,

we have

(3)" $X_n = HP'$ and $p^k h_k = 1$.

On U, we have the following global vector field tangent to the real hypersurfaces $h = \text{constant}$:

(4) $T = \frac{1}{i} (P' - \bar{P}')$

Note that on $M \cap V$, $\{X_\alpha, \overline{X_\alpha}, \frac{H}{\sqrt{2}} T\}$ form a local orthonormal frame for $\mathbb{C}TM$. Throughout this note, small Greek (resp. Latin) indices always run from 1 to $n-1$ (resp. 1 to n).

Let $\iota : M \to \tilde{M}$ be the inclusion map and let

(5) $\xi^n = \iota^* (\frac{i}{\sqrt{2}} (\zeta^n - \bar{\zeta}^n)) = \iota^* (\sqrt{2}\, i\, \zeta^n)$.

Dual to $\{X_\alpha, \overline{X}_\alpha, \frac{H}{\sqrt{2}} T\}$, $\{\iota^*(\zeta^\alpha), \iota^*(\overline{\zeta^\alpha}), \xi^n\}$ is an orthonormal frame of $\mathbb{C}TM^*$. Let

$${}^oT'(M) = \mathbb{C}TM \cap T^{1,0}(\tilde{M})|_M ,$$

$${}^oT''(M) = \overline{{}^oT'(M)} \quad \text{and} \quad {}^oT(M) = {}^oT'(M) \oplus {}^oT''(M)$$

$<\ ,\ >$ restricted to ${}^oT(M)$ is a special choice of the Levi form. Denote by F the subbundle of TM generated by the global vector field T. Thus, we have the orthogonal decomposition

$\mathbb{C}TM = {}^oT'(M) \oplus {}^oT''(M) \oplus \mathbb{C}F$, and we have also set up orthonormal frames for the various vector bundles. Writing $\zeta^i = \zeta^i_j dz^j$ and $X_i = x^j_i \frac{\partial}{\partial z^j}$ on V, we note that

(6) $$\zeta^n_j = H^{-1} h_j , \quad x^j_n = H\, p^j$$

and, since $\{X_i\}$ is an orthonormal frame,

(6)' $$x^j_i \overline{x^k_i} = h^{j\bar{k}} \quad \text{or} \quad x^j_\alpha \overline{x^k_\alpha} = h^{j\bar{k}} - p^j H^2 \overline{p^k} .$$

On U, we have the metric connection $\tilde{\nabla}$ associated to $<\ ,>$. Let $\rho : \mathbb{C}TM|_M \to {}^oT(M)$ be the orthogonal projection. As usual, let Γ denote the space of global C^∞ sections. We define the mapping

$$\nabla : \Gamma(\mathbb{C}TM) \times \Gamma({}^oT(M)) \to \Gamma({}^oT(M)) \quad \text{by}$$

(7) $$\nabla(X, Y) := \nabla_X Y = \rho(\tilde{\nabla}_X Y) .$$

It is easy to check that ∇ satisfies the following properties

(8) If $Y \in \Gamma({}^oT'(M))$ (resp. $\Gamma({}^oT''(M))$), then $\nabla_X Y \in \Gamma({}^oT'(M))$ (resp. $\Gamma({}^oT''(M))$)

(9) For C^∞ functions f, g on M, $\nabla_{fX+gY} Z = f\nabla_X Z + g\nabla_Y Z$,

$$\nabla_X(fY) = (Xf)Y + f\nabla_X Y , \quad \nabla_X(Y+Z) = \nabla_X Y + \nabla_X Z .$$

(10) $$X <Y, Z> = <\nabla_X Y, Z> + <Y, \nabla_X Z>$$

(11) $$\nabla_X Y - \nabla_Y X = \rho[X, Y]$$

whenever the symbols make sense.

Furthermore, these properties characterize the restriction of ∇ to $\Gamma({}^{o}T(M)) \times \Gamma({}^{o}T(M))$: (8) and (11) determine $\nabla_X Y$ when X and Y are of different types, and then (10) determines $\nabla_X Y$ when they are of the same type. Note that

(11)' $\quad \nabla_X Y - \nabla_Y X = [X, Y]$ if X and Y are of the same type.

We define the curvature as for ordinary connections:

(12) $$R(X, Y)\, Z = \nabla_X \nabla_Y Z - \nabla_Y \nabla_X Z - \nabla_{[X,Y]} Z ,$$

where $X, Y \in \Gamma(\mathbb{C}TM)$ and $Z \in \Gamma({}^{o}T(M))$

By (9), $R(fX, gY)(pZ) = fgp\, R(X,Y)Z$ for any C^∞ functions f, g, p on M.

We now write down the curvature in terms of h alone. Let $\tilde{R}$ be the curvature tensor associated with $\tilde{\nabla}$ on U. We recall the following local formulas [3]:

(13) $$\tilde{\nabla}_{\frac{\partial}{\partial z^{\bar j}}} \frac{\partial}{\partial z^{\bar k}} = h_{m\bar j\bar k} h^{\bar l m} \frac{\partial}{\partial z^{\bar l}} , \qquad \tilde{\nabla}_{\frac{\partial}{\partial z^{\bar l}}} \frac{\partial}{\partial z^{k}} = 0$$

(14) $$\tilde{R}\left(\frac{\partial}{\partial z^{\bar i}}, \frac{\partial}{\partial z^{j}}\right) \frac{\partial}{\partial z^{\bar k}} = - \frac{\partial}{\partial z^{j}} \left(h_{r\bar i\bar k}\, h^{\bar m r} \right) \frac{\partial}{\partial z^{\bar m}}$$

Set

(15) $$L(X) = \rho\, (\tilde{\nabla}_X X_n) , \text{ for } X \in \Gamma(\mathbb{C}TM)$$

<u>Proposition 1</u> For the basis $\{ \overline{X}_\alpha = x^{\bar i}_{\alpha} \frac{\partial}{\partial z^{\bar i}} \}$ of ${}^{o}T''(M)$

(a) $$R(\overline{X}_\alpha, X_\beta)\, \overline{X}_\gamma = \rho\, \tilde{R}(\overline{X}_\alpha, X_\beta)\, \overline{X}_\gamma + \langle \overline{X}_\gamma , L(\overline{X}_\beta)\rangle L(\overline{X}_\alpha) - \langle \overline{X}_\gamma , L(X_\alpha) \rangle L(X_\beta)$$

Let $K_{\bar i j \bar k l} = -h_{\bar i j \bar k l} + h_{\bar m j l}\, h_{p \bar i \bar k} h^{\bar m p} - H^{-2} (h_{jl} - h_m h^{\bar p m} h_{\bar p j l})(h_{\bar i \bar k} - h_{\bar m} h^{\bar m p} h_{p \bar i \bar k})$

and $\tilde{K}_{\bar\alpha\beta\bar\gamma\rho} = K_{\bar i j \bar k l}\, x^{\bar i}_{\alpha}\, x^{j}_{\beta}\, x^{\bar k}_{\gamma}\, x^{l}_{\rho}$. Then

(b) $$R(\overline{X}_\alpha, X_\beta)\, \overline{X}_\gamma = (H^{-2} \delta^{\gamma}_{\beta}\, \delta^{\alpha}_{\rho} + \tilde{K}_{\bar\alpha\beta\bar\gamma\rho})\, \overline{X}_\rho$$

Proof: By definitions (7), (15) and the metric property of $\tilde{\nabla}$,

(16) $$\tilde{\nabla}_X \overline{X}_\alpha = \nabla_X \overline{X}_\alpha - \langle \overline{X}_\alpha , L(\overline{X})\rangle \overline{X}_n \quad \text{for any } X \in \Gamma(\mathbb{C}TM)$$

Substituting (16) in $\tilde{R}(\overline{X}_\alpha, X_\beta)\overline{X}_\gamma$ and computing modulo $\overline{X}_n$, we get (a). Next,

(17) $$\rho\tilde{R}(\overline{X}_\alpha, X_\beta)\overline{X}_\gamma = \langle \tilde{R}(\overline{X}_\alpha, X_\beta)\overline{X}_\gamma, \overline{X}_\rho\rangle \overline{X}_\rho$$

$$= -\overline{x^i_\alpha}\, x^j_\beta\, \overline{x^k_\gamma} \frac{\partial}{\partial z^j}(h_{p\bar{i}\bar{k}}\, h^{\bar{m}p})\, h_{l\bar{m}}\, x^l_\rho \overline{X}_\rho \qquad \text{by (14)}$$

$$= \overline{x^i_\alpha}\, x^j_\beta\, \overline{x^k_\gamma}\, x^l_\rho [-h_{\bar{i}j\bar{k}l} + h_{\bar{m}jl}\, h_{p\bar{i}\bar{k}}\, h^{\bar{m}p}]\overline{X}_\rho$$

We shall use $h^{\bar{m}p} h_{l\bar{m}} = \delta^p_l$ to shift derivatives without mention.

(18) $$\tilde{\nabla}_{\overline{X}_\alpha} X_n = \overline{x^j_\alpha} \frac{\partial}{\partial \overline{z^j}}\left(\frac{h_m h^{\bar{p}m}}{H}\right)\frac{\partial}{\partial \overline{z^p}} + \overline{x^j_\alpha} \frac{h_m h^{\bar{p}m}}{H} h_{\bar{k}\bar{j}\bar{p}} h^{\bar{l}k} \frac{\partial}{\partial \overline{z^l}} \qquad \text{by (3), (13)}$$

$$= \overline{x^j_\alpha} \frac{\partial}{\partial \overline{z^j}}\left(\frac{h_m}{H}\right) h^{\bar{p}m} \frac{\partial}{\partial \overline{z^p}}$$

Then

(18)' $$L(\overline{X}_\alpha) = \overline{x^j_\alpha} \frac{\partial}{\partial \overline{z^j}}\left(\frac{h_m}{H}\right) x^m_\rho \overline{X}_\rho$$

$$= H^{-1}\overline{X}_\alpha$$

using $h_m x^m_\rho = 0$ and $\overline{x^j_\alpha} h_{m\bar{j}} x^m_\rho = \delta^\alpha_\rho$. Hence

(18)" $$\langle \overline{X}_\gamma, L(\overline{X}_\beta)\rangle L(\overline{X}_\alpha) = H^{-2}\delta^\gamma_\beta \delta^\alpha_\rho \overline{X}_\rho .$$

Computing $L(X_\alpha)$ is a similar way, we get

(19) $$\langle L(X_\alpha), \overline{X}_\gamma\rangle = [x^i_\alpha \frac{\partial}{\partial z^i}\left(\frac{h_m h^{\bar{p}m}}{H}\right)]\, h_{k\bar{p}}\, x^k_\gamma$$

$$= H^{-1} x^i_\alpha x^k_\gamma (h_{ik} - h_m h^{\bar{p}m} h_{\bar{p}ik}) .$$

Denoting the last expression by L_α^γ ,

(19)' $$- \langle \overline{X_\gamma}, L(X_\alpha)\rangle \; L(X_\beta) = - \overline{\langle L(X_\alpha), \overline{X_\gamma}\rangle} \; \langle L\,(X_\beta), \overline{X_\rho} \rangle \; X_\rho$$

$$= - \overline{L_\alpha^\gamma} \, L_\beta^\rho \, X_\rho$$

(b) follows from (a) by (17), (18)", (19) and (19)' q.e.d.

<u>Example</u>: For the sphere in $\mathbb{C}^n$, $h = z^j \overline{z^j} - \varepsilon^2 = 0$, $H = 1$, $K_{ijkl} = 0$ and $R(\overline{X_\alpha}, X_\beta)\, \overline{X_\gamma} = \delta_\beta^\gamma \, \overline{X_\alpha}$

To conclude this section, we relate the curvature in Proposition 1 to the Chern-Moser invariants, using Webster's pseudo-Hermitian approach [6]. Recall that for the local orthonormal frame $\{\zeta^i\}$ on V ,

(20) $$d\zeta^i = \zeta^j \wedge \psi_j^i \quad ,$$

where $\psi_j^i + \overline{\psi_i^j} = 0$ and $\psi_j^i(X)\, X_i = \tilde{\nabla}_X X_j$

(20)' $$d\psi_j^i = \psi_j^k \wedge \psi_k^i + \Phi_j^i \quad ,$$

where $\Phi_j^i\,(X_k, \overline{X_l})\, X_i = \tilde{R}\,(X_k, \overline{X_l})\, X_j$

Let $\theta = \iota^*(i\partial h)$ and $\theta^\alpha = \iota^*(\zeta^\alpha)$. It is easy to check that

(21) $$d\theta = - i\theta^\alpha \wedge \overline{\theta^\alpha} \quad ;$$

in fact, one may use $\zeta^\alpha = h_{j\bar{k}} \, \overline{x_\alpha^k} \, dz^j$, (6)' and $\iota^*(dh) = 0$.

Pulling back (20) for $i = 1, \ldots , n-1$ gives

$$d\theta^\alpha = \theta^\beta \wedge \iota^*(\psi_\beta^\alpha) + \theta\wedge(-iH^{-1}\iota^*\psi_n^\alpha) .$$

Since $\iota^*(-iH^{-1}\psi_n^\alpha) \equiv -iH^{-1} \langle L(X_\beta), X_\alpha\rangle \, \theta^\beta \mod \theta, \; \overline{\theta^\gamma}$

$$= -iH^{-2}\theta^\alpha \quad ,$$

if we take $\omega_\beta^\alpha = \iota^*(\psi_\beta^\alpha) + iH^{-2}\, \delta_\beta^\alpha \theta$, then

(21)' $d\theta^\alpha = \theta^\beta \wedge \omega_\beta^\alpha + \theta \wedge \tau^\alpha$

with $\tau^\alpha \equiv 0 \mod \overline{\theta^\gamma}$ and $\omega_\beta^\alpha + \overline{\omega_\alpha^\beta} = 0$.

Thus we obtain the intrinsic forms in [6 , Theorem 1.1]

Pulling back (20)' and using the definition of ω_β^α, we get

$d\omega_\beta^\alpha - \omega_\beta^\gamma \wedge \omega_\gamma^\alpha \equiv H^{-2}\delta_\beta^\alpha \theta^\gamma \wedge \overline{\theta^\gamma} + \iota^*(\psi^n \wedge \psi_n^\alpha + \phi_\beta^\alpha) \mod \theta$.

Pulling back (20) for $i = n$, we see that $\iota^*(\psi_\beta^n) \equiv H^{-1}\overline{\theta^\beta} \mod \theta$.

Together with $\iota^*(\psi_n^\alpha) \equiv H^{-1}\psi^\alpha \mod \theta, \overline{\theta^\gamma}$, we get

$$R_{\alpha\bar\beta\rho\bar\sigma} = \tilde K_{\alpha\bar\beta\rho\bar\sigma} + H^{-2}(\delta_\alpha^\beta\delta_\rho^\sigma + \delta_\alpha^\sigma\delta_\rho^\beta)$$

where $\tilde K_{\alpha\bar\beta\rho\bar\sigma} = \overline{\tilde K_{\bar\alpha\beta\bar\rho\sigma}}$ as in Proposition 1 and $R_{\alpha\bar\beta\rho\bar\sigma}$ as in [6 , Theorem 1.1a] .

Finally it follows that $\tilde K_{\alpha\bar\beta\rho\bar\sigma}$ and $R_{\alpha\bar\beta\rho\bar\sigma}$ are related to the Chern-Moser invariant $S_{\alpha\bar\beta\rho\bar\sigma}$ in the same manner (cf [6] , Formula (3.8)) :

(22) $$S_{\alpha\bar\beta\rho\bar\sigma} = \tilde K_{\alpha\bar\beta\rho\bar\sigma} - \frac{1}{n+1}(\tilde K_{\alpha\bar\beta}\delta_\rho^\sigma + \tilde K_{\rho\bar\beta}\delta_\alpha^\sigma + \tilde K_{\alpha\bar\sigma}\delta_\rho^\beta + \tilde K_{\rho\bar\sigma}\delta_\alpha^\beta)$$
$$+ \frac{\tilde K}{n(n+1)}(\delta_\alpha^\beta\delta_\rho^\sigma + \delta_\alpha^\sigma\delta_\rho^\beta) .$$

where $\tilde K_{\alpha\bar\beta} = \tilde K_{\alpha\bar\beta\rho\bar\rho}$ and $\tilde K = \tilde K_{\alpha\bar\alpha}$.

By (22), one can compute the Chern-Moser invariants directly from any strictly plurisubharmonic defining function.

§3 Computation of $\Box_b$

We assume that M is compact and restrict our computation to purely antiholomorphic forms. Thus let $\Lambda_b(o, q) = \Gamma(\Lambda^q({}^oT''(M))^*)$. Each element $u \in \Lambda_b^{(o,q)}$ will be given locally by the values

(23) $u_{\bar\alpha_1 \cdots \bar\alpha_q} = u(\overline{X}_{\alpha_1}, \ldots, \overline{X}_{\alpha_q})$ with $\overline{X}_\alpha$ as above.

$\bar\partial_b u \in \Lambda_b(o, q+1)$ is then defined by

(24) $$(\bar\partial_b u)_{\bar\alpha_1\cdots\bar\alpha_{q+1}} = \sum_{i=1}^{q+1} (-1)^{i+1}\,\bar X_{\alpha_i}\, u_{\bar\alpha_1\cdots\hat{\bar\alpha}_i\cdots\bar\alpha_{q+1}}$$

$$+ \sum_{i<k} (-1)^{i+k} u([\bar X_{\alpha_i}, \bar X_{\alpha_k}], \ldots, \hat{\bar X}_{\alpha_i}, \ldots, \hat{\bar X}_{\alpha_k} \ldots, \bar X_{\alpha_{q+1}})$$

where as usual $\wedge$ means deletion of index.

Let γ be any volume form on M. For $u, v \in \Lambda_b^{(o,q)}$, let

(25) $$(u, v) = \frac{1}{q!} \int u_{\bar\alpha_1\cdots\bar\alpha_q}\, \overline{v_{\bar\alpha_1\cdots\bar\alpha_q}}\, \gamma$$

A simple integration by parts shows that for any $X \in \Gamma(\mathbb{C}TM)$. there is a unique C^∞ function a_X on M such that

(26) $\int (Xf)\gamma = \int a_X f \gamma$, for any C^∞ function f on M. The mapping ∇ in §2 induces the following operator on $\Lambda_b^{(o,q)}$: for any $X \in \Gamma(\mathbb{C}TM)$

(27) $$(\nabla_X u)_{\bar\alpha_1\cdots\bar\alpha_q} = X u_{\bar\alpha_1\cdots\bar\alpha_q} - \sum_{i=1}^{q} u(\bar X_{\alpha_1}, \ldots, \nabla_X \bar X_{\alpha_i}, \ldots, \bar X_{\alpha_q})$$

We denote $\nabla_{\bar X_\alpha} u$ (resp. $a_{\bar X_\alpha}$) by $\nabla_{\bar\alpha} u$ (resp. $a_{\bar\alpha}$). Let $\bar\partial_b^*$ and ∇_X^* be the adjoint operator of $\bar\partial_b$ and ∇_X with respect to (,).

We now compute $\Box_b = \bar\partial_b\bar\partial_b^* + \bar\partial_b^*\bar\partial_b$ in terms of ∇_X and ∇_X^*. Since such computation of Laplacians is standard, we only give the crucial steps. Techniques in steps 3 and 4 are, however, special for $\Box_b$ and will be given in greater detail.

<u>Step 1</u>. Let $u \in \Lambda_b^{(o,q)}$ and $X \in \Gamma(\mathbb{C}TM)$.

(28) $(\bar\partial_b u)_{\bar\alpha_1 \cdots \bar\alpha_{q+1}} = \sum_{i=1}^{q+1} (-1)^{i+1} (\nabla_{\bar\alpha_i} u)_{\bar\alpha_1 \cdots \hat{\bar\alpha}_i \cdots \bar\alpha_{q+1}}$, using (11)'

Integrating by parts and using (10), we get

(29) $\nabla^*_X u = -\nabla_{\bar X} u + a_{\bar X} u$

(30) $\bar\partial^*_b u = \nabla^*_{\bar\alpha} (u \lrcorner \bar X_\alpha)$

where $(u \lrcorner \bar X_\alpha)_{\bar\alpha_1 \cdots \bar\alpha_{q-1}} = u_{\bar\alpha\bar\alpha_1 \cdots \bar\alpha_{q-1}}$

<u>Step 2</u> A careful application of (28) - (30) using the properties of ∇ gives

(31) $(\Box_b u)_{\bar\alpha_1 \cdots \bar\alpha_q} = (\nabla^*_{\bar\alpha} \nabla_{\bar\alpha} u)_{\bar\alpha_1 \cdots \bar\alpha_q}$

$+ \sum_{i=1}^{q} (-1)^{i+1} (\nabla_\alpha \nabla_{\bar\alpha_i} - \nabla_{\bar\alpha_i} \nabla_\alpha - \nabla_{\rho[X_\alpha, \bar X_{\alpha_i}]} u)_{\bar\alpha\, \bar\alpha_1 \cdots \hat{\bar\alpha}_i \cdots \bar\alpha_q}$

+ terms with $\nabla^*_{\bar\alpha} \bar X_\alpha$,

where $\nabla^*_{\bar X} \bar Y = -\nabla_X \bar Y + a_X \bar Y$.

<u>Step 3</u> We shall choose γ on M such that $\nabla^*_{\bar\alpha} \bar X_\alpha = 0$ for each local $\{X_\alpha\}$. Let

(32) $\sigma = i^n n! g \, dz^1 \wedge d\bar z^1 \wedge \ldots \wedge dz^n \wedge d\bar z^n$,

where $g = \det (h_{j\bar k})$, be the volume form on U associated with $\langle\ ,\ \rangle$. Fix a $(2n-1)$ form σ_o on U such that

(33) $\sigma_o \wedge d\, h = H^2 \sigma$.

We now show that $\gamma = \iota^*(\sigma_o)$ satisfies our requirement. First we extend the definition of ∇ to the ambient space. For this purpose, we consider vector fields Y, Z, W on U such that at each point $p \in U$, if $p \in M_c = \{h=c, \text{ constant}\}$, then $Y_p, Z_p, W_p \in {}^{o}T_p(M_c$ We define $\nabla_Y Z$ and $\overset{*}{\nabla}_Y Z$ on each level real hypersurface as before, using the pull-back of σ_o as volume form on each surface. As in (26), we write

(34) $$\int (Xf)\sigma = \int b_X f \sigma$$

where X is any vector field and f any C^∞ function on U. Now for Y, Z as above, we set ${}^{a}\overset{*}{\nabla}_Y Z = -\nabla_{\bar{Y}} Z + b_{\bar{Y}} Z$. $\overset{*}{\nabla}_Y Z$ and ${}^{a}\overset{*}{\nabla}_Y Z$ are of the same type as Z. Further, by (33) they satisfy the same adjoint condition:

$$\int < \ , W > \sigma = \int < Z , \nabla_Y W > \sigma$$

for any W as above and with compact support in U. Hence $\overset{*}{\nabla}_Y Z = {}^{a}\overset{*}{\nabla}_Y Z$ and it clearly suffices to show that ${}^{a}\overset{*}{\nabla}_{\bar{\alpha}} \bar{X}_\alpha = 0$ on V. Next, to facilitate computation, let

(35) $$Z_j = \rho\left(\frac{\partial}{\partial z^j}\right) = \frac{\partial}{\partial z^j} - h_j P'$$

We can write $X_\alpha = x^j_\alpha Z_j$. One easily checks the following formulas:

(36) $$p^j Z_j = 0 , \quad \text{since} \quad p^j h_j = 1 .$$

(37) $$\nabla_{Z_j} \bar{Z}_k = Z_j (-p^{\bar{l}} h_{\bar{k}}) \bar{Z}_l = - (Z_j p^{\bar{l}}) h_{\bar{k}} \bar{Z}_l$$

(38) $$Z_j (x^j_\alpha \overline{x^k_\alpha}) = \frac{\partial}{\partial z^j} (x^j_\alpha \overline{x^k_\alpha}) + p^l h_{jl} x^j_\alpha \overline{x^k_\alpha} , \quad \text{since} \quad h_j x^j_\alpha = 0 .$$

Integration by parts give

$$b_{Z_j} \equiv -\frac{\partial}{\partial z^j}(\log H^2 + \log g) + p^1 h_{j1}\ , \ \text{mod}\ \ h_j \ .$$

Hence

(39) $$b_{Z_j} x^j_\alpha \overline{x^k_\alpha} = \left(-\frac{\partial}{\partial z^j}(\log H^2 + \log g) + p^1 h_{j1}\right) x^j_\alpha \overline{x^k_\alpha}$$

Finally,

(40) $$a\nabla^*_{\overline{\alpha}} \overline{X}_\alpha = -\nabla_{Z_j}(x^j_\alpha \overline{x^k_\alpha} \overline{Z}_k) + b_{Z_j} x^j_\alpha \overline{x^k_\alpha} \overline{Z}_k \ .$$

$$= (-Z_j(x^j_\alpha \overline{x^k_\alpha}) + b_{Z_j} x^j_\alpha \overline{x^k_\alpha}) \overline{Z}_k \quad \text{by} \quad (37)$$

$$= \overline{A^k} \overline{Z}_k$$

where $\overline{A^k} = -\left[\frac{\partial}{\partial z^j}(x^j_\alpha \overline{x^k_\alpha}) + \left(\frac{\partial}{\partial z^j}(\log H^2 + \log g)\right) x^j_\alpha \overline{x^k_\alpha}\right]$,

by (38), (39).

Using (6)' for $x^j_\alpha \overline{x^k_\alpha}$ and the well-known formula $\frac{\partial}{\partial z^j}\log g = h_{jk\overline{1}} h^{\overline{1}k}$, one checks that $\overline{A^k} \equiv 0 \mod \overline{p^k}$. By (36), this finishes the proof.

From now on we fix this choice of γ.

<u>Step 4</u> We shall deal with the second term on the right hand side of (31), which contains a derivative in the T direction (4).

First note that

(41) $$[X, \overline{Y}] = \rho\,[X, \overline{Y}] + i < X, Y > T$$

for any $X, Y \in \Gamma(^oT'M)$, by operating $\theta = \iota^*(i\partial h)$ on both sides.

Using (41), it is not difficult to check that for $u \in \Lambda^{(o,q)}_b$

(42) $$(\nabla_X \nabla_{\overline{Y}} - \nabla_{\overline{Y}} \nabla_X - \nabla_{\rho[X, \overline{Y}]})\, u = i < X, Y > \nabla_T u + u\,(R(\overline{Y}, X))$$

where $u(R(\overline{Y}, X))_{\overline{\alpha}_1 \cdots \overline{\alpha}_q} = \sum_{i=1}^{q} u(\overline{X}_{\alpha_1}, \ldots, R(\overline{Y}, X)\overline{X}_{\alpha_i}, \ldots, \overline{X}_{\alpha_q})$.

Next, observe that

(43) $$(\overset{*}{\nabla}_\alpha \nabla_\alpha - \overset{*}{\nabla}_{\bar\alpha} \nabla_{\bar\alpha})\, u$$

$$= \nabla_{\rho[X_\alpha, \bar X_\alpha] + a_{\bar\alpha} X_\alpha - a_\alpha \bar X_\alpha}\, u + (n-1) i\, \nabla_T u + u\,(R(\bar X_\alpha, X_\alpha))$$

by (29), (42), and that the first term on the right vanishes by (11) and $\overset{*}{\nabla}_{\bar\alpha} X_\alpha = 0$. Eliminating $\nabla_T u$ by (42) and (43), (41) becomes

(44) $$\square_b u = \frac{n-q-1}{n-1} \overset{*}{\nabla}_{\bar\alpha} \nabla_{\bar\alpha} u + \frac{q}{n-1} (\overset{*}{\nabla}_\alpha \nabla_\alpha u - u\,(R(\bar X_\alpha, X_\alpha))) + u_R$$

where $(u_R)_{\bar\alpha_1 \cdots \bar\alpha_q} = \sum_{i=1}^{q} (-1)^{i+1} u(R(\bar X_{\alpha_i}, X_\alpha))_{\alpha \bar\alpha_1 \cdots \hat\alpha_i \cdots \bar\alpha_q}$

A similar formula has been obtained by Tanaka [4]. Our derivation is more explicit, so that we can write the curvature terms using h alone, as follows:

<u>Proposition 2</u> For any $u \in A_b^{(o,q)}$,

$$(\square_b u, u) = \frac{n-q-1}{n-1} (\nabla_{\bar\alpha} u, \nabla_{\bar\alpha} u) + \frac{q-1}{n-1} (\nabla_\alpha u, \nabla_\alpha u) + nq \left(\frac{n-q-1}{n-1}\right) (H^{-1} u, H^{-1} u)$$

$$+ \frac{n-q-1}{n-1} \int \sum_{i=1}^{q} \tilde K_{\bar\alpha_i \beta}\, u_{\bar\alpha_1 \cdots (\bar\beta)_i \cdots \bar\alpha_q}\, \overline{u}_{\bar\alpha_1 \cdots \bar\alpha_i \cdots \bar\alpha_q}\, \gamma$$

where $\tilde K_{\bar\alpha\beta} = \tilde K_{\bar\alpha\beta\bar\rho\rho}$ with $\tilde K_{\bar\alpha\beta\bar\gamma\rho}$ as in Proposition 1 and $(\beta)_i$ means that β occurs in the ith place.

<u>Proof.</u> One simply writes down $-\frac{q}{n-1} u\,(R(\bar X_\alpha, X_\alpha)) + u_R = \tilde u$ in components using (b) in Proposition 1. After some cancellation, one gets

$$\tilde u_{\bar\alpha_1 \cdots \bar\alpha_q} = \left(-\frac{q^2}{n-1} - \frac{2q(q-1)}{2} + q\,(n-1)\right) H^{-2}\, u_{\bar\alpha_1 \cdots \bar\alpha_q}$$

$$+ \left(1 - \frac{q}{n-1}\right) \sum_{i=1}^{q} u_{\bar{\alpha}_1 \cdots \bar{\beta} \cdots \bar{\alpha}_q} K_{\bar{\alpha}_i \beta} \quad .$$

The formula then follows immediately q.e.d.

§4 Application

(A) Tubular neighbourhood of holomorphic negative line bundle L over compact complex manifold $M^{\#}$ of dimension $n-1$. Let $\{f_{\lambda\mu}\}$ be the transition functions of L with respect to a covering $\{W_\lambda\}$ of $M^{\#}$. Thus $w_\lambda = f_{\lambda\mu} w_\mu$ on $W_\lambda \cap W_\mu$, where w_ν is the fibre coordinate on W_ν . By assumption, there exists a metric on L , given by r_ν on W_ν with $r_\mu = |f_{\lambda\mu}|^2 r_\lambda$ on $W_\lambda \cap W_\mu$, such that the following curvature condition is satisfied:

(45) $-i\Theta = i\partial\bar{\partial} \log r$ is a positive form. (We drop the index ν from now on.) Equivalently, in local coordinates $z^1, \ldots, z^{n-1}$ on W,

(45)' $(r\, r_{\alpha\bar{\beta}} - r_\alpha r_{\bar{\beta}})$ is positive definite, where subscripts denote partial derivatives with respect to z^α .

Let $\rho_{\alpha\bar{\beta}} = r\, r_{\alpha\bar{\beta}} - r_\alpha r_{\bar{\beta}}$ and $\rho_{\alpha\bar{\beta}}\rho^{\bar{\beta}\gamma} = \delta_\alpha^\gamma$.

The boundary M of the tubular neighborhood is given by the equation

$$h = r\,|w|^2 - 1$$

<u>Proposition 3</u> If the Ricci curvature corresponding to the Kähler form $-i\Theta$ on $M^{\#}$ is positive definite, then there is no nontrivial form $u \in \Lambda_b^{(o,q)}$ on M such that $\Box_b u = 0$, for $1 \le q \le n-2$.

<u>Proof</u>: Write $z^n = w$ and $A = r_{\bar{\alpha}} \rho^{\bar{\alpha}\beta} r_\beta$. One easily checks by (45)' that

(46) $$(h_{j\bar{k}})_{1\le j,k\le n} = \begin{pmatrix} |w|^2 r_{\alpha\bar{\beta}} & w r_\alpha \\ w r_{\bar{\beta}} & r \end{pmatrix} \quad \text{is positive definite,}$$

Moreover $H = 1$ and

(46)' $$(h^{\bar{k}l}) = \begin{pmatrix} r\,|w|^{-2}\,\rho^{\bar{\beta}\gamma} & -\bar{w}^{-1}\rho^{\bar{\beta}\sigma} r_\sigma \\ -w^{-1}\rho^{\bar{\sigma}\gamma} r_{\sigma} & r^{-1}(1+A) \end{pmatrix} .$$

One may write down the partial derivatives of h in terms of those of r, e.g. $h_{jl} = |w|^2 r_{jl}$, and compute $K_{\bar{i}j\bar{k}l}$ on M using $|w|^2 = r^{-1}$. First observe that

(47) $$h_{jl} - h_m h^{\bar{p}m} h_{\bar{p}jl} = 0$$

Then a careful computation shows that

(48) $$K_{\bar{i}jkl} = 0 \quad \text{if any index equals } n .$$

while

(48)' $$K_{\bar{\alpha}\beta\bar{\gamma}\rho} = -r^{-1} r_{\bar{\alpha}\beta\bar{\gamma}\rho} + r^{-2} r_{\beta\rho} r_{\bar{\alpha}\bar{\gamma}} .$$

$$+ (r_{\bar{\tau}\beta\rho} + r^{-1} r_{\bar{\tau}} r_{\beta\rho})\rho^{\bar{\tau}\sigma} (r_{\sigma\bar{\alpha}\bar{\gamma}} + r^{-1} r_\sigma r_{\bar{\alpha}\bar{\gamma}})$$

Now $\{X_\alpha\}$ has the form $X_\alpha = x_\alpha^\beta \left(\frac{\partial}{\partial z^B} - r^{-1} r_\beta w \frac{\partial}{\partial w}\right)$, with the orthonormality condition

(49) $$x_\alpha^\gamma \rho_{\gamma\bar{\sigma}} \overline{x_\beta^\sigma} = r^2 \delta_\alpha^\beta ,$$

which implies

(49)' $$x_\gamma^\alpha \overline{x_\gamma^\beta} = r^2 \rho^{\alpha\bar{\beta}} .$$

The Kähler metric we take on $M^\#$ is

(50) $g_{\alpha\bar\beta}\, dz^{\alpha} \otimes d\bar z^{\beta} := (\log r)_{\alpha\bar\beta}\, dz^{\alpha} \otimes d\bar z^{\beta} = r^{-2} \rho_{\alpha\bar\beta}\, dz^{\alpha} \otimes d\bar z^{\beta}$.

The curvature of this metric is given by

$$R^{\#}_{\alpha\bar\beta\gamma\bar\rho} = (\log r)_{\alpha\bar\beta\gamma\bar\rho} - r^{2} \rho^{\bar\tau\sigma} (\log r)_{\bar\tau\beta\rho} (\log r)_{\sigma\bar\alpha\bar\gamma}$$

Using this formula and (48)' , we check that

(51) $K_{\alpha\bar\beta\gamma\bar\rho} = R^{\#}_{\alpha\bar\beta\gamma\bar\rho} - (g_{\beta\bar\alpha}\, g_{\rho\bar\gamma} + g_{\beta\bar\gamma}\, g_{\rho\bar\alpha})$, $g_{\alpha\bar\beta} = r^{-2} \rho_{\alpha\bar\beta}$.

Finally, if we substitute (48)', (51) into the last integral in Proposition 2 and use (49), (49)' , then we get

$$\frac{n-q-1}{n-1} \int \sum_{i=1}^{q} (R^{\#}_{\bar\tau\sigma}\, \overline{x^{\tau}_{\alpha_i}}\, x^{\sigma}_{\beta} - n\delta^{\alpha_i}_{\beta})\, \bar u_{\bar\alpha_1 \cdots \bar\alpha_i \cdots \bar\alpha_q} \cdots u_{\bar\alpha_1 \cdots (\bar\beta)_i \cdots \bar\alpha_q}$$

where $R^{\#}_{\bar\tau\sigma} = R^{\#}_{\bar\tau\sigma\bar\alpha\beta}\, r^{2} \rho^{\bar\alpha\beta}$ is the Ricci curvature.

The negative term cancels with $nq\left(\frac{n-q-1}{n-1}\right)(H^{-1} u, H^{-1} u)$. The proposition then follows from standard argument. q.e.d.

Example: The universal line bundle over $\mathbb{C}P^{n-1}$ with the usual metric on the fibres. In this case, the Kähler metric on $\mathbb{C}P^{n-1}$ as stated in Proposition 3 is the Fubini-Study metric, which has positive definite Ricci curvature. Hence the proposition applies.

B. Cone over complex hypersurface $M^{\#}$ in $\mathbb{C}P^{n}$. Let $M^{\#}$ be given by the equation $P(\zeta^{0}, \ldots, \zeta^{n}) = 0$, where P is a homogeneous polynomial in the homogeneous coordinates $\zeta^{0}, \ldots, \zeta^{n}$, with $dP \neq 0$. The same equation defines a cone $\tilde M$ in $\mathbb{C}^{n+1}$. In studying the isolated singularity of $\tilde M$ at the origin, one naturally considers $\tilde M \cap S^{2n+1}$, that is, the real hypersurface $\tilde M$ in M defined by the equation

$h(x) = \|x\|^2 - 1$, $x \in M$. We prove here the following proposition.

Proposition 4 If the Ricci curvature of M with respect to the induced Fubini-Study metric is positive definite, then there is no nontrivial harmonic $(o, q)_b$ form on M for $1 \leq q \leq n-2$.

Proof: Without loss of generality, suppose that we can locally solve for $Q^o(z^1, \ldots, z^n)$, holomorphic and homogeneous of degree 1, such that

(52) $$P(Q^o(z^1, \ldots, z^n), z^1, \ldots, z^n) = 0 .$$

We use $z^1, \ldots, z^n$ as local coordinates on $\tilde{M}$. h is then given by

(53) $$h(z^1, \ldots, z^n) = | Q^o(z^1, \ldots, z^n) |^2 + z^j \overline{z^j} - 1 .$$

We use subscripts to denote partial derivatives of P and Q also. Clearly

(54) $$(h_{j\bar{k}}) = (Q^o_j \overline{Q^o_k} + \delta^k_j) \text{ is positive definite}$$

and

(54)' $$(h^{\bar{k}l}) = (\delta^l_k - (1+\|Q'\|^2)^{-1} Q^o_k \overline{Q^o_l}) , \text{ where } \|Q'\|^2 = Q^o_j \overline{Q^o_j}$$

A careful computation then shows that

(55) $$K_{\bar{i}j\bar{k}l} = -\overline{Q^o_{ik}} Q^o_{jl} H^{-2} (1+\|Q'\|^2)^{-1}$$

Let $\{X^{\#}_\alpha\}$ be a local orthonormal frame of $(1, 0)$ vectors in $M^{\#}$ with respect to the induced metrice and let $\{X_\alpha\}$ be the lifting in ${}^{o}T'(M)$. In the z coordinates, write $X_\alpha = x^j_\alpha \frac{\partial}{\partial z^j}$ as before, $\{X_\alpha\}$ being orthonormal with respect to $h_{j\bar{k}} dz^j \otimes d\bar{z}^k$.

As vectors in $\mathbb{C}^{n+1}$, $X_\alpha = \sum_{A=0}^{n} x^A_\alpha \frac{\partial}{\partial \zeta^A}$, where $x^o_\alpha = x^j_\alpha Q^o_j$.

Then one checks that

(56) $$P_{AC}\, x^A_\alpha\, x^C_\gamma = P_o\, Q^o_{ik}\, x^i_\alpha\, x^k_\gamma \;,$$

where capital Latin indices run from 0 to n .

The curvature $R^{\#}$ of $M^{\#}$ is given by (cf [5 , p. 825]).

(57) $$\langle R^{\#}(\bar{X}^{\#}_\alpha , X^{\#}_\beta)\; \bar{X}^{\#}_\gamma, \bar{X}^{\#}_\rho\rangle = \delta^\alpha_\beta\, \delta^\gamma_\rho + \delta^\alpha_\rho\, \delta^\gamma_\beta - \|P'\|^{-2}\, \overline{P_{AC}}\, \overline{x^A_\alpha}\, \overline{x^C_\gamma}\, P_{BD}\, x^B_\beta\, x^D_\rho \;,$$

where $\|p'\|^2 = P_A \overline{P_A}$.

(57)' The Ricci tensor on $(\bar{X}^{\#}_\alpha , X^{\#}_\beta)$ equals $n\,\delta^\alpha_\beta - \|p'\|^{-2}\overline{P_{AC}} P_{BD} \overline{x^A_\alpha}\, \overline{x^C_\gamma}\, x^B_\beta x^D_\gamma$.

The proposition then follows from Proposition 2 by the observation that

$$nq(H^{-1}u, H^{-1}u) + \int\sum K_{\bar{\alpha}_i\beta}\; \bar{u}_{\bar{\alpha}_i \cdots \bar{\alpha}_i \cdots \bar{\alpha}_q}\; u_{\bar{\alpha}_1 \cdots (\bar{\beta})_i \cdots \bar{\alpha}_q}\; \gamma$$

$$= \int\sum \left(n\, \delta^\beta_{\alpha_i} - \frac{\overline{Q^o_{ik}}\; Q^o_{jl}}{(1+\|Q'\|^2)}\, \overline{x^i_{\alpha_i}}\, \overline{x^k_\gamma}\, x^j_\beta\, x^l_\gamma\right) \frac{\bar{u}_{\bar{\alpha}_1 \cdots \bar{\alpha}_i \cdots \bar{\alpha}_q}}{H} \frac{u_{\bar{\alpha}_1 \cdots (\bar{\beta})_i \cdots \bar{\alpha}_q}}{H}\, \gamma$$

by (55), and the term in parenthesis equals, by (56)

$$n\,\delta^\beta_{\alpha_i} - \|P'\|^{-2}\, \overline{P_{AC}}\, P_{BD}\, \overline{x^A_{\alpha_i}}\, \overline{x^C_\gamma}\, x^B_\beta\, x^D_\gamma$$, which is the Ricci curvature (57)' q.e.d.

<u>Remark</u> In both cases, we have been very explicit in relating the boundary curvature to the curvature of the base $M^{\#}$. In this way, we hope to set up a framework for considering $(p, q)_b$ forms on M. Vanishing theorems on these would give significant information on the isolated singularities associated to both situations (of [2, 7]) .

References

[1] Chern, S.S., Moser, J.: Real hypersurfaces in complex manifolds. Acta Math., 133, 219-271 (1974)

[2] Kuranishi, M.: Application of $\overline{\partial}_b$ to deformation of isolated singularities Proc. Sympos. Pure Math. A.M.S., 30 part 1, 97-106 (1977)

[3] Morrow J., Kodaira, K.: Complex manifolds, Holt, Rinehart and Winston, New York, (1971).

[4] Tanaka, N.: A differential geometric study on strongly pseudoconvex manifolds. Lectures in Math., vol. 9, Kyoto University, Kinokuniya Book Store Co. Ltd., Tokyo, (1975)

[5] Vitter, A.: On the curvature of complex hypersurfaces. Indiana Univ. Math. J. 23, 813-826 (1974)

[6] Webster, S.: Pseudo-hermitian structures on a real hypersurface. J. Differential Geometry, 13, 25-41 (1978)

[7] Yau, Stephen S.T.: Kohn-Rossi cohomology and its application to the complex Plateau problem, I. Ann. of Math., 113, 67-110 (1981)

Section Two

Methods of Differential Geometry

Several Complex Variables
Proceedings of the 1981 Hangzhou Conference

GEOMETRIE DES COMPACTIFICATIONS DES ESPACES HERMITIENS LOCALEMENT SYMETRIQUES

Paul GERARDIN
Université Paris VII *

Abstract. D.Mumford and others gave in [*] new compactifications of the locally symmetric hermitian spaces. This paper shows that they are also obtained from a completion of the universal covering, as in the case of the Satake-Baily-Borel compactifications. The case of the Siegel modular space is explained in detail.

1. L'espace hermitien symétrique attaché à un espace vectoriel symplectique

On part d'un espace vectoriel symplectique réel V de dimension 2n, dont on écrit $[\ |\ ]$ la forme symplectique et S le groupe des automorphismes symplectiques ; le groupe S est un groupe de Lie presque simple de rang n ; son complexifié $S(\underline{\underline{C}})$ est le groupe de la forme symplectique étendue au complexifié $V \otimes \underline{\underline{C}}$.

Le groupe S opère transitivement sur l'ensemble $D = D(V)$ des structures complexes J sur V pour qui la forme hermitienne

$$u,v \in V \longmapsto (u|v)_J = [u|Jv] + i[u|v]$$

est définie positive ; un tel J est un automorphisme symplectique, et l'action d'un $s \in S$ dessus revient à la conjugaison par s ; ceci fait apparaître D comme sous-variété fermée de S. De plus, le complexifié de $J \in D$ a i et -i pour valeurs propres, et les sous-espaces propres associés L(J) et $\overline{L(J)}$ respectivement sont lagrangiens transverses. Ceci permet de plonger D comme ouvert de la variété complexe projective $D^{\vee} = D(V)$ des lagrangiens de $V \otimes \underline{\underline{C}}$ (l'espace symétrique dual de D), et ainsi D est un espace hermitien, symétrique puisque le sous-groupe d'isotropie de $J \in D$ dans S est son centralisateur, à savoir le groupe unitaire de la forme $(\ |\ )_J$, sous-groupe compact maximal de S.

*Cet exposé a pu être donné à la conférence grâce à la Commission d'Echanges entre la Chine et la France.

Received 1 Dec. 1981

2. L'action géodésique de l'immeuble vectoriel de S sur l'espace symétrique

Désignons par $|S|$ la partie du groupe S formée des éléments qui sont diagonalisables à valeurs propres positives ; en ordonnant les valeurs propres de l'élément $s \in |S|$ par valeurs décroissantes, on définit une filtration de V associée à s :

$$0 \subset W_1 \subset \ldots \subset W_r \subsetneq W_r \subset \ldots \subset W_1 \subset V .$$

Notons $I(S)$ l'ensemble des classes de $|S|$ suivant la relation d'équivalence suivante : avoir mêmes valeurs propres et même filtration", et munissons-le de la métrique définie par le procédé suivant. Pour chaque paire $Z = \{Z',Z''\}$ formée de deux ensembles de n droites de V dont les sommes constituent deux lagrangiens supplémentaires, soit S_Z le sous-groupe de S des éléments qui conservent chacune des $2n$ droites de Z, et $|S_Z|$ la trace de S_Z sur $|S|$; c'est un groupe vectoriel, sous-groupe de Lie de S qu'on munit de la structure d'espace vectoriel euclidien transportée de celle de son algèbre de Lie grâce à la forme de Killing de Lie S. De plus, la projection $|S| \longrightarrow I(S)$ restreinte à S_Z est injective, et deux éléments quelconques de $I(S)$ sont dans un même $|S_Z|$, leur distance dans l'un ne dépendant pas du choix ; enfin, ceci définit une distance sur $I(S)$, qui apparaît comme réunion des espaces euclidiens $|S_Z|$. On dit que $I(S)$ est l'immeuble de S, et que les $|S_Z|$ en sont les appartements. En appelant convexe toute partie de $I(S)$ dont les traces sur les appartements sont convexes, les appartements apparaissent comme les sous-espaces convexes plats maximaux. Le groupe S opère par isométries sur $I(S)$.

Pour $J \in D$ et $\lambda \in I(S)$, on définit un élément λJ de D de la façon suivante : la donnée de J définit une structure hermitienne sur V avec $(\ |\ )_J$, et donc un supplémentaire orthogonal de chaque élément d'une filtration de V dans le suivant ; soit $s \in S$ l'élément hermitien positif pour J qui se projette sur λ : ses sous-espaces propres s'obtiennent de la filtration de V définie par λ par le procédé précédent ; alors λJ est le transformé de J par s. L'application ainsi définie

$$I(S) \times D \longrightarrow D$$

est l'action géodésique de l'immeuble $I(S)$ sur l'espace symétrique D ;

avec Z et $|S_Z|$ comme ci-dessus, on introduit la partie D_Z de D constituée des strucrures complexes J pour qui les $2n$ droites de Z sont orthogonales relativement à la forme $(\ |\ )_J$: l'action géodésique se restreint en une action

$$S_Z \times D_Z \longrightarrow D_Z$$

qui fait apparaître D_Z comme espace affine euclidien de direction $|S_Z|$. De plus, pour $J \in D$, la partie $|S|_J$ de $|S|$ formée des éléments hermitiens positifs pour $(\ |\ )_J$ constituent un espace vectoriel via le logarithme, euclidien, et la projection de $|S|$ sur $I(S)$ envoie $|S|_J$ bijectivement sur $I(S)$, de façon équivariante sous l'action du stabilisateur de J dans S. Enfin, l'action géodésique est séparément bijective, et pour $J \in D$ fixé, la composée de $|S|_J \longrightarrow I(S)$ avec $\lambda \in I(S) \longmapsto \lambda J \in D$ correspond à l'application exponentielle entre l'espace tangent $T_J D = \mathrm{Log}|S|_J$ et la variété riemannienne D ; les bijections ainsi définies, pour chaque $J \in D$:

$$I(S) \longrightarrow D \longrightarrow |S|_J$$

diminuent les distances. Les parties D_Z définies ci-dessus sont aussi les sous-espaces convexes plats maximaux de D, et sont appelés les appartements (affines) de D.

De façon similaire avec le groupe symplectique complexe $S(\underline{\underline{C}})$, on introduit: la partie $|S(\underline{\underline{C}})|$ des éléments diagonalisables à valeurs propres > 0, le quotient $I(V \otimes \underline{\underline{C}})$ de $|S(\underline{\underline{C}})|$ par la relation d'équivalence analogue, les appartements $|S(\underline{\underline{C}})_Z|$ qui sont des espaces vectoriels euclidiens de dimension n, et la métrique sur $I(V \otimes \underline{\underline{C}})$ qui prolonge celle des appartements ; les points fixes de la conjugaison complexe opérant sur $I(V \otimes \underline{\underline{C}})$ redonnent $I(V)$.

Le groupe $\underline{\underline{R}}$ opère sur $|S(\underline{\underline{C}})|$ par $t \in \underline{\underline{R}}$, $s \in |S(\underline{\underline{C}})| \longmapsto s^t$, cette action passe au quotient sur $I(V \otimes \underline{\underline{C}})$, et le quotient de $I(V \otimes \underline{\underline{C}})$ privé de l'image de $1 \in |S(\underline{\underline{C}})|$ est noté $SI(V \otimes \underline{\underline{C}})$. Les éléments de $S(\underline{\underline{C}})$ qui opèrent scalairement sur un lagrangien donné se projettent sur un même élément de $SI(V \otimes \underline{\underline{C}})$, et on injecte ainsi l'ensemble $D^{\vee}$ des lagrangiens complexes dans $SI(V \otimes \underline{\underline{C}})$. On en déduit une injection de l'espace hermitien symétrique D dans $SI(V \otimes \underline{\underline{C}})$:

$$D \longrightarrow SI(V \otimes \underline{\underline{C}}).$$

3. L'achèvement de Satake de l'espace hermitien symétrique

Désignons par $GS(V)$ la grassmannienne symplectique de V, formée des sous-espaces totalement isotropes de V. Pour $W \in GS(V)$, la restriction à $W^\perp$ de la forme symplectique admet W pour noyau, et fait donc de $W^\perp/W$ un espace symplectique, qui possède en particulier un espace hermitien symétrique $D(W^\perp/W)$. La partie de l'espace $D^\vee$ des lagrangiens complexes formée de ceux des lagrangiens L qui vérifient :

$$L \cap \bar{L} = W \otimes \underline{\underline{C}} \quad \text{et} \quad w \in L,\ w \neq 0, \Rightarrow i[\bar{w}|w] > 0$$

est une sous-variété localement fermée de $D^\vee$ que l'application qui envoie L sur son image dans $W^\perp \otimes \underline{\underline{C}} / W \otimes \underline{\underline{C}}$ met en isomorphisme avec $D(W^\perp/W)$; on identifie de cette façon les $D(W^\perp/W)$ avec des sous-variétés de $D^\vee$. Si W est un lagrangien de V, l'espace $D(W^\perp/W)$ est réduit à un point ; si W est $\{0\}$, l'espace $D(W^\perp/W)$ est D lui-même. L'adhérence $\bar{D}$ de D dans D est la réunion des $D(W^\perp/W)$ lorsque W parcourt $GS(V)$; on dira que les $D(W^\perp/W)$ sont les composants de $\bar{D}$. On dispose aussi d'une projection de D sur chacun des $D(W^\perp/W)$, obtenue ainsi : à $J \in D$ on associe la décomposition de V en somme directe $W + W^\perp \cap JW^\perp + JW$, ce qui permet d'identifier $W^\perp/W$ avec $W^\perp \cap JW^\perp$, et définit un élément $J_W \in D(W^\perp/W)$ en prenant la restriction de J à $W^\perp \cap JW^\perp$. Ces projections diminuent les distances.

L'achèvement de Satake $\operatorname{Sat} D$ a même ensemble sous-jacent que $\bar{D}$, et sa topologie a pour base les parties (Ω, W) définies ainsi : Ω est un ouvert de D, $W \in GS(V)$, on appelle U_W le radical unipotent du stabilisateur de W dans S, et $[U_W \Omega]_{W'}$, pour $W' \subset W$ l'image de l'enveloppe convexe de $U_W \Omega$ dans $D(W'^\perp/W')$, ~~et~~ alors (Ω, W) est la réunion des $[U_W \Omega]_{W'}$, quand W' parcourt les sous-espaces vectoriels de W. On appellera achèvement de Satake dans la direction $W \in GS(V)$, la partie $(\operatorname{Sat} D)_W = \bigsqcup_{W' \subset W} D(W'^\perp/W')$.

A chaque $W \in GS(V)$, on associe donc le groupe U_W des automorphismes symplectiques qui opèrent trivialement sur les quotients successifs de la filtration $0 \subset W \subseteq W^\perp \subset V$, et le groupe Z_W sous-groupe de U_W formé de ceux des éléments opérant trivialement sur $W^\perp$ et V/W ; en fait, Z_W est le centre de U_W, le quotient U_W/Z_W étant commutatif. L'action du stabilisateur de W dans S sur Z_W par conjugaison est en fait une action du groupe $GL(W)$; l'application qui à $z \in Z_W$ associe la forme quadratique $v \mapsto [(z-1)v|v]$ sur $V/W^\perp$ permet de voir Z_W comme l'espace vectoriel des formes quadratiques sur $V/W^\perp$, et comme cet espace est le dual de W grâce à la forme symplectique, on a une identification naturelle entre Z_W et l'espace $S_2(W)$ des polynômes homogènes de degré 2 en W ; dans cette bijection, l'action de $GL(W)$ sur Z_W correspond à son action naturelle sur $S_2(W)$. En conséquence, il y a une orbite ouverte C_W de $GL(W)$ dans Z_W, qui correspond au cône convexe ouvert autoadjoint $S_2(W)^{\times}_{+}$ des formes définies positives; de plus, l'adhérence de ce cône C_W dans Z_W est la réunion disjointe de tous les cônes $C_{W'}$ dans les $Z_{W'}$ pour $W' \subset W$, et ceci donne la décomposition de $\bar{C}_W$ en ses facettes (classes suivant la relation sur $\bar{C}_W$ donnée par : avoir même position par rapport à chaque hyperplan d'appui de $\bar{C}_W$).

Pour $W \in GS(V)$, le complexifié $Z_W(\underline{\underline{C}})$ se décompose en $Z_W Z_W^i$, où Z_W^i désigne les points de $Z_W(\underline{\underline{C}})$ que la conjugaison complexe envoie sur leur inverse ; on a aussi un isomorphisme d'espaces vectoriels réels : $z \in Z_W \mapsto z^i \in Z_W^i$, obtenu en faisant agir sur $Z_W(\underline{\underline{C}})$ un automorphisme symplectique induisant sur $W \otimes \underline{\underline{C}}$ l'homothétie $e^{i\pi/4}$; cet isomorphisme envoie le cône C_W sur un cône C_W^i de Z_W^i, et la partie $Z_W C_W^i$ de $Z_W(\underline{\underline{C}})$ est un tube, demi-espace de Siegel usuel.

Le groupe $Z_W(\underline{\underline{C}})$ opère librement sur l'ouvert $Z_W(\underline{\underline{C}})D = Z_W^i D$ de D, et la restriction à D de la fibration $Z_W^i D \longrightarrow Z_W(\underline{\underline{C}}) \backslash Z_W^i D$ fait apparaître D comme fibré en tubes $Z_W C_W^i$ sur $Z_W(\underline{\underline{C}}) \backslash Z_W^i D$; de plus, ceci factorise la projection de D sur $D(W^{\perp}/W)$:

$$D \longrightarrow Z_W(\underline{\underline{C}}) \backslash Z_W^i D \longrightarrow D(W^{\perp}/W),$$

la seconde fibration étant principale de groupe U_W/Z_W.

4. Achevés polyédraux d'espaces vectoriels

On se donne un espace vectoriel E de dimension finie sur $\underline{\underline{R}}$, muni d'un cône C de sommet 0, convexe, saillant (c'est-à-dire ne contenant pas de droite) et ouvert dans son support. Les facettes de C forment un ensemble $\Phi(C)$, contenant l'origine et C notamment. Le cône dual $C^{\vee}$ est constitué des formes linéaires sur E positives sur C ; on suppose en plus que C est simplicial, c'est-à-dire que ses facettes de dimension 1 sont des demi-droites d'une base de E. L'ensemble des applications de $C^{\vee}$ dans l'intervalle $]-\infty,+\infty]$ compatibles avec l'addition sur C et l'action de $\underline{\underline{R}}_+$ forme naturellement une variété à coin où E se plonge comme ouvert dense ; on la note $\mathrm{Ach}_C E$; le groupe E opère dessus, et la décomposition en orbites est la réunion des espaces vectoriels quotients par les supports des facettes du cône C :

$$\mathrm{Ach}_C E = \coprod_{\Phi(C)} \langle F\rangle\backslash E \ ;$$

en plus, l'intérieur de l'adhérence de C dans $\mathrm{Ach}_C E$ est la réunion des images $\langle F\rangle\backslash C$ de C dans les composants de $\mathrm{Ach}_C E$. Une base d'ouverts de la topologie de $\mathrm{Ach}_C E$ est formée des $\coprod_{F'<F} \langle F'\rangle\backslash U+F$ où U est un ouvert de E et $F\in\Phi(C)$. On peut voir aussi $\mathrm{Ach}_C E$ comme se projetant sur $E/\langle C\rangle$ avec fibres $\mathrm{Ach}_C\langle C\rangle$.

Si l'on a deux cônes C et C' comme ci-dessus dont l'intersection des adhérences est l'adhérence d'une facette de chacun d'eux, soit C'' , alors $\mathrm{Ach}_{C''}E$ se plonge comme ouvert (sous-coin) de $\mathrm{Ach}_C E$ et de $\mathrm{Ach}_{C'}E$, et le recollement qui s'en déduit est noté $\mathrm{Ach}_{\{C,C'\}}E$. Plus généraleeent, on appelle éventail dans E la donnée d'un ensemble $\mathcal{E}$ de cônes comme ci-dessus tels que l'intersection des adhérences de deux d'entre eux soit l'adhérence d'une facette de chacun ; on peut donc recoller les $\mathrm{Ach}_C E$ pour $C\in\mathcal{E}$, et on obtient ainsi la variété à coins $\mathrm{Ach}_{\mathcal{E}}E$, sur qui E opère, les orbites étant les $\langle F\rangle\backslash E$ où F parcourt l'ensemble des cônes de E facettes des cônes de $\mathcal{E}$:

$$\mathrm{Ach}_{\mathcal{E}}E = \coprod_{\Phi(\mathcal{E})} \langle F\rangle\backslash E \ , \quad \Phi(\mathcal{E}) = \bigcup_{C\in\mathcal{E}} \Phi(C) .$$

On dit que $\Phi(\mathcal{E})$ est une dissection de la partie de E réunion des $F\in\Phi(\mathcal{E})$.

Lorsque A est un espace affine sous E , on a donc des variétés à coins associées aux éventails de E : $\mathrm{Ach}_{\mathcal{E}}A = \mathrm{Ach}_{\mathcal{E}}E \times^E A$. En particulier, avec Z, S_Z $|S_Z|$ et D_Z comme au §2, les racines longues par rapport au sous-groupe de Cartan S_Z de S définissent 2^n quadrants dans $|S_Z|$, et l'achèvement associé de l'appartement D_Z est son adhérence dans l'achèvement de Satake de D: ce sont des hypercubes.

Avec un cône simplicial C comme ci-dessus dans E , on note $\mathrm{Ach}_C E\otimes\underline{\underline{C}}$ l'espace topologique suivant : c'est la réunion disjointe sur $\Phi(C)$ des espaces vectoriels complexes $\langle F\rangle\otimes\underline{\underline{C}}\backslash E\otimes\underline{\underline{C}}$, et une base d'ouverts est donnée à partir des ouverts U de E et des facettes F de C en prenant les parties de $\mathrm{Ach}_C E\otimes\underline{\underline{C}}$ réunion des $\langle F'\rangle\otimes\underline{\underline{C}}\backslash U+\langle F\rangle+iF$ sur les facettes $F'<F$. Cet espace se projette sur l'achevé $\mathrm{Ach}_C E$ précédent en prenant les parties imaginaires ; la partie réelle le projette sur la somme directe des $\langle F\rangle\backslash E$, $F\in\Phi(C)$. Avec un éventail $\mathcal{E}$ de E , les espaces $\mathrm{Ach}_C E\otimes\underline{\underline{C}}$ se recollent en $\mathrm{Ach}_{\mathcal{E}}E\otimes\underline{\underline{C}}$, réunion disjointe des $\langle F\rangle\otimes\underline{\underline{C}}\backslash E\otimes\underline{\underline{C}}$ quand F parcourt $\Phi(C)$.

Lorsque l'espace $E\otimes\underline{\underline{C}}$ opère librement sur un espace B, on définit des espaces $\mathrm{Ach}_{\mathcal{E}}B$ pour chaque éventail $\mathcal{E}$ de E par $\mathrm{Ach}_{\mathcal{E}}B = \mathrm{Ach}_{\mathcal{E}}E\otimes\underline{\underline{C}} \times^{E\otimes\underline{\underline{C}}} B$, un espace fibré sur $E\otimes\underline{\underline{C}}\backslash B$ en $\mathrm{Ach}_{\mathcal{E}}E\otimes\underline{\underline{C}}$, qui se décompose en $\coprod_{\Phi(\mathcal{E})} \langle F\rangle\otimes\underline{\underline{C}}\backslash B$.

Si l'éventail $\mathcal{E}$ est adapté à un réseau R de E en ce sens que tout cône de $\mathcal{E}$ est engendré par une partie d'une base de R, l'action de R décompose $\mathrm{Ach}_{\mathcal{E}}E\otimes\underline{\underline{C}}$ en les $[(\langle F\rangle\cap R)\backslash(\langle F\rangle\otimes\underline{\underline{C}})]\backslash(R\backslash E\otimes\underline{\underline{C}})$, $F\in\Phi(\mathcal{E})$, qui sont des quotients du tore complexe $R\backslash E\otimes\underline{\underline{C}}$, isomorphe à $R\otimes\underline{\underline{C}}^{\times}$, par les sous-tores $\langle F\rangle\cap R\backslash\langle F\rangle\otimes\underline{\underline{C}}$, isomorphes à $(\langle F\rangle\cap R)\otimes\underline{\underline{C}}^{\times}$: on retrouve les variétés toriques introduites par Mumford notamment, recollées des $\mathrm{Spec}\,\underline{\underline{C}}[F_R^{\vee}]$ pour chaque facette $F\in\Phi(\mathcal{E})$, en notant $F_R^{\vee}$ l'ensemble des formes linéaires sur E entières sur R et $\geqslant 0$ sur F ; ainsi, $R\backslash\mathrm{Ach}_{\mathcal{E}}E\otimes\underline{\underline{C}}$ apparaît comme une variété algébrique lisse.

5. Compactifications des quotients arithmétiques de l'espace D

On se donne une forme entière R de l'espace symplectique V, c'est-à-dire un réseau vérifiant $[R|R] = \underline{\underline{Z}}$. Appelons $GS^R(V)$ la partie de $GS(V)$ des sous-espaces totalement isotropes W de V pour qui $W\cap R$ est un réseau. On désigne par $\mathrm{Sat}^R D$ le sous-espace de $\mathrm{Sat}\,D$ réunion des $D(W^{\perp}/W)$ pour W dans $GS^R(V)$; le sous-groupe de S qui conserve $R\otimes\underline{\underline{Q}}$ opère continument sur $\mathrm{Sat}^R D$. Pour $W\in GS^R(V)$, on écrit $(\mathrm{Sat}^R D)_W = (\mathrm{Sat}\,D)_W \cap \mathrm{Sat}^R D$.

Dans le groupe S, on introduit la partie $C^R(V)$ réunion des cônes C_W pour $W\in GS^R(V)$. A chaque $W\in GS^R(V)$ est associé un réseau Z_W^R de Z_W défini comme le sous-groupe de Z_W qui conserve R. On se donne une dissection Φ de $C^R(V)$, c'est-à-dire un ensemble de parties de $C^R(V)$, chacune étant contenue dans un C_W, $W\in GS^R(V)$, telles que les F adhérents à un C_W constituent une dissection Φ_W de l'adhérence de C_W dans $C^R(V)$ adaptée au réseau Z_W^R. Pour $F\in\Phi$, on note $\{F\}$ l'élément W de $GS^R(V)$ dont le cône C_W contient F ; on écrit Φ_W^o pour l'ensemble des $F\in\Phi$ de $\{F\} = W$, ce qui décompose Φ en partition $\Phi = \coprod_{GS^R(V)} \Phi_W^o$.

Chaque Φ_W définit une variété à coins $\mathrm{Ach}_{\Phi_W} Z_W = \coprod_{\Phi_W} \langle F\rangle\backslash Z_W$, où l'intérieur de l'adhérence du cône C_W est la réunion

$$\mathrm{Ach}_{\Phi_W} C_W = \coprod_{\Phi_W} F\backslash C_W \quad ;$$

dans cette dernière écriture, les morceaux stables sous Z_W sont ceux associés aux $F\in\Phi_W^o$, valant $\langle F\rangle\backslash C_W = \langle F\rangle\backslash Z_W$. L'action libre de l'espace vectoriel complexe $Z_W(\mathbb{C})$ sur $Z_W(\mathbb{C})D = Z^i_W D$ donne, comme indiqué au §4, un espace Ach $Z^i_W D$ réunion disjointe des $\langle F\rangle\otimes\mathbb{C}\backslash Z^i_W D$ pour $W\in\Phi_W$, et où l'intérieur de l'adhé-^{W} rence de D apparaît comme un espace $\mathrm{Ach}_{\Phi_W} D$, fibré sur $Z_W(\mathbb{C})\backslash Z^i_W D$ en fibres $\mathrm{Ach}_{\Phi_W} Z_W C^i_W$, intérieur de l'adhérence du tube $Z_W C^i_W$ dans $\mathrm{Ach}_{\Phi_W} Z_W(\mathbb{C})$. La partie de $\mathrm{Ach}_{\Phi_W} D$ correspondant à $\overset{o}{\Phi}_W$ est formée des $\langle F\rangle\otimes\mathbb{C}\backslash Z^i_W D$, pour $\{F\} = W$.

On recolle ensuite les espaces $\mathrm{Ach}_{\Phi_W} Z^i_W D$: on a $\Phi_W \cap \Phi_{W'} = \Phi_{W\cap W'}$, et $\mathrm{Ach}_{\Phi_{W\cap W'}} Z^i D$ est un ouvert commun aux deux espaces $\mathrm{Ach}_{\Phi_W} Z^i_W D$ et $\mathrm{Ach}_{\Phi_{W'}} Z^i_{W'} D$; on en déduit un recollement de tous les espaces $\mathrm{Ach}_{\Phi_W} D$ en un espace

$$\mathrm{Ach}_\Phi D = \coprod_{\Phi} \langle F\rangle\otimes\mathbb{C}\backslash Z^i_{\{F\}} D .$$

De plus, pour $F\in\Phi$ et $\{F\} = W$, on a une projection du composant $\langle F\rangle\otimes\mathbb{C}\backslash Z^i_W D$ sur $D(W^\perp/W)$ en utilisant l'action du groupe $U_W Z_W(\mathbb{C})$:

$$\langle F\rangle\otimes\mathbb{C}\backslash Z^i_W D \longrightarrow Z_W(\mathbb{C})\backslash Z^i_W D \longrightarrow D(W^\perp/W),$$

décomposition en deux fibrations principales, de groupes $Z_W(\mathbb{C})/\langle F\rangle\otimes\mathbb{C}$ puis U_W/Z_W. Ceci donne une projection de $\mathrm{Ach}_\Phi D$ sur $\mathrm{Sat}^R D$, l'image réciproque de $(\mathrm{Sat}^R D)_W$ étant la réunion des composants associés aux $F\in\Phi_W$.

Soit maintenant un groupe arithmétique Γ, sous-groupe d'indice fini du stabilisateur du réseau R dans S, net en ce sens que 1 est la seule racine de l'unité produit de valeurs propres d'éléments de Γ. Il opère donc proprement sur D, et on a une variété lisse complexe $\Gamma\backslash D$. Le groupe Γ opère aussi sur $\mathrm{Sat}^R D$, et on sait, par Satake-Baily-Borel, que le quotient $\Gamma\backslash\mathrm{Sat}^R D$ est compact et naturellement une variété projective, compactification "minimale" de $\Gamma\backslash D$. Avec une dissection Φ de $C^R(V)$ stable sous Γ et finie modulo Γ, on obtient un espace $\mathrm{Ach}_\Phi D$ sur qui Γ opère, et le quotient $\Gamma\backslash\mathrm{Ach}_\Phi D$ est compact, muni naturellement d'une structure d'espace algébrique, comme l'a démontré Mumford ; de plus, on a une projection :

$$\Gamma\backslash\mathrm{Ach}_\Phi D \longrightarrow \Gamma\backslash\mathrm{Sat}^R D$$

qui prolonge l'identité sur $\Gamma\backslash D$. Pour chaque sous-espace vectoriel $W\in GS^R(V)$, soit Γ_W le sous-groupe de Γ conservant W ; on a alors une projection du sous-espace de $\Gamma\backslash\mathrm{Ach}_\Phi D$ donné par $\Gamma_W \coprod_{\{F\} = W} \langle F\rangle\otimes\mathbb{C}\backslash Z^i_W D$ sur $\Gamma_W\backslash D(W^\perp/W)$, qui se décompose modulo l'action de $Z^i_W(\mathbb{C})$ en deux fibrations.

6. Compactifications des espaces hermitiens localement symétriques

On part d'un domaine hermitien symétrique de type non compact D : la composante neutre de son groupe des automorphismes est un groupe de Lie, composante neutre du groupe S des points réels d'un groupe algébrique semi-simple sur $\underline{\underline{R}}$, et D est aussi l'espace symétrique de S ; la structure complexe sur D détermine pour chaque point de D un élément de l'algèbre de Lie de S induisant la structure complexe sur l'espace tangent au point considéré, et cet élément de l'algèbre de Lie détermine un sous-groupe à un paramètre de $S(\underline{\underline{C}})$, dont le sous-groupe contracté est un sous-groupe parabolique maximal dit spécial ; ceci définit une injection complexe de D dans l'espace symétrique dual D , formé des paraboliques spéciaux de $S(\underline{\underline{C}})$. L'adhérence $\bar{D}$ de D dans D se partitionne en D et les espaces hermitiens symétriques D_P provenant des sous-groupes paraboliques maximaux P de S , et on définit comme au §3 l'achèvement de Satake $\mathrm{Sat}\, D$, de même ensemble sous-jacent que $\bar{D}$. Chaque P a un radical unipotent U_P dont le centre Z_P est de conoyau commutatif, et l'action de P par conjugaison sur Z_P admet une orbite qui est un cône convexe ouvert auto-adjoint ; de plus, le groupe $Z_P(\underline{\underline{C}})$ opère librement sur le saturé $Z_P(\underline{\underline{C}})D = Z_P^i D$ de D dans $\check{D}$ sous $Z_P(\underline{\underline{C}})$; l'espace D apparaît comme fibré sur $Z_P(\underline{\underline{C}})\backslash Z_P^i D$ en fibre-type le cône C_P précédent, et la base est elle-même fibrée sur D_P , fibration principale de groupe U_P/Z_P.

La donnée d'une structure entière R sur S permet de définir les sous-groupes paraboliques maximaux adaptés à R , et donne un achèvement $\mathrm{Sat}^R D$ en se limitant dans $\mathrm{Sat}\, D$ aux D_P provenant des P adaptés à R . On introduit aussi la réunion $C^R \subset S$ de 1 et des cônes C_P provenant de ces P , et si Φ est une dissection de C^R au sens du §5, on a un espace $\mathrm{Ach}_\Phi D$, décomposé en D et les $\langle F\rangle \otimes \underline{\underline{C}} \backslash Z_P^i D$ pour $F \in \Phi$ et F dans le cône C_P. Cet espace se projette sur $\mathrm{Sat}^R D$.

Si maintenant Γ est un sous-groupe arithmétique net de S pour la structure entière R , on sait par Ash qu'il y a une dissection Φ qui est stable par Γ et finie modulo Γ ; alors le groupe Γ opère sur $\mathrm{Ach}_\Phi D$, et le quotient $\Gamma\backslash \mathrm{Ach}_\Phi D$ est un espace compact se projetant sur l'espace compact $\Gamma\backslash \mathrm{Sat}^R D$, comme le démontre Mumford, obtenant de cette façon un espace algébrique au-dessus de la variété projective $\Gamma\backslash \mathrm{Sat}^R D$, compactifications de $\Gamma\backslash D$:

$$\begin{array}{ccc} & & \Gamma\backslash \mathrm{Ach}_\Phi D \\ & \nearrow & \downarrow \\ \Gamma\backslash D & & \\ & \searrow & \Gamma\backslash \mathrm{Sat}^R D \end{array} \quad .$$

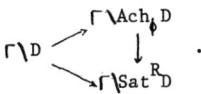

REFERENCES

Sur le groupe symplectique, en plus de N.BOURBAKI, Algèbre Ch.IX :

P.GERARDIN Groupes Symplectiques réels et Domaines de Siegel, Ch.VII dans "Sur les Groupes Classiques",Publications Mathématiques de l'I.R.M.A. n°1,Abidjan, Côte d'Ivoire, 1979,P.95 à 147.

C.L.SIEGEL Symplectic Geometry. Amer.J.Math. 65(1965),1-76. Réédité par Academic Press en 1964.

Sur les compactifications de Satake-Baily-Borel :

W.L.BAILY et A.BOREL Compactifications of arithmetic quotients of bounded symmetric domains. Ann.of Math. (2)84(1966),442-526.

SEMINAIRE E.N.S. PARIS, 10ème année, 1957-58.

I.I.PYATECKII-SHAPIRO Groupes arithmétiques sur les domaines complexes. Uspehi Mat.Nauk 19(6)(1964),93-121 (en russe).

Sur les compactifications polyédriques :

* A.ASH, D.MUMFORD, M.RAPOPORT, Y.TAI Smooth compactification of locally symmetric varieties. Math. Sci. Press. Brookline, Mass.,U.S.A.1975.

J.L.BRYLINSKI Détermination de la fibre du morphisme de la compactification de Ash Mumford... vers la compactification de Satake. Manuscrit, octobre 1978.

J.L. BRYLINSKI "1-motifs" et formes automorphes (théorie arithmétique des domaines de Siegel). Prépublication du Centre de Mathématiques de l'Ecole Polytechnique, Octobre 1979.

P. DELIGNE Espaces hermitiens symétriques. Cours à l'I.H.E.S. mai-juin 1973.

Several Complex Variables
Proceedings of the 1981 Hangzhou Conference

Holomorphic Projective Structures and Invariant Distances

Shoshichi Kobayashi

§ 1. Introduction.

In analogy with the intrinsic pseudo-distance on complex analytic spaces (see [3]), I introduced a projectively invariant pseudo-distance on affine and projective manifolds, [4]. The same construction can be applied to holomorphic affine and, more generally, projective structures to produce an intrinsic pseudo-distance which depends not only on the complex structure but on the given holomorphic projective structure. In this lecture, I will discuss a few examples of holomorphic projective structures and their projective pseudo-distances, referring for details to [7].

§ 2. Holomorphic affine and projective structures.

Let M be an n-dimensional complex manifold. A holomorphic affine structure on M is given by an atlas $\{U_\alpha, \varphi_\alpha\}$ whose coordinate changes are given by holomorphic affine transformations of $\mathbb{C}^n$. More precisely, it is given by an atlas $\{U_\alpha, \varphi_\alpha\}$ satisfying the following conditions :

(i) $\{U_\alpha\}$ is an open cover of M and $\varphi_\alpha : U_\alpha \to \mathbb{C}^n$ is a local coordinate chart ;

(ii) When $U_\alpha \cap U_\beta$ is non-empty, $\varphi_\beta \circ \varphi_\alpha^{-1} : \varphi_\alpha(U_\alpha \cap U_\beta) \longrightarrow \varphi_\beta(U_\alpha \cap U_\beta)$ is given by a complex affine transformation of $\mathbb{C}^n$.

Replacing $\mathbb{C}^n$ by the projective space $\mathbb{P}_n\mathbb{C}$ and requiring that each coordinate change $\varphi_\beta \circ \varphi_\alpha^{-1}$ is given by a projective

Received 1 December, 1981

transformation of $\mathbb{P}_n\mathbb{C}$, we arrive at the notion of holomorphic projective structure.

As usual, two affine or projective structures $\{U_\alpha, \varphi_\alpha\}$ and $\{V_\lambda, \psi_\lambda\}$ on a fixed complex manifold M are considered as identical if $\psi_\lambda \circ \varphi_\alpha^{-1}$ is affine or projective whenever $U_\alpha \cap V_\lambda$ is non-empty.

For the general theory of holomorphic affine and projective structures and the classification of compact complex surfaces with such structures, I mention the following articles, [1],[2], [6],[9].

§ 3. Projective pseudo-distance.

Let M be a complex manifold with a fixed holomorphic projective structure. We can define a projectively invariant pseudo-distance δ_M replacing holomorphic mappings by projective mappings in the definition of the holomorphically invariant pseudo-distance d_M (Kobayashi pseudo-distance). It suffices therefore to clarify what we mean by a projective mapping. Let $\xi^0, \xi^1, \ldots, \xi^n$ and $\zeta^0, \zeta^1, \ldots, \zeta^k$ be homogeneous coordinates for $P_n\mathbb{C}$ and $P_k\mathbb{C}$, respectively. Let U and V be domains in $P_n\mathbb{C}$ and $P_k\mathbb{C}$, respectively. Then a mapping $f : V \longrightarrow U$ is said to be projective if it is given by linear equations

$$\xi^i = \sum_{j=0}^{k} a^i_j \zeta^j.$$

In particular, if k=1, then f is projective if it is given, in terms of the inhomogeneous coordinates $z^i = \xi^i/\xi^0$, $i=1,\ldots,n$, and $t = \zeta^1/\zeta^0$, by equations of the form :

$$z^i = (a^i t + b^i)/(ct + d), \quad i=1,\ldots,n.$$

Since the pseudo-distance δ_M is defined by projective maps which are more restrictive than holomorphic mappings, we have the inequality :

$$\delta_M \geqq d_M$$

If d_M(resp. δ_M) is a distance, M is said to be hyperbolic(resp. projective-hyperbolic).

As in the real case [5], the pseudo-distance δ_M can be defined for a complex manifold with a holomorphic projective connection,[7]. The corresponding infinitesimal pseudo-metric can be also defined as in the real case.

§ 4. Examples.

(a) For the complex line $\mathbb{C}$ with the natural affine structure, we have $\delta_{\mathbb{C}} = 0$ as well as $d_{\mathbb{C}} = 0$

(b) Since $\exp : \mathbb{C} \longrightarrow \mathbb{C}^*$ is a covering map, we have $d_{\mathbb{C}^*} = 0$. However, the exponential map is not projective with respect to the natural affine structure of $\mathbb{C}$ and $\mathbb{C}^*$, and $\delta_{\mathbb{C}^*}$ is a distance, [7].

(c) Let L be a lattice in $\mathbb{C}$. Then for the torus $T = \mathbb{C}/L$ with the induced affine structure, we have $\delta_T = 0$ by (a). Let α be the transformation of $\mathbb{C}^*$ sending z to $2z$, and $\langle\alpha\rangle$ the group generated by α. Then for the torus $T' = \mathbb{C}^*/\langle\alpha\rangle$ with the induced affine structure, $\delta_{T'}$ is a distance by (b).

(d) Let $T = \mathbb{C}^n/L$ be a complex torus of dimension n, where L is a lattice in $\mathbb{C}^n$. The complex structures in T are in one-to-one correspondence with the commutative, associative algebra structures in $\mathbb{C}^n$ over $\mathbb{C}$, [8].

The correspondence is given as follows. A holomorphic affine connection on T is given by a set of constants Γ^i_{jk}, (Christoffel's symbols). These constants, used as structure constants, define an algebra structure in $\mathbb{C}^n$. The algebra structure is commutative if and only if the corresponding connection Γ^i_{jk} is torsion-free. The commutative algebra structure is associative if and only if the corresponding connection has no curvature. Markowitz [7] has shown that an affine structure (i.e., an affine connection with no torsion and curvature) on T is projective hyperbolic if and only if the corresponding commutative, associative algebra is semi-simple.

Bibliography

1. R. Gunning, On uniformization of complex manifolds : the role of connections, Math. Notes No.22, Princeton Univ., Press 1978.
2. M. Inoue, S. Kobayashi and T. Ochiai, Holomorphic affine connections on compact complex surfaces, J. Fac. Sci. Univ. Tokyo 27(1980) 247-264.
3. S. Kobayashi, Hyperbolic manifolds and holomorphic mappings. Marcel Dekker, 1970.
4. __________________, Intrinsic distances associated with flat affine or projective structures. J. Fac. Sci. Univ. Tokyo 24(1977), 129-135.
5. __________________, Projective structures of hyperbolic type, Minimal Submanifolds and Geodesics, Kaigai Publications, Tokyo 1978, 85-92.
6. S. Kobayashi and T. Ochiai, Holomorphic projective structures

on compact complex surfaces, Math. Ann. 249(1980), 75-94 ; II ibid. 255(1981), 519-521.

7. M. Markowitz, Holomorphic affine and projective connections of hyperbolic type, Math. Ann. 245(1979),55-62.

8. Y. Matsushima, Affine structures on complex manifolds, Osaka J. Math. 5 (1968), 215-222.

9. T. Ochiai, A survey on holomorphic G-structures. Proc. of DDI Symposium in Beijing, 1980.

University of California,
Berkeley
and
University of Tokyo

Several Complex Variables
Proceedings of the 1981 Hangzhou Conference

COMPLEX-ANALYTICITY OF HARMONIC MAPS AND VANISHING THEOREMS

Yum-Tong Siu

The purpose of this talk is to point out the similarity between the methods used in investigating the rigidity of compact complex manifolds and those employed in studying their strong rigidity. We hope that in understanding more fully this similarity we can obtain strong rigidity results for Einstein manifolds by using the techniques used in obtaining known results on the rigidity of Einstein manifolds.

A compact complex manifold N is called <u>rigid</u> if any holomorphic family of compact complex manifolds which contains N as a fiber must be holomorphically locally trivial at that fiber. A sufficient condition for a compact complex manifold N to be rigid is the vanishing of the first cohomology group $H^1(N,T_N)$ of N with coefficients in the tangent bundle T_N of N. A simplified schematic illustration of this relationship between the rigidity of N and the vanishing of $H^1(N,T_N)$ is given in Fig.1.

Figure 1

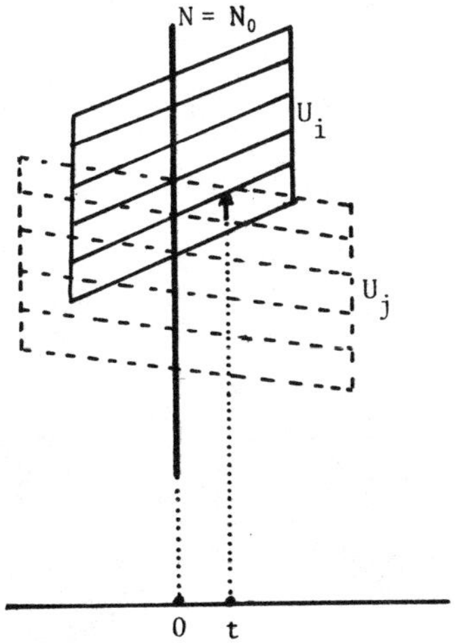

Received 7 July 1982.

Suppose N is the fiber N_0 at $t=0$ of a holomorphic family η of compact complex manifolds N_t parametrized by t. The fiber N_0 which is represented by a vertical line segment is covered by coordinate charts U_i, U_j, etc. of η. These charts have "vertical coordinates" along the fibers of η. The "horizontal coordinates" of two different charts U_i, U_j in general cannot be "parallel" except in the case when the family η is locally trivial at the fiber N_0. When one starts from a point in N_0 and travels along the two different "horizontal coordinates" of U_i and U_j for a distance measured by the parameter t, one ends up at two different points. One joins these two points together by a "vector", divides it by the parameter t, and, upon letting $t \to 0$, obtains a tangent vector of N_0 as limit. This way one gets a tangent vector field ξ_{ij} on $U_i \cap U_j \cap N_0$. Clearly the collection $\{\xi_{ij}\}$ forms a cocycle, because the cocycle condition corresponds to using the three sides of a triangle to define the addition of vectors. When the family η is locally trivial at N_0, there is a common "horizontal coordinate direction" in a neighborhood of N_0, though the "horizontal coordinates" of an arbitrarily chosen coordinate chart U_i may not be along this common "horizontal coordinate direction". In the same way that ξ_{ij} is constructed, from the discrepancy of the "horizontal coordinate" of U_i and the common "horizontal coordinate direction" we construct a tangent vector field ξ_i on $U_i \cap N_0$. Again, by using the sides of a triangle to add vectors, we conclude that $\xi_{ij} = \xi_j - \xi_i$. In other words, when η is locally trivial at N_0, the cocycle $\{\xi_{ij}\}$ is the coboundary of $\{\xi_i\}$. This illustrates how intuitively the rigidity of N is related to the vanishing of $H^1(N,T_N)$.

The most common way of getting the vanishing of $H^1(N,T_N)$ is to invoke the vanishing theorem of Kodaira which uses the technique first introduced by Bochner to conclude the vanishing of a harmonic form from conditions on the curvature tensor. This technique is the same as applying integration by parts to the global square norm of the gradient of a harmonic form. In the complex case the gradient of a harmonic form can be decomposed into two parts. One part is the (0,1)-gradient and the other is the (1,0)-gradient. Integration by parts applied to the global square norm of the (0,1)-gradient yields the vanishing theorem for positive bundles. We call this method of getting vanishing theorems the $\bar{\nabla}$ Bochner-Kodaira technique. Integration by parts applied to the global square norm of the (1,0)-gradient yields the vanishing theorem for negative bundles. We call this method of getting vanishing theorems the ∇ Bochner-Kodaira technique. For a (0,q)-form $\varphi = (\varphi^{\alpha}_{\bar{J}_q})$ on a compact Kähler manifold N with values in a Hermitian holomorphic vector bundle E over N, the key formulas for the $\bar{\nabla}$ and ∇ Bochner-Kodaira techniques are respectively

$$(*) \qquad \Box\varphi = -(\mathrm{tr}\,\nabla\bar{\nabla})\varphi - \Omega\varphi - \mathrm{Ric}\,\varphi$$

$$(\dagger) \qquad \Box\varphi = -(\mathrm{tr}\,\bar{\nabla}\nabla)\varphi - \Omega\varphi + (\mathrm{tr}\,\Omega)\varphi\ .$$

The meanings of the notations in these two formulas are given below (standard notations being used without explanations).

$$\Box = \bar{\partial}\bar{\partial}^* + \bar{\partial}^*\bar{\partial}$$

$$\mathrm{tr}\,\nabla\bar{\nabla} = \sum_i \nabla_i \nabla_{\bar{i}}$$

$$\mathrm{tr}\,\bar{\nabla}\nabla = \sum_i \nabla_{\bar{i}} \nabla_i$$

$$(\Omega\varphi)^{\alpha}_{\bar{J}_q} = \sum_{\tau=1}^{q} \Omega_{\beta}{}^{\alpha\bar{\ell}}{}_{\bar{j}_\tau}\, \varphi^{\beta}_{\bar{j}_1 \cdots (\bar{\ell})_\tau \cdots \bar{j}_q}$$

where

$$\Omega_{\alpha\bar{\beta}i\bar{j}} = \partial_i\partial_{\bar{j}} h_{\alpha\bar{\beta}} - h^{\lambda\bar{\mu}} \partial_i h_{\alpha\bar{\mu}} \partial_{\bar{j}} h_{\lambda\bar{\beta}}$$

is the curvature tensor of the Hermitian metric $h_{\alpha\bar{\beta}}$ along the fibers of E,

$$\bar{J}_q = (\bar{j}_1, \ldots, \bar{j}_q),$$

$(\bar{\ell})_\tau$ means that $\bar{\ell}$ takes the place of the τth index (i.e. $\bar{j}_\tau$), $\alpha, \beta, \ldots$ are indices for coordinates along the fibers of E, and $i, j, \ldots$ are indices for coordinates of N.

$$((\mathrm{tr}\ \Omega)\varphi)^{\alpha}_{\bar{J}_q} = \Omega_{\beta}{}^{\alpha} \varphi^{\beta}_{\bar{J}_q}$$

where

$$\Omega_{\alpha\bar{\beta}} = g^{i\bar{j}} \Omega_{\alpha\bar{\beta}i\bar{j}}$$

and $g_{i\bar{j}}$ is the Kähler metric of the manifold N.

$$(\mathrm{Ric}\ \varphi)^{\alpha}_{\bar{J}_q} = \sum_{\tau=1}^{q} R^{\bar{\ell}}{}_{\bar{j}_\tau} \varphi^{\alpha}_{\bar{j}_1 \ldots (\bar{\ell})_\tau \ldots \bar{j}_q}$$

where

$$R_{i\bar{j}} = \partial_i\partial_{\bar{j}} \log \det (g_{k\bar{\ell}})$$

is the Ricci tensor of N.

The $\bar{\nabla}$ and ∇ Bochner-Kodaira techniques consist of taking the pointwise inner product with φ of both sides of the formulas (*) and (†) and integrating over N when φ is harmonic. The results obtained by these two techniques are equivalent by Serre duality. Moreover, the equivalence can be seen directly from the two formulas (*) and (†) by using the following identity in multilinear algebra

$$\frac{1}{n!(n-q-1)!}\Omega_{\alpha}{}^{\beta\bar{s}}{}_{\bar{t}}\,\psi_{\beta i_1\ldots i_n \bar{s}\bar{j}_{q+2}\ldots\bar{j}_n}\,\overline{\psi^{\bar{\alpha}\bar{i}_1\ldots\bar{i}_n t j_{q+2}\ldots j_n}}$$

$$=\frac{1}{q!}\Omega_{\alpha}{}^{\beta}\varphi^{\alpha}_{\bar{j}_1\ldots\bar{j}_q}\overline{\varphi_{\bar{\beta}}{}^{j_1\ldots j_q}}-\frac{1}{(q-1)!}\Omega_{\alpha}{}^{\beta\bar{s}}{}_{\bar{t}}\varphi^{\alpha}_{\bar{s}\bar{j}_2\ldots\bar{j}_q}\overline{\varphi_{\bar{\beta}}{}^{t j_2\ldots j_q}}$$

where n is the complex dimension of N and $\psi_{\alpha i_1\ldots i_n \bar{j}_{q+1}\ldots\bar{j}_n}$ is the E^*-valued $(n,n-q)$-form which is obtained by applying the Hodge star operator to $\bar{\varphi}$.

The Hermitian bundle E is said to be <u>Nakano</u> q-<u>positive</u> if at any point of N with $g_{i\bar{j}} = \delta_{ij}$ (the Kronecker delta), for any nonzero set of complex numbers $\zeta^{\alpha}_{J_q}$ which is skew-symmetric in the q-tuple J_q of indices the expression

$$-\Sigma_{\alpha,\beta,k,\ell,J_{q-1}}\Omega_{\alpha\bar{\beta}k\bar{\ell}}\,\zeta^{\alpha}_{kJ_{q-1}}\overline{\zeta^{\beta}_{\ell J_{q-1}}}$$

is positive. Similarly one defines semipositivity, negativity, and semi-negativity.

The dual of a Nakano q-positive bundle is in general not Nakano q-negative. It is, however, q-negative in the dual Nakano sense according to the definition given below.

E is said to be q-<u>positive in the dual Nakano sense</u> if at every point of N with $g_{i\bar{j}} = \delta_{ij}$, for any nonzero set of complex numbers $\zeta^{\alpha}_{J_q}$ which is skew-symmetric in the q-tuple J_q of indices, the expression

$$- \Sigma_{\alpha,\beta,k,\ell,J_{q-1}} \Omega_{\alpha\bar{\beta}k\bar{\ell}} \zeta^{\alpha}_{\ell J_{q-1}} \overline{\zeta^{\beta}_{kJ_{q-1}}}$$

is positive.

The $\bar{\nabla}$ Bochner-Kodaira technique from formula (*) yields the vanishing of $H^q(N, E\otimes K_N)$ if E is Nakano q-positive (K_N = canonical line bundle of N). By the identity in multilinear algebra given above, the ∇ Bochner-Kodaira technique from formula (†) yields the vanishing of $H^q(N,E)$ if E is (n-q)-negative in the dual Nakano sense. These two results are equivalent by Serre duality. It does not matter which one is used if one wants to apply it to get the rigidity of N from the vanishing of $H^1(N,T_N)$. However, when we apply their analogs to get strong rigidity later, the analog of formula (†) is more direct.

Another Bochner-Kodaira technique which we call the $\partial\bar{\partial}$ Bochner-Kodaira technique consists of computing $\partial\bar{\partial}(h_{\alpha\bar{\beta}}\varphi^{\alpha}\wedge\overline{\varphi^{\beta}}\wedge\omega_N^{n-q-1})$ and integrating it over N, where ω_N is the Kähler form of N. Because of the identity in multilinear algebra given above, the $\partial\bar{\partial}$ Bochner-Kodaira technique and the ∇ Bochner-Kodaira technique are identical.

When N is Kähler-Einstein and $E = T_N$, by the identity in multilinear algebra given above, T_N is (n-q)negative in the dual Nakano sense if $\kappa > \frac{1}{2}(q+1)\chi$, where κ is given by $R_{i\bar{j}} = \kappa g_{i\bar{j}}$ and χ is the largest eigenvalue of the Hermitian form

$$(\zeta^{ik}) \mapsto R_{i\bar{j}k\bar{\ell}} \zeta^{ik} \overline{\zeta^{j\ell}}$$

($R_{i\bar{j}k\bar{\ell}} = \partial_i\partial_{\bar{j}} g_{k\bar{\ell}} - g^{r\bar{s}} \partial_i g_{r\bar{\ell}} \partial_{\bar{j}} g_{k\bar{s}}$ is the curvature tensor of N).

When N is a compact quotient of an irreducible bounded symmetric domain of complex dimension ≥ 2, Calabi-Vesentini [3] and Borel [2] computed the value χ. Their results yield the ρ-negativity of T_M in the dual Nakano sense for the following values of ρ.

$\rho = (m-1)(n-1) + 1$	for the domain defined by $m \times n$ matrices
$\rho = \frac{1}{2}(n-2)(n-3) + 1$	for the domain defined by skew-symmetric $n \times n$ matrices
$\rho = \frac{1}{2}n(n-1) + 1$	for the domain defined by symmetric $n \times n$ matrices
$\rho = 2$	for the domain defined by n-vectors
$\rho = 6$	for the exceptional domain of complex dimension 16
$\rho = 11$	for the exceptional domain of complex dimension 27.

One has the rigidity of such mainifolds N from the vanishing of $H^1(N,T_N)$ due to the ρ-negativity of T_N in the dual Nakano sense.

We now discuss strong rigidity and point out how strong rigidity can be obtained by using a formula analogous to (†). We consider only the Kähler case.

A compact Kähler manifold M is said to be strongly rigid if any compact Kähler manifold N which is of the same homotopy type as M is either biholomorphic or antibiholomorphic to M.

In the case of rigidity we use harmonic (0,1)-forms with coefficients in the tangent bundle and try to show that they are all zero. In the case of strong rigidity we use instead harmonic maps.

A map $f: N \to M$ is said to be harmonic if it is critical with respect to the energy functional $E(f)$ defined by

$$E(f) = \int_N g^{i\bar{j}} \partial_i f^\alpha \overline{\partial_j f^\beta} h_{\alpha\bar{\beta}}$$

where $h_{\alpha\bar{\beta}}$ is the Kähler metric of M. An equivalent definition is that the Laplacian of f is zero where the Laplacian is defined by using the connections of M and N.

According to Eells - Sampson [4], there is a harmonic map in every homotopy class of maps from N to M if M has nonpositive sectional curvature. From now on we assume that M has nonpositive sectional curvature. We seek to impose additional curvature conditions on M to make it strongly rigid.

Suppose N is of the same homotopy type as M and $f: N \to M$ is a harmonic map which is a homotopy equivalence, We want to investigate when we have the vanishing of either $\bar{\partial} f$ or ∂f. Since f is harmonic, $\bar{\partial} f$ is a (0,1)-form with values in $f^* T_M$ which is harmonic with respect to the connections of M and N. The vanishing of $\bar{\partial} f$ can be proved by using the Bochner-Kodaira techniques in a way analogous to the proof of the vanishing of the harmonic T_N - valued (0,1)-form φ in the study of rigidity. The difference is that in the case of φ the bundle T_N over N is holomorphic whereas in the case of $\bar{\partial} f$ the bundle $f^* T_M$ over N is not known to be holomorphic and, as a matter of fact, may be anti-holomorphic even after we have the strong rigidity of M. So the Bochner-Kodaira techniques will give more complicated curvature terms in the case of $\bar{\partial} f$. Moreover, since only curvature conditions on M are allowed, the formula for the Bochner-Kodaira technique should not contain the Ricci curvature tensor of N. Hence one can only use the ∇ Bochner-Kodaira technique (or the $\partial\bar{\partial}$ Bochner-Kodaira technique which is identical to it). If one wants to use the $\bar{\nabla}$ Bochner-Kodaira technique, one has to use it after applying the Hodge star operator to the complex conjugate of $\bar{\partial} f$. The formula for the ∇ Bochner-Kodaira technique in the case of $\bar{\partial} f$ is

$$\langle \square \bar{\partial} f , \bar{\partial} f \rangle = \langle \nabla \bar{\partial} f, \nabla \bar{\partial} f \rangle + 2R_{\alpha\bar{\beta}\gamma\bar{\delta}} f^{\bar{\beta}\gamma}_{ij} \overline{f^{\bar{\alpha}\delta}_{k\ell}} g^{i\bar{k}} g^{j\bar{\ell}}$$

where $\langle \cdot , \cdot \rangle$ is the pointwise inner product with respect to the metrics of M and N, ∇ is the covariant differential operator in the $(1,0)$-direction, $R_{\alpha\bar{\beta}\gamma\bar{\delta}}$ is the curvature tensor of M, and $f^{\bar{\alpha}\beta}_{ij}$ is defined by

$$\overline{\partial f^{\alpha}} \wedge \partial f^{\beta} = \frac{1}{2} f^{\bar{\alpha}\beta}_{ij} \, dz^i \wedge dz^j$$

($z^1, \ldots, z^n$ are the local coordinates of N).

When T_M is 1-negative in the dual Nakano sense, it follows from the above formula that either $\bar{\partial} f$ or ∂f is zero if the rank of the differential df of f over $\mathbb{R}$ is ≥ 3 at some point of N. The rank condition is automatically satisfied when $n \geq 2$ and f is a homotopy equivalence.

This method is not enough to yield the strong rigidity of compact quotients of irreducible bounded symmetric domains of complex dimension ≥ 2, because in general their tangent bundles are not 1-negative in the dual Nakano sense. To handle this case, we have to apply the Bochner-Kodaira techniques to the wedge product of p copies of $\bar{\partial} f$. Let ζ be the wedge product. The formula is

$$\langle \square\zeta, \zeta \rangle = \langle \nabla\zeta, \nabla\zeta \rangle +$$

$$\frac{p+1}{p!(p-1)!} R_{\alpha_1\bar{\beta}_1\gamma\bar{\delta}} f^{\bar{\beta}_1\ldots\bar{\beta}_p\gamma}_{i_1\ldots i_{p+1}} \overline{f^{\bar{\alpha}_1\ldots\bar{\alpha}_p\delta}_{j_1\ldots j_{p+1}}} h_{\alpha_2\bar{\beta}_2} \cdots h_{\alpha_p\bar{\beta}_p} g^{i_1\overline{j_1}} \cdots g^{i_{p+1}\overline{j_{p+1}}}$$

where $f^{\bar{\alpha}_1 \ldots \bar{\alpha}_p \beta}_{i_1 \ldots i_{p+1}}$ is defined by

$$\overline{\partial f^{\alpha_1}} \wedge \ldots \wedge \overline{\partial f^{\alpha_p}} \wedge \partial f^{\beta} = \frac{1}{(p+1)!} f^{\bar{\alpha}_1 \ldots \bar{\alpha}_p \beta}_{i_1 \ldots i_{p+1}} dz^{i_1} \wedge \ldots \wedge dz^{i_{p+1}} .$$

We say that the bisectional curvature of M is _strongly_ q-_nondegenerate_ when the following holds. If k and ℓ are positive integers, and $\xi_{(1)}, \ldots, \xi_{(k)}$ (respectively $\eta_{(1)}, \ldots, \eta_{(\ell)}$) are $\mathbb{C}$-linearly independent tangent vectors of M of type (1,0) at any point of M such that

$$R_{\alpha\bar{\beta}\gamma\bar{\delta}} \xi^{\alpha}_{(\mu)} \overline{\xi^{\beta}_{(\mu)}} \eta^{\gamma}_{(\nu)} \overline{\eta^{\delta}_{(\nu)}} = 0$$

for all $1 \leq \mu \leq k$ and $1 \leq \nu \leq \ell$, then $k + \ell \leq q$.

The above formula involving ζ yields the following.

Theorem. _Let M be a compact Kähler manifold of complex dimension m. Let $1 \leq p \leq m-1$. Assume that T_M is 1-seminegative and p-negative in the dual Nakano sense. Assume also that the bisectional curvature of M is strongly p-nondegenerate. If f is a harmonic map from a compact Kähler manifold N to M and the rank of df over $\mathbb{R}$ is $\geq 2p+1$ at some point of N, then f is either holomorphic or antiholomorphic._

Corollary. _A compact Kähler manifold M of complex dimension m is strongly rigid if T_M is 1-seminegative and (m-1)-negative in the dual Nakano sense and the bisectional curvature of M is strongly (m-1)-nondegenerate._

The tangent bundles of irreducible bounded symmetric domains are 1-seminegative in the dual Nakano sense and, as we saw earlier, are also ρ-negative in the dual Nakano sense with the value ρ given above. Their bisectional curvatures are strongly ρ-nondegenerate. This was verified in [8] for the classical domains. For the exceptional domains it was verified by Zhong [10]. Hence the compact quotients of irreducible bounded symmetric domains of complex dimension ≥ 2 are strongly rigid.

The term "strong rigidity" was introduced by Mostow. He used it in a slightly different sense. He showed that a compact locally symmetric Riemannian manifold of nonpositive curvature with no totally geodesic 1- or 2-dimensional submanifolds which are local direct factors is strongly rigid in the sense that any two such manifolds which are homeomorphic must be isometric after renormalization of the metrics [7]. Our strong rigidity result is stronger than Mostow's in the complex case because for our result curvature conditions are needed only for one of the two manifolds. The analog of our strong rigidity result in the real case should be the strong rigidity of compact Einstein manifolds. One seeks to impose suitable negativity conditions on the curvature tensor of a compact Einstein manifold to make it strongly rigid in the sense that any compact Einstein manifold of the same homotopy type must be isometric to it after renomalization of the metrics. There are rigidity results on compact Einstein manifolds [1, 5, 6], but strong rigidity results are still unknown. We hope that the similarity between the methods used to study rigidity and strong rigidity in the complex case which we point out here may be of some help in trying to obtain strong rigidity results from rigidity results in the real case.

Details of the discussion given in this talk can be found in [9]. (Remark 2 on p.75 of [9] holds only for $E = T_M$ which is the only case used there. $\eta^{\beta}_{(\nu)}$ in (5.8.1) of [9, p. 89] should read $\eta^{\delta}_{(\nu)}$.)

References.

1. M. Berger & D. Ebin, Some decomposition of the space of symmetric tensors of a Riemannian manifold, J. Diff. Geom. 3 (1969), 379-392.

2. A. Borel, On the curvature tensor of the Hermitian symmetric manifolds, Ann. of Math. 71 (1960), 508-521.

3. E. Calabi & E. Vesentini, On compact locally symmetric Kähler manifolds, Ann. of Math. 71 (1960), 472-507.

4. J. Eells & J.H. Sampson, Harmonic mappings of Riemannian manifolds, Amer. J. Math. 86 (1964), 109-160.

5. N. Koiso, Non-deformability of Einstein metrics, Osaka J. Math. 15 (1978), 419-433.

6. N. Koiso, Rigidity and stability of Einstein metrics - the case of compact symmetric spaces, Osaka J. Math. 17 (1980), 51-73.

7. G.D. Mostow, Strong Rigidity of Locally Symmetric Spaces, Ann. of Math. Studies 78 (1973), Princeton University Press.

8. Y.T. Siu, Strong rigidity of compact quotients of exceptional bounded symmetric domains, Duke Math. J. 48 (1981), 857-871.

9. Y.-T. Siu, Complex-analyticity of harmonic maps, vanishing and Lefschetz theorems, J. Diff. Geom. 17 (1982), 55-138.

10. J.-C. Zhong, The degree of strong nondegeneracy of the bisectional curvature of exceptional bounded symmetric domains, Proc. Intern. Conf. Several Complex Variables, Hangzhou, China 1981.

Author's address: Department of Mathematics, Stanford University, Stanford, California 94305, U.S.A.

Several Complex Variables
Proceedings of the 1981 Hangzhou Conference

THE CHARACTERIZATION OF STRICTLY PARABOLIC SPACES

Wilhelm Stoll

Department of Mathematics University of Notre Dame

Notre Dame, Indiana, USA

The famous Riemann mapping theorem asserts that a simple connected Riemann surface is biholomorphically equivalent to the Riemann sphere $\mathbb{P}_1$, the complex plane $\mathbb{C}$ or the unit disc $\mathbb{C}(1)$. No equivalent theorem exists in several variables. Already Poincaré observed that the unit ball and the polydisc are not biholomorphically equivalent. Hence purely topological means will not suffice to classify complex manifolds. Here an exhaustion is used.

Let M be an irreducible complex space of dimension m. Let τ be a non-negative function of class C^∞ on M. Define $\Delta = \sup_M \sqrt{\tau}$ as the <u>maximal radius</u> of τ. Assume that $\sqrt{\tau} < \Delta \leq \infty$ on M. Hence M is not compact. For each $r > 0$ define the

closed pseudoball: $M[r] = \{x \in M \mid \tau(x) \leq r^2\}$

<u>open pseudoball</u>: $M(r) = \{x \quad M \mid \tau(x) < r^2\}$

<u>pseudosphere</u>: $M\langle r\rangle = \{x \in M \mid \tau(x) = r^2\}$

<u>center</u>: $M[0] = \{x \in M \mid \tau(x) = 0\}$

<u>periphery</u>: $M_* = \{x \in M \mid \tau(x) > 0\}$.

The function τ is said to be an exhaustion of maximal radius Δ, if $M[r]$ is compact for every $r \in \mathbb{R}[0,\Delta)$.

Received 27 November, 1981

The exterior derivative splits into $d = \partial + \bar{\partial}$ and twists to $d^c = \frac{i}{4\pi}(\bar{\partial} - \partial)$. The function τ is said to be parabolic if

(1) $$dd^c \log \tau \geq 0 \qquad (dd^c \log \tau)^m \equiv 0 \qquad (dd^c\tau)^m \not\equiv 0$$

on M_*. If τ is parabolic and an exhaustion with maximal radius Δ, we call τ a parabolic exhaustion and (M,τ) a parabolic space of dimension m and maximal radius Δ.

The name "parabolic" was suggested by Griffiths and King [2]. In [4] the following properties of parabolic manifolds and spaces were proved: Let (M,τ) be a parabolic space. Let $\tilde{M}$ be an irreducible complex space with $\dim \tilde{M} = \dim M$. Let $\pi : \tilde{M} \to M$ be a proper, surjective holomorphic map. Then $\tilde{\tau} = \tau \circ \pi$ is a parabolic exhaustion of M with the same maximal radius as τ. Define $\tau_0 : \mathbb{C}^m \to \mathbb{R}_+$ by

(2) $$\tau_0(z) = |z_1|^2 + \ldots + |z_m|^2.$$

Then $(\mathbb{C}^m,\tau_0)$ is a parabolic manifold of dimension m and maximal radius Δ. Every irreducible, affine algebraic space of dimension m can be spread over $\mathbb{C}^m$ by a proper, surjective holomorphic map and, consequently carries a parabolic exhaustion of infinite maximal radius. $(\mathbb{C} - \mathbb{Z}) \times \mathbb{C}^{m-1}$ is a parabolic manifold with infinite maximal radius but is not affine algebraic. For $j = 1, \ldots ,n$, let (M_j,τ_j) be parabolic spaces of infinite maximal radii. Then $M = M_1 \times \ldots \times M_n$ carries a parabolic exhaustion τ of infinite maximal radius defined by

(3) $$\tau(x_1, \ldots, x_n) = \tau_1(x_1) + \ldots + \tau_n(x_x).$$

A non-compact Riemann surface carries a parabolic exhaustion of maximal radius ∞ if and only if every subharmonic function bounded from above is constant.

An effective Nevanlinna theory can be developed on parabolic manifolds ([2],[4]). Certain advantages were to be gained on so-called strictly parabolic manifolds. Here a parabolic manifold (M,τ) is said to be <u>strict</u> if $dd^c\tau > 0$, hence if

(4) $$dd^c\tau > 0 \quad \text{on} \quad M \qquad dd^c \log \tau \geq 0 \qquad (dd^c \log \tau)^m \equiv 0 \quad \text{on} \quad M_* .$$

If $0 < \Delta \leq \infty$ and if τ_0 is defined by (2) and if $\mathbb{C}^m(\Delta) = \{z \in \mathbb{C}^m \mid \tau_0(z) < \Delta^2\}$, then $(\mathbb{C}^m(\Delta), \tau_0)$ is a strictly parabolic manifold of dimension m and maximal radius Δ.

<u>Theorem 1</u>. Let (M,τ) be a strictly parabolic manifold of dimension m and maximal radius Δ. Then there exists a biholomorphic isometry $h : \mathbb{C}^m(\Delta) \to M$ with $\tau \circ h = \tau_0$.

Orginally [3], an additional assumption was needed which was eliminated by Dan Burns [1]. The proof of Theorem 1 appeared in [5]. Subsequently, Dan Burns [1] and Pit-Mann Wong [7] gave alternative proofs.

Now, strictly parabolic complex spaces shall be defined. Let M be an irreducible complex space of dimension m. A proper, injective, holomorphic map $j : U \to G$ of an open subset U of M into an open subset

G of $\mathbb{C}^n$ is called a chart of M if $j : U \to U' = j(U)$ is biholomorphic. If $U = U'$ is identified such that $j : U \to G$ becomes the inclusion, the chart is called embedded. (M,τ) is called a strictly parabolic space of dimension m and maximal radius Δ if

(1) M is an irreducible complex space of dimension m.

(2) $\tau : M \to \mathbb{R}_+$ is an exhaustion with maximal radius Δ.

(3) Let $\mathfrak{R}(M)$ be the set of regular points of M. Then $\tau \mid \mathfrak{R}(M)$ is a strictly parabolic function.

(4) For every point $a \in M$ there exists an embedded chart $j : U \to G$ with $a \in U$ and a non-negative function θ of class C^∞ on G such that $\theta \mid U = \tau \mid U$ and such that $dd^c\theta > 0$ on G. Moreover for every point $p \in U \cap M_*$ there exists an open neighborhood V_p of p in G such that $\theta \mid V_p > 0$ and $dd^c \log \theta \geq 0$ on V_p.

The function θ is called a strictly parabolic extension of τ. Then

(5) $$(dd^c \log \theta)^n = 0 \qquad \text{on } U \cap M_*$$

but not necessarily on any open subset of G.

Let K be an irreducible, analytic cone of dimension m with vertex 0 in $\mathbb{C}^n$. Define $K_* = K - \{0\}$ and $\mathbb{C}^n_* = \mathbb{C}^n - \{0\}$. Define $\theta_0 : \mathbb{C}_n \to \mathbb{R}_+$ by

(6) $$\theta_0(z) = |z_1|^2 + \ldots + |z_n|^2.$$

Then $\tau_0 = \theta_0 \mid K$ is an exhaustion of maximal radius ∞ of K. Obviously $dd^c\tau_0 > 0$ on $\mathfrak{R}(K)$ and $dd^c \log \tau_0$ on $\mathfrak{R}(K_*)$. Let $\mathbb{P} : \mathbb{C}^n_* \to \mathbb{P}_{n-1}$ be the standard projection. Then $K' = \mathbb{P}(K_*)$ is an irreducible analytic subset of $\mathbb{P}_{n-1}$ with $\dim K' = m - 1$. Let $\iota : K' \to \mathbb{P}_{n-1}$ and $j : K \to \mathbb{C}^n$ be the inclusions. Then $j : K \to \mathbb{C}^n$ is an embedded chart. Moreover $\iota \circ \mathbb{P} = \mathbb{P} \circ j$. Let Ω be the Fubini-Study form on $\mathbb{P}_{n-1}$. Then

(7) $$dd^c \log \theta_0 = \mathbb{P}^*(\Omega).$$

For dimension reasons, $\iota^*(\Omega)^m = 0$ on K'. Therefore

$$(dd^c \log \tau_0)^m = j^*(dd^c \log \theta_0)^m = j^*\mathbb{P}^*(\Omega^m) = \mathbb{P}^*\iota^*(\Omega^m)$$
$$= \mathbb{P}^*(\iota^*(\Omega)^m) = \mathbb{P}^*(0) = 0.$$

Consequently, $\tau_0 \mid \mathfrak{R}(K)$ is strictly parabolic. Obviously, θ_0 satisfies (4) and is a strictly parabolic extension of τ_0. Consequently, τ_0 is a parabolic exhaustion of K. Take $0 < \Delta \leq \infty$ and define

(8) $$K(\Delta) = \{z \in K \mid \tau_0(z) < \Delta^2\} = K \cap \mathbb{C}^n(\Delta).$$

Then $(K(\Delta),\tau_0)$ is a strictly parabolic space of dimension m and maximal radius Δ.

<u>Theorem 2</u>. Let (M,τ) be a strictly parabolic space of dimension m and radius Δ. Then there exists an irreducible, affine algebraic cone K of dimension m embedded into some $\mathbb{C}^n$ with $m \leq n$ and a biholomorphic iso-

metry $h : K(\Delta) \to M$ such that $\tau_0 = \tau \circ h$.

The cone K can be identified. It is shown, that the center $M[0]$ consists of one and only one point 0_M. Then K is the Whitney tangent cone at 0_M embedded into the Zariski tangent space $\mathfrak{m}/\mathfrak{m}^2$ which is identified with $\mathbb{C}^n$. Thus n is the embedding dimension at 0_M. The proof of Theorem 2 is given in [6] and is not a direct generalization of the original proof of Theorem 1, since the singularities of M provide considerable difficulties. Only the steps of the proof shall be sketched here

1. Step. The concept of a vector field of clan C^∞ on a complex space is introduced and the standard theory of integral curves is extended to these types of vector fields.

2. Step. The exterior form $dd^c\tau > 0$ defines a Kaehler metric on $\mathfrak{R}(M)$. The real vector fields

$$F = (1/2)\operatorname{grad} \tau \qquad Y = F/\sqrt{\tau} = \operatorname{grad} \sqrt{\tau} \tag{9}$$

extend to vector fields of clan C^∞ on M respectively M_*.

3. Step. A flow $\psi : \mathbb{R}(0,\Delta) \times M_* \to M_*$ of clan C^∞ is defined such that

$$\dot{\psi}(t,p) = Y(\psi(t,p)) \tag{10}$$

$$\psi(\sqrt{\tau(p)},p) = p \tag{11}$$

$$\tau(\psi(t,p)) = t^2 \tag{12}$$

4. Step. The center $M[0]$ consists of one and only one point 0_M.

5. Step. Put $\Delta_0 = \log \Delta$ and define $\chi : \mathbb{R}(-\infty,\Delta_0) \times M_* \to M_*$ by

(13) $$\chi(x,p) = \psi(e^x,p).$$

Then

(14) $$\chi(x,p) = F(\chi(x,p)).$$

6. Step. The rotated vector field $\mathfrak{J}F$ is complete and defines a one parameter group of diffeomorphisms $\sigma : \mathbb{R} \times M_* \to M_*$ such that

(15) $$\sigma(0,p) = 0 \qquad \tau(\sigma(y,p)) = \tau(p) \qquad \sigma(y,p) = F(\sigma(y,p)).$$

If $p \in M\langle r\rangle$, then $\sigma(y,p) \in M\langle r\rangle$ for all $y \in \mathbb{R}$. Since $[F, F] = 0$

(16) $$\mathfrak{w}(x + iy,p) = \chi(x,\sigma(y,p)) = \sigma(y,\chi(x,p)).$$

The map $z \to \mathfrak{w}(z,p)$ is holomorphic in z on $D = \mathbb{R}(-\infty,\Delta_0) \quad \mathbb{R}$.

7. Step. Let $j : U \to G \subseteq \mathbb{C}^n$ be an embedded chart with $0_M \in U$ and $j(0_M) = 0$ such that there is a strictly parabolic extension θ on G. Take $0 < r_0 < \Delta$ such that $M[r_0] \subset G$. Let K be the Whitney tangent cone K of M at $0_M = 0$ in $\mathbb{C}^n$ and let $K[r]$, $K\langle r\rangle$ and $K(r)$ be defined in respect to the strictly parabolic exhaustion τ_0 of K. Then ψ extends to a map $\psi : \mathbb{R}[0,\Delta) \times M_* \to M$ with $\psi(0,p) = 0_M$ such that $\psi(t,p)$ is geodesic as a function of $t \in \mathbb{R}[0,r_0]$ in respect to the Kaehler metric $dd^c\theta > 0$. Then $\psi(0,p) \in K\langle 1\rangle$ and the map $p \to \psi(0,p)$ defines diffeomorphism from $M\langle r_0\rangle$ onto $K\langle 1\rangle$ whose inverse is denoted by

(17) $$\mathfrak{y} : K\langle 1\rangle \to M\langle r_0\rangle.$$

Then $\sigma(y, (\xi)) \in M\langle r_0\rangle$ for all $y \in \mathbb{R}$ and $\xi \in K\langle 1\rangle$. Define

(18) $$\zeta(Y,\xi) = \psi(0,\sigma(y,\eta(\xi))) = \eta^{-1}(\sigma(y,\eta(\xi))).$$

Then $\zeta(0,\xi) = \xi$ for all $\xi \in K\langle 1\rangle$. Local analysis shows that

(19) $$\zeta_y(y,\xi) = i\zeta(y,\xi).$$

Therefore

(20) $$\zeta(y,\xi) = e^{iy}\xi.$$

8. Step. Consequently

$$\mathfrak{w}(x + iy,\eta(\xi)) = \chi(x,\sigma(y,\eta(\xi)))$$

$$= \chi(x,\eta(\zeta(y,\xi))) = \mathfrak{w}(x + iy + 2\pi ik,\eta(\xi))$$

for all $k \in \mathbb{Z}$. Therefore a flow of class C^∞

(21) $$\mathfrak{v} : \mathbb{C}(\Delta) \times K\langle 1\rangle \to M$$

is defined by

(22) $$\mathfrak{v}(e^z,\zeta) = \mathfrak{w}(z,\eta(\zeta)) \qquad \mathfrak{v}(0,\zeta) = 0_M .$$

The map $z \to \mathfrak{v}(z,\xi)$ is holomorphic and injective on $\mathbb{C}(\Delta)$.

9. Step. Define $h : K(\Delta) \to M$ by $h(0) = 0_M$ and by

(23) $$h(z) = \psi(||z||,\eta(\frac{z}{||z||}))$$

if $0 \neq z \in K(\Delta)$. If $t_0 > 0$ is small enough, then $h(z) = \exp_0(z)$ for $z \in K(t_0)$. Hence h is a diffeomorphism of class C^∞.

10. Step. Take $0 \neq z \in C(\Delta)$. Then $x \in \mathbb{R}$ and $y \in \mathbb{R}$ exist such that $e^{x+iy} = z$. Take $\xi \in K\langle 1\rangle$. Then

$$h(z\xi) = \psi(e^x, \mathfrak{y}(z\xi e^{-x})) = \chi(x, \mathfrak{y}(e^{iy}\xi))$$

$$= \mathfrak{w}(x + iy, \mathfrak{y}(\xi)) = \mathfrak{v}(z, \mathfrak{y}(\xi)).$$

The map h is holomorphic on each disc $\mathbb{C}(\Delta)\xi$. Since h is of class C^∞ on $K(\Delta)$, this implies that h is holomorphic. A holomorphic diffeomorphism of class C^∞ is biholomorphic. Hence $h : K(\Delta) \to M$ is biholomorphic. Since

$$\tau(h(z)) = \tau(\psi(||z||, \mathfrak{y}(\frac{z}{||z||}))) = ||z||^2 = \tau_0(z)$$

the map h is an isometry; q.e.d,

REFERENCES

[1] Burns, D., " Curvature of Monge-Ampère foliation and parabolic manifolds," preprint, 50 pp of ms.

[2] Griffiths, Ph.A. and J. King, " Nevanlinna theory and holomorphic mappings between algebraic varieties," Acta Math., 30(1973), 145-220.

[3] Stoll, W., " Variétés strictement parabolique," C.R. Acad. Sci. Paris, 285(1977) Série A, 757-759.

[4] Stoll, W., " Value distribution on parabolic spaces," Lecture Notes in Mathematics, 600(1977), 216. Springer-Verlag.

[5] Stoll, W., " The characterization of strictly parabolic manifolds," Ann. Scuola Norm. Sup. Pisa, 7(1980), 87-154.

[6] Stoll, W., " The characterization of strictly parabolic spaces," Compositio Math., 44(1981), 305-373.

[7] Wong, P.-M., " Geometry of the complex homogeneous Monge-Ampère equation," Invent. Math., 67(1982), 261-274.

This research as well as Stoll's participation in the Hangzhou conference was support in part by the National Science Foundation Grant MCS 8003257.

Several Complex Variables
Proceedings of the 1981 Hangzhou Conference

THE CHARACTERISTIC NUMBERS OF 4-DIMENSIONAL KÄHLER MANIFOLDS

Y.L. Xin

(Institute of Mathematics, Fudan University
Shanghai, China)

Using the decomposition of the curvature tensor, we obtain relations between the Euler number and the Pontrjagin number for 4-dimensional k-Ricci pinched and λ-holomorphically pinched Kähler manifolds.

More precisely we have the following results.

Theorem 1. Let M be a compact 4-dimensional Kähler manifold with Euler number χ and Pontrjagin number p. If M is k-Ricci pinched with $k \geq \frac{\sqrt{2}}{2}$, then the inequalities

$$\chi + \frac{3-5k^2}{2k} p \geq 0 \tag{1}$$

and

$$\chi + \frac{1}{2} p \geq 0 \tag{2}$$

are valid. Furthermore, if equality (1) occurs, the M must be in one of the following three cases:

(1) M has constant holomorphic sectional curvature;

(2) The universal covering manifold of M is a K3 surface;

(3) M is flat.

Received 1 June 1982

If equality (2) occurs, then M must be in one of cases (2) and (3) above.

By a k-Ricci pinched manifold we mean a Riemannian manifold in which

$$\frac{1}{4}|s| \geq k \left|\text{any eigenvalue of Ricci curvature}\right|$$

where s is the scalar curvature. Note that for Einstein manifolds k = 1.

Theorem 1 is a generalization of Donneley's result [2].

Theorem 2. Let M be a compact 4-dimensional Kähler manifold which is λ-holomorphically pinched with $\lambda \geq 0$; then the following inequalities hold:

$$\begin{cases} \chi + \frac{1}{2}p \geq 0 \\ \chi + \min\left(\frac{1-2\lambda-5\lambda^2}{6\lambda^2}, \frac{\lambda^2}{\lambda^2-4}\right)p \geq 0 \end{cases} \qquad \text{if} \quad \lambda \in [\tfrac{1}{4},1]$$

$$\begin{cases} \chi + \frac{\lambda^2}{1-4\lambda^2} p \geq 0 \\ \chi + \frac{\lambda^2}{\lambda^2-4} p \geq 0. \end{cases} \qquad \text{if} \quad \lambda \notin [\tfrac{1}{4},1].$$

By the λ-holomorphically pinching condition we mean that there is a constant A satisfying $\lambda A \leq H \leq A$, where H is holomorphic sectional curvature.

The above result is a generalization of Bishop-Goldberg's theorem [1].

REFERENCES

[1] R.L. Bishop and I.S. Goldberg, "Some implications of the generalized Gauss-Bonnet theorem", Trans. Amer. Math. Soc. 112 (1964), 508-535.

[2] H. Donnelly, "Topology and Einstein Kaehler metrics", J. Differential Geometry 11 (1976), 259-264.

Several Complex Variables
Proceedings of the 1981 Hangzhou Conference

ON THE SCHWARZ LEMMA FOR COMPLETE HERMITIAN MANIFOLDS

Yang Hong-cang

(Institute of Mathematics, Academic Sinica)

and

Chen Zhi-hua

(Institute of Mathematics, Academic Sinica)

Abstract

This paper generalizes a result from Chen, Cheng and Lu [1] and improves a result from Yau [2]. Let M be a complete Hermitian manifold whose holomorphic sectional curvature is bounded from below by k_1 (or whose second Ricci curvature is bounded from below by R_1^T). Let N be a Hermitian manifold whose holomorphic sectional curvature is bounded from above by $k_2 < 0$. We shall prove that if $f: M \longrightarrow N$ is a holomorphic mapping and some conditions on the curvature and torsion of M and N are given, then

$$f^*ds_N^2 \leq \frac{k_1}{k_2} ds_M^2$$

$$\text{(or} \qquad f^*ds_N^2 \leq \frac{R_1^T}{k_2} ds_M^2).$$

1. INTRODUCTION

Yau [2] proved a general Schwarz lemma:

Let M be a complete Kaehler manifold whose Ricci curvature is bounded from below by R_1. Let N be a Hermitian manifold

Received 1 Dec. 1981

whose holomorphic bisectional curvature is bounded from above by $K_2 < 0$. If $f: M \longrightarrow N$ is a non-constant holomorphic mapping, then

$$f^* ds_N^2 \leq \frac{R_1}{K_2} ds_M^2. \tag{1}$$

Chen, Cheng and Lu [1] proved a general Schwarz lemma different from (1):

Let M be a complete Kaehler manifold whose holomorphic sectional curvature is bounded from below by k_1 and whose Riemannian sectional curvature is also bounded from below. Let N be a Hermitian manifold whose holomorphic sectional curvature is bounded from above by $k_2 < 0$. If $f: M \longrightarrow N$ is a non-constant holomorphic mapping, then

$$f^* ds_N^2 \leq \frac{k_1}{k_2} ds_M^2 . \tag{2}$$

H.L. Royden [3] proved the following:

Let M be a complete Kaehler manifold whose Ricci curvature is bounded from below by R_1. Let N be a Kaehler manifold whose holomorphic sectional curvature is bounded from above by $k_2 < 0$. If $f: M \longrightarrow N$ is a non-constant holomorphic mapping, then

$$f^* ds_N^2 \leq \frac{2k}{1+k} \cdot \frac{R_1}{k_2} ds_M^2 , \tag{3}$$

where k = max rank f.

The general Schwarz lemmas given above have a common condition that M is a Kaehler manifold. We shall prove that formulae (1) and (2) can be generalized to Hermitian manifolds. In particular, we shall prove (1) for Hermitian manifolds. The formulae we got differ from Royden's formulae. The principal idea is due to Chen, Cheng and Lu [1]. As an application, we shall give a generalization of Liouville's theorem.

2. NOTATIONS. ELEMENTARY FORMULAE

We use mainly the terminology in Lu [4] and [1]. Let M be an m-dimensional Hermitian manifold whose unitary frame is $\{e_i\}$ with dual frame $\{\theta^i\}$, $i = 1,\cdots,m$. Let N be an n-dimensional Hermitian manifold whose unitary frame is $\{\tilde{e}_\alpha\}$ with dual frame $\{\omega_\alpha\}$, $\alpha = 1,\cdots,n$. The Hermitian metric of M is

$$ds_M^2 = \sum_i \theta^i \overline{\theta}^i , \tag{4}$$

and the Hermitian metric of N is

$$ds_N^2 = \sum_\alpha \omega^\alpha \overline{\omega}^\alpha , \tag{5}$$

where the indices i, α under $\sum$ run from 1 to m,n respectively.

It is well known that there exist connexion-forms $\{\theta_j^i\}$ on M, such that

$$\begin{aligned}
&d\theta^i + \sum_j \theta_j^i \wedge \theta^j = \frac{1}{2} \sum_{j,k} T_{jk}^i \theta^j \wedge \theta^k, \\
&\qquad \theta_j^i + \overline{\theta}_i^j = 0, \quad T_{jk}^i = - T_{kj}^i = T_{j\bar{i}k}. \\
&d\theta_j^i + \sum_k \theta_k^i \wedge \theta_j^k = \frac{1}{2} \sum_{k,\ell} R_{jk\bar{\ell}}^i \theta^k \wedge \overline{\theta}^\ell, \\
&\qquad R_{jk\bar{\ell}}^i = R_{j\bar{i}k\bar{\ell}}, \quad \overline{R_{i\bar{j}k\bar{\ell}}} = R_{j\bar{i}k\bar{\ell}}.
\end{aligned} \tag{6}$$

where T^i_{jk} is the torsion tensor of M and $R^i_{jk\bar{\ell}}$ is the curvature tensor of M. In particular, if M is a Kaehler manifold, then $T^i_{jk} \equiv 0$.

For every fixed point $x_0 \in M$, let $\xi = \sum_i \xi^i e_i$ and $\eta = \sum_i \eta^i e_i$ be two (1,0)-type tangent vectors of M at x_0. The holomorphic bisectional curvature determined by ξ and η is

$$K(\xi,\eta;x_0) = \sum_{i,j,k,\ell} R_{i\bar{j}k\bar{\ell}}\xi^i\bar{\xi}^j\eta^k\bar{\eta}^\ell/(\sum_i \xi^i\bar{\xi}^i)(\sum_i \eta^i\bar{\eta}^i), \tag{7}$$

and the holomorphic sectional curvature determined by ξ is

$$k(\xi;x_0) = \sum_{i,j,k,\ell} R_{i\bar{j}k\bar{\ell}}\xi^i\bar{\xi}^j\xi^k\bar{\xi}^\ell/(\sum_i \xi^i\bar{\xi}^i)^2. \tag{8}$$

The Ricci curvature determined by ξ is

$$R(\xi;x_0) = \sum_{i,j} R_{i\bar{j}}\xi^i\bar{\xi}^j/(\sum_i \xi^i\bar{\xi}^i), \quad R_{i\bar{j}} = \sum_k R_{k\bar{k}i\bar{j}}, \tag{9}$$

and the second Ricci curvature determined by ξ is

$$R^T(\xi;x_0) = \sum_{i,j} R^T_{i\bar{j}}\xi^i\bar{\xi}^j/\sum_i \xi^i\bar{\xi}^i, \qquad R^T_{i\bar{j}} = \sum_k R_{i\bar{j}k\bar{k}}. \tag{10}$$

The torsion vector determined by ξ and η is

$$T(\xi,\eta;x_0) = \sum_k T_k(\xi,\eta;x_0)\theta^k, \tag{11}$$

where

$$T_k(\xi,\eta;x_0) = \sum_{i,j} T_{i\bar{j}k}\xi^i\bar{\eta}^j/(\sum_i \xi^i\bar{\xi}^i \cdot \sum_j \eta^j\bar{\eta}^j)^{\frac{1}{2}}, \tag{12}$$

and the torsion is

$$\|T(\xi,\eta;x_0)\| = [\sum_k |T_k(\xi,\eta,x_0)|^2]^{\frac{1}{2}}. \tag{13}$$

If M is a Kaehler manifold, then

$$R^T(\xi,x_0) \equiv R(\xi,x_0), \quad \|T(\xi,\eta;x_0)\| \equiv 0. \tag{14}$$

The holomorphic bisectional curvature, the holomorphic sectional curvature and the Ricci curvature of N are defined in the same way as above. We use $R^{*\cdot}\ldots$ and $T^{*\cdot}\ldots$ to denote the curvature tensor and torsion tensor of N.

Assuming that

$$f: M \longrightarrow N$$

is a holomorphic mapping (it can be written $f \in Hol(M,N)$), we define

$$f^*\omega^\alpha = \sum_i a_i^\alpha \theta^i . \tag{15}$$

Then

$$f^*ds_N^2 = \sum_{i,j} (\sum_\alpha a_i^\alpha \bar{a}_j^\alpha)\theta^i\bar{\theta}^j . \tag{16}$$

Defining the covariant differential

$$Da_i^\alpha = da_i^\alpha - \sum_k a_k^\alpha \theta_i^k + \sum_\beta a_i^\beta \, \omega_\beta^\alpha$$
$$\equiv \sum_k (a_{ik}^\alpha \theta^k + a_{i\bar{k}}^\alpha \bar{\theta}^k), \tag{17}$$

and

$$Da_{ij}^\alpha = da_{ij}^\alpha - \sum_k a_{kj}^\alpha \theta_i^k - \sum_k a_{ik}^\alpha \theta_j^k + \sum_\beta a_{ij}^\beta \omega_\beta^\alpha$$
$$\equiv \sum_k (a_{ijk}^\alpha \theta^k + a_{ij\bar{k}}^\alpha \bar{\theta}^k), \tag{18}$$

we have

$$\begin{cases} a_{ij}^\alpha - a_{ji}^\alpha = \sum_{\beta,\gamma} T^{*\alpha}_{\beta\gamma} a_j^\beta a_i^\nu - \sum_k T^k_{ji} a_k^\alpha \\ a_{i\bar{j}}^\alpha = 0 \end{cases} \tag{19}$$

and

$$\begin{cases} a_{ik\bar{j}}^\alpha = \frac{1}{2} \sum_p R_{i\bar{p}k\bar{j}} a_p^\alpha - \frac{1}{2} \sum_{\beta,\gamma,\delta} R^*_{\bar{\beta}\alpha\gamma\bar{\delta}} a_i^\beta a_k^\gamma \bar{a}_j^\delta, \\ a_{ikj}^\alpha - a_{ijk}^\alpha = \sum_p T^p_{kj} a_p^\alpha . \end{cases} \tag{20}$$

Let $A_{i\bar{j}} = \sum_\alpha a_i^\alpha \bar{a}_j^\alpha$. Then it is a (1,1)-form on M. We can define its successive covariant differentials with respect to the connexion forms θ_j^i. Using (20), we can see that

$$A_{i\bar{j},p\bar{q}} = (\sum_\alpha a_i^\alpha \bar{a}_j^\alpha)_{p\bar{q}}$$
$$= \sum_\alpha a_{ip}^\alpha \bar{a}_{jq}^\alpha + \frac{1}{2} \sum_{k,\alpha} R_{i\bar{k}p\bar{q}} a_k^\alpha \bar{a}_j^\alpha - \frac{1}{2} \sum_{\alpha,\beta,\gamma,\delta} R^*_{\bar{\alpha}\beta\gamma\bar{\delta}} a_i^\alpha \bar{a}_j^\beta a_p^\gamma \bar{a}_q^\delta \tag{21}$$

and

$$\Delta_c \ln(\det A_{i\bar{j}}) \equiv 4 \sum_p \ln(\det A_{i\bar{j}})_{p\bar{p}}$$

$$= 2(S_1 - \sum_{\alpha,\beta,p} R^*_{\alpha\bar{\beta}} a^\alpha_p \bar{a}^\beta_p) \,, \tag{22}$$

where $S = \sum_{i,j} R_{i\bar{i}j\bar{j}}$ is the scalar curvature of M.

Assume that M is a complete Hermitian manifold with a pole at the point $z \in M$. Let $\rho(x,z)$ be the distance function from $x \in M$ to z. It can be regarded as differentiable. We have estimates for the Levi forms and the complex Laplacian of ρ which follow from the complex Hessian comparison theorem (cf. Chen and Yang [5], R. Greene and Wu [6]).

1. Let M be a Hermitian manifold whose holomorphic bisectional curvature is bounded from below by $-A^2$ $(A > 0)$ with torsion bounded by $T > 0$. Then $\forall \xi \in T_x^{(1,0)}$, $\|\xi\| = 1$,

$$\sum_{i,j} \rho_{i\bar{j}} \xi^i \bar{\xi}^j \leq \frac{1}{2\rho} [1+(A+2T)\rho] \tag{23}$$

2. Let M be a Hermitian manifold whose second Ricci curvature is bounded from below by $-A^2$ $(A > 0)$ with torsion bounded by $T > 0$. Then

$$\Delta_c \rho \equiv 4 \sum_i \rho_{i\bar{i}}$$

$$\leq \frac{1}{2\rho}[4m + 4(A+2mT)\rho] \,. \tag{24}$$

3. Let M be a Kaehler manifold whose Riemannian sectional curvature satisfies

$$k'(\xi',\eta';x) \leq \frac{1}{4}\cdot\frac{1}{[\varepsilon+\rho(x,z)]^2}, \quad (\varepsilon > 0) \quad \forall \xi',\eta' \in T_x. \tag{25}$$

Then

$$\sum_{i,j} \rho_{i\bar{j}}\xi^i\xi^j \geq \frac{1}{8\rho}, \qquad \sum_{i,j} \rho^2_{i\bar{j}}\xi^i\bar{\xi}^j \geq \frac{1}{2}, \tag{26}$$

and

$$\sum_i \rho^2_{i\bar{i}} \geq \frac{2m+1}{4}. \tag{27}$$

The formulae (26) and (27) follow from the following inequality given in [7]:

$$\forall f \in C[0,\infty) \quad \text{with} \quad \dot{f} \in L^2[0,\infty), \quad f(0) = 0,$$
$$\int_0^{+\infty} \left(\dot{f}^2 - \frac{1}{4t^2}f^2\right)dt \geq 0. \tag{28}$$

3. SCHWARZ LEMMA FOR COMPLETE HERMITIAN MANIFOLDS

Let M,N be two Hermitian manifolds and $f: M \longrightarrow N$ be a holomorphic mapping. We now consider

$$f^*ds^2_N = \sum_{i,j} A_{i\bar{j}}(x)\theta^i\bar{\theta}^j.$$

It is known that $\forall x_0 \in M$ there exist eigenvalues $\{\lambda_i(x_0)\}$ of $A_{i\bar{j}}$ such that $\lambda_1(x_0) \geq \cdots \geq \lambda_m(x_0) \geq 0$. Assume that a unit eigenvector with eigenvalue $\lambda_1(x_0)$ is $\xi(x_0) = \sum_i \xi^i(x_0)e_i$. This implies that ξ^i satisfies the following conditions

$$\begin{cases} \sum_i A_{i\bar{j}}(x_0)\xi^i = \lambda_1(x_0)\xi^j, \\ \sum_{i,j} A_{i\bar{j}}(x_0)\xi^i\bar{\xi}^j = \lambda_1(x_0), \\ \sum_i \xi^i(x_0)\xi^i(x_0) = 1 . \end{cases} \tag{29}$$

Let $\xi(x) = \sum_i \xi^i(x)e_i$ be a differentiable (1,0)-type local vector field defined in a neighbourhood U of x_0 which coincides with $\xi(x_0)$ at x_0 and satisfies the conditions:

$$\begin{cases} \xi^i_j(x_0) = \xi^i_{\bar{j}}(x_0) = 0, \\ \sum_i \xi^i(x)\bar{\xi}^i(x) = 1, \end{cases} \tag{30}$$

where ξ^i_j, $\xi^i_{\bar{j}}$ represent respectively the covariant derivatives of ξ^i in the directions of e_j and $\bar{e}_j$ which are defined by

$$\begin{aligned} D\xi^i &= d\xi^i + \sum_j \xi^j\theta^i_j \\ &\equiv \sum_j (\xi^i_j\theta^j + \xi^i_{\bar{j}}\bar{\theta}^j). \end{aligned} \tag{31}$$

We assert that there exists such a local vector field and, furthermore, it is easy to construct a lot of them. Using $\xi(x)$, we can construct a function defined in U:

$$\lambda(x) = \sum_{i,j} A_{i\bar{j}}(x)\xi^i(x)\overline{\xi}^j(x). \tag{32}$$

It is obvious that $\lambda(x)$ is differentiable in a neighbourhood U of x_0 and $\lambda(x_0) = \lambda_1(x_0)$. Applying (29) and (30), we can see by direct computation

$$\lambda_{k\bar{\ell}}(x_0) = \sum_{i,j} A_{i\bar{j},k\bar{\ell}}(x_0)\xi^i\overline{\xi}^j. \tag{33}$$

And then we have two lemmas which follow from (21) and (33):

<u>Lemma 1</u>. $\forall f \in \mathrm{Hol}(M,N)$ and $\forall x_0 \in M$, if $\lambda(x)$ be defined by (32), then we have

$$\sum_{k,\ell} \lambda_{k\bar{\ell}}(x_0)\xi^i\overline{\xi}^j \geq \frac{1}{2}\lambda(x_0)[k(\xi;x_0)-\lambda(x_0)k^*(f_*\xi;f\circ x_0)], \tag{34}$$

where $k(\xi;x_0)$ is the holomorphic sectional curvature of M determined by $\xi(x_0)$ and $k^*(f_*\xi;f\circ x_0)$ is the holomorphic sectional curvature of N determined by $f_*\xi = \sum_{i,\alpha} a_i^\alpha \xi^i(x_0)e_\alpha$.

<u>Lemma 2</u>. Assume that the holomorphic bisectional curvature of N is non-positive. Then $\forall f \in \mathrm{Hol}(M,N)$ and $\forall x_0 \in M$, we have

$$\begin{aligned} \Delta_c\lambda(x_0) &\equiv 4\sum_k \lambda_{k\bar{k}}(x_0) \\ &\geq 2\lambda(x_0)[R^T(\xi;x_0)-\lambda(x_0)k^*(f_*\xi;f\circ x_0)]. \end{aligned} \tag{35}$$

Assume that M is complete. Let $B_a(z)$ be a geodesic ball with centre z, which is a pole of M, and with geodesic radius a. We set

$$K_a = \inf_{\substack{x\in B_a(z)\\ \xi,\eta\in T_x^{(1,0)}}} K(\xi,\eta;x), \quad R_a^T = \inf_{\substack{x\in B_a(z)\\ \xi\in T_x^{(1,0)}}} R^T(\xi,x), \quad T_a = \sup_{\substack{x\in B_a(z)\\ \xi,\eta\in T_x^{(1,0)}}} \|T(\xi,\eta;x)\|. \tag{36}$$

Now we prove our main theorems.

Theorem 1. Let M be a complete Hermitian manifold whose holomorphic sectional curvature is bounded from below by k_1 with holomorphic bi-sectional curvature and torsion satisfying

$$\lim_{a\to\infty} \frac{K_a}{a^2} = 0 \qquad \text{and} \qquad \lim_{a\to\infty} \frac{T_a}{a} = 0 \tag{37}$$

respectively. Let N be a Hermitian manifold whose holomorphic sectional curvature is bounded from above by $k_2 < 0$. Then $\forall f \in \mathrm{Hol}(M,N)$,

$$f^*ds_N^2 \leq \frac{k_1}{k_2}\, ds_M^2 . \tag{38}$$

Theorem 2. Let M be a complete Hermitian manifold whose second Ricci curvature is bounded from below by R_1^T with torsion satisfying $\lim_{a\to\infty} T_a/a = 0$. Let N be a Hermitian manifold whose holomorphic sectional curvature is bounded from above by $k_2 < 0$ with non-positive holomorphic bi-sectional curvature. Then $\forall f \in \mathrm{Hol}(M,N)$,

$$f^*ds_N^2 \leq \frac{R_1^T}{k_2}\, ds_M^2 . \tag{39}$$

Proof. (See Chen, Cheng and Lu [1]).

$\forall x \in M$, define $\rho(x)$ as the distance from x to z, which can be regarded as a differentialble function on M. For every fixed point $x_1 \in M$, $\rho(x_1) = \rho_1$, let $a > \rho_1$. Define

$$\phi_1(x) = [a^2-\rho^2(x)]^2\lambda_1(x) \tag{40}$$

where $\lambda_1(x)$ is the maximal eigenvalue of $A_{i\bar{j}}(x)$. Then obviously $\phi_1(x)$ is a continuous function defined on $\overline{B_a(z)}$ and $\phi_1\big|_{\partial B_a(z)} = 0$. Assume that $\phi_1(x)$ achieves its maximum at a point $x_0 \in B_a(z)$. We construction a function $\lambda(x)$ in a neighbourhood of x_0 as in (32). Then the function

$$\phi(x) = [a^2-\rho^2(x)]^2\lambda(x) \tag{41}$$

is differentiable in a neighbourhood of x_0 and achieves its maximum at x_0.

Applying the maximum principle to $\phi(x)$, we obtain

$$\begin{cases} \phi_i(x_0) = \phi_{\bar{i}}(x_0) = 0 \\ \sum_{i,j} \phi_{i\bar{j}}\xi^i\bar{\xi}^j(x_0) \le 0 \end{cases} \quad \text{and} \quad \begin{cases} \phi_i(x_0) = 0 \\ \Delta_c\phi(x_0) \le 0 \end{cases} \tag{42}$$

From (42) it follows that

$$0 \ge \sum_{k,\ell} \frac{\lambda_{k\bar{\ell}}\xi^k\bar{\xi}^\ell}{\lambda} - 6\,\frac{|\sum_k (a^2-\rho^2)_k\xi^k|^2}{(a^2-\rho^2)^2} + 2\,\frac{\sum_{k,\ell}(a^2-\rho^2)_{k\bar{\ell}}\xi^k\bar{\xi}^\ell}{a^2-\rho^2}, \tag{43}$$

and

$$0 \ge \frac{\Delta_c\lambda}{\lambda} - 24\,\frac{\sum_k|(a^2-\rho^2)_k|^2}{(a^2-\rho^2)^2} + 2\,\frac{\Delta_c(a^2-\rho^2)}{a^2-\rho^2}\ . \tag{44}$$

By Gauss lemma,

$$\sum_k |(a^2-\rho^2)_k|^2 = \rho^2, \qquad \sum_k |(a^2-\rho^2)_k \xi^k|^2 \le \rho^2. \tag{45}$$

If the holomorphic bi-sectional curvature of M in $B_a(z)$ is bounded from below by $K_a < 0$ and the torsion bounded by $T_a > 0$, then using formula (23), we get

$$\sum_{k,\ell} (a^2-\rho^2)_{k\bar{\ell}} \xi^k \bar{\xi}^\ell \ge -[2 + (\sqrt{-K_a} + 2T_a)a]. \tag{46}$$

Applying (46), (45) and lemma 1 to (43), we have

$$0 \ge \frac{1}{2}[k_1(\xi,x_0) - \lambda(x_0)k^*(f_*\xi, f\circ x_0)] - \frac{6a^2}{[a^2-\rho^2(x_0)]^2} - \frac{2[2+a(2T_a+\sqrt{-K_a})]}{a^2-\rho^2(x_0)}. \tag{47}$$

By the hypothesis in theorem 1 and (47), we obtain

$$\lambda_1(x_1) \le \left[\frac{a^2-\rho^2(x_0)}{a^2-\rho_1^2}\right]^2 \lambda(x_0)$$

$$\le \left(\frac{a^2}{a^2-\rho_1^2}\right)^2 \cdot \frac{k_1}{k_2} + \frac{4}{-k_2}\,\frac{3a^2}{(a^2-\rho_1^2)^2} + \frac{2+a(2T_a+\sqrt{-K_a})}{(a^2-\rho_1^2)^2}\,a^2 . \tag{48}$$

As $a \longrightarrow \infty$, we obtain immediately

$$\lambda_1(x_1) \le \frac{k_1}{k_2} . \tag{49}$$

On the other hand, obviously $f^* ds_N^2(x) \le \lambda_1(x)\, ds_M^2$, from which theorem 1 follows.

Similarly, from the hypothesis of theorem 2 and formulae (24), (45) and lemma 2, we have

$$0 \geq 2[R^T(\xi, x_0) - \lambda(x_0)k^*(f_*\xi, f \circ x_0)] - \frac{24a^2}{[a^2-\rho^2(x_0)]^2} - \frac{8[2m+1+a(2mT_a+\sqrt{-R_a^T})]}{a^2-\rho^2(x_0)}, \tag{50}$$

from which one can easily prove theorem 2.

In the same way, we can prove the following:

Theorem 3. Let M be a complete m-dimensional Hermitian manifold whose scalar curvature is bounded from below by S_1 with second Ricci curvature and torsion satisfying

$$\lim_{a\to\infty} \frac{R_a^T}{a^2} = 0 \qquad \text{and} \qquad \lim_{a\to\infty} \frac{T_a}{a} = 0. \tag{51}$$

Let N be an m-dimensional Hermitian manifold whose Ricci curvature is bounded from above by $R_2 < 0$. Then $\forall f \in \mathrm{Hol}(M,N)$,

$$f^* dV_N \leq \left(\frac{S_1}{mR_2}\right)^m dV_m . \tag{52}$$

4. APPLICATION

The following propositions 1-3 follow immediately from theorems 1-3.

Proposition 1. Let M be a complete Hermitian manifold with non-negative holomorphic sectional curvature and with holomorphic bi-sectional curvature and torsion satisfying (37). Let N be a Hermitian manifold whose holomorphic sectional curvature is bounded from below by a negative constant. Then, $\forall f \in \mathrm{Hol}(M,N)$, f is a constant mapping.

Proposition 2. Let M be a complete Hermitian manifold with non-negative second Ricci curvature and torsion satisfying $\lim_{a\to\infty} T_a/a = 0$. Let N be a Hermitian manifold whose holomorphic sectional curvature is bounded from above by a negative constant with non-positive holomorphic bi-sectional curvature. Then, $\forall f \in \mathrm{Hol}(M,N)$, f is a constant mapping.

Proposition 3. Let M be a complete m-dimensional Hermitian manifold with non-negative scalar curvature and with second Ricci curvature and torsion satisfying (51). Let N be an m-dimensional Hermitian manifold whose Ricci curvature is bounded from above by a negative constant. Then $\forall f \in \mathrm{Hol}(M,N)$, f is degenerate everywhere.

As an application of proposition 2, we shall prove a theorem which generalizes the classical Liouville theorem. First of all, we have

Proposition 4. Let M be a complete Hermitian manifold with non-negative second Ricci curvature and bounded torsion. Let N be a complete Kaehler manifold whose Riemannian sectional curvature satisfies (25). Assume $f \in \mathrm{Hol}(M,N)$. If $\exists\, \rho_0 < +\infty$ such that $f(M) \subset B_{\rho_0}(z)$, then f is a constant mapping. That is, there is no non-constant bounded holomorphic mapping from M onto N.

Proof. Let $h: N \longrightarrow R$ be a differentiable function and $ds^2_{B_{\rho_0}(z)}(x) = e^h ds^2_M$. $B_{\rho_0}(z)$ can be regarded as a Hermitian manifold with metric $ds^2_{B_{\rho_0}(z)}$, and

$$K_{B_{\rho_0}(z)}(\xi,\eta;x) = [K_N(\xi,\eta;x) - \sum_{i,j} h_{i\bar{j}}(x)\xi^i\bar{\xi}^j]e^{-h(x)}. \qquad (53)$$

Assume

$$K_N(\xi,\eta;x) \leq B^2 \quad . \tag{54}$$

Letting $h(x) = 2(B^2+1)\rho^2(x)$ and using formula (26), we have

$$\begin{aligned} K_{B_{\rho_0}(x)}(\xi,\eta;x) &\leq [B^2 - 2(B^2+1) \sum_{i,j} \rho^2_{i\bar{j}} \ \xi^i\bar{\xi}^j]e^{-2(B^2+1)\rho^2} \\ &\leq -e^{-2(B+1)\rho_0^2} \\ &< 0 . \end{aligned} \tag{55}$$

Applying proposition 2 to the holomorphic mapping $\tilde{f}$: $M \longrightarrow B_{\rho_0}(z)$, we obtain proposition 4.

This theorem was proved by Yu [8] originally. We give some improvement here. Now we prove

<u>Theorem 4.</u> (Liouville theorem) Let M be a complete m dimensional Kaehler manifold ($m > 2$) whose Riemannian sectional curvature satisfies

$$k'(\xi',\eta';x) \leq \frac{1}{4} \cdot \frac{1}{[\varepsilon+\rho(x)]^2} , \quad \varepsilon > 0, \tag{56}$$

and whose Ricci curvature satisfies

$$R(\xi;x) \geq - \frac{2m-3}{4[\varepsilon+\rho^2(x)]} . \tag{57}$$

Then every bounded holomorphic mapping from M onto itself is a constant mapping.

Proof. Let $h(x) = \ln \frac{1}{\varepsilon+\rho^2(x)}$ and

$$ds^2_{\widetilde{M}} = e^{h(x)} ds^2_M(x). \tag{58}$$

Then M can be regarded as a Hermitian manifold $\widetilde{M}$ with metric $ds^2_{\widetilde{M}}$, which is still complete. By calculation, we have

$$\| T_{\widetilde{M}}(\xi,\eta;x) \| < 4 \tag{59}$$

and

$$\begin{aligned} R^T_{\widetilde{M}}(\xi;x) &= [R_M(\xi;x) - \sum_i h_{i\bar{i}}(x)]e^{-h(x)} \\ &= [R_M(\xi;x) + \frac{\sum \rho^2_{i\bar{i}}}{(\varepsilon+\rho^2)} - \frac{\sum \rho^2_i \rho^2_{\bar{i}}}{[\varepsilon+\rho^2]^2}]e^{-h(x)}. \end{aligned} \tag{60}$$

Since $4 \sum_i \rho_i \rho_{\bar{i}} = 1$, using formulae (27), we have

$$\begin{aligned} R^T_{\widetilde{M}}(\xi;x) &\geq [R_M(\xi;x) + \frac{2m+1}{4(\varepsilon+\rho^2)} - \frac{\rho^2}{(\varepsilon+\rho^2)^2}](\varepsilon+\rho^2) \\ &\geq [R_M(\xi,x) + \frac{2m-3}{4(\varepsilon+\rho^2)}](\varepsilon+\rho^2) \geq 0 . \end{aligned} \tag{61}$$

Then, applying proposition 4 to holomorphic mapping

$$\tilde{f}: M \longrightarrow M,$$

we can see $\tilde{f} \equiv$ const. when $\exists \rho_0 < +\infty$ such that $\tilde{f}(\widetilde{M}) \subset B_{\rho_0}(z)$. Thus theorem 4 is proved.

Remark. We do not know whether a Kaehler manifold satisfying (56) and (57) is biholomorphic to $\mathbb{C}^m$ or not. In the light of theorem 4, we know that it possesses some properties of $\mathbb{C}^m$.

The work of the first author was done under the direction of Professor Lu Qi-keng to whom he would like to express his indebtedness.

Bibliography

[1] Chen Zhi-hua, Shiu-yuen Cheng and Lu Qi-keng: On the Schwarz lemma for complete Kaehler manifolds, Science Sinica (1979) 9.

[2] Yau, S. T.: A general Schwarz lemma for Kaehler manifolds, Amer. J. of Math. 100(1978).

[3] H.L. Royden: The Ahlfors-Schwarz lemma in several complex variables, Comment. Math. Helvetici 55 (1980).

[4] Lu Qi-keng: Differnential geometry, Science Press, Beijing, 1981.

[5] Chen Zhi-hua and Yang Hong-cang: An estimation for the Levi forms of distance function on Hermitian manifolds and som applications, Acta Math. Sinica, to appear.

[6] R. Greene and Wu H.: Functions on manifolds which possess a pole, Lecture Notes in Math. 699.

[7] G.H. Hardy, J.E. Littlewood, and G. Polya: Inequalities, 2nd ed., Cambridge Univ. Press, 1952.

[8] Yu Qi-huang: Holomorphic maps and conformal transformation on Hermitian manifolds.

Several Complex Variables
Proceedings of the 1981 Hangzhou Conference

HOLOMORPHIC MAPS AND CONFORMAL TRANSFORMATION ON HERMITIAN MANIFOLDS

Qi-huang Yu

(Institute of Applied Math., Academia Sinica)

Let (N,h) be a Hermitian manifold and let $\phi: N \longrightarrow \mathbb{R}^+$ be a C^∞ map, then $(N,\tilde{h} = \phi^4 h)$ also is a Hermitian manifold. If h is a Kähler metric, the metric $\tilde{h} = \phi^4 h$ in general is not a Kähler metric. But under certain conditions we can obtain some properties of (N,h) by using conformal transformation. In this paper we obtain the following three results: 1) the Schwarz lemmas of holomorphic maps between complex manifolds whose curvatures are bounded from above by nonnegative constants; 2) Liouville-type theorems of holomorphic maps; 3) a class of Kähler manifolds not biholomorphic to $\mathbb{C}^n$.

In this paper Einstein's summation convention is used.

The author would like to express his gratitude to Prof. L.K. Hua and Prof. S. Kung for their kind direction.

Consider the Hermitian manifolds (N,h) and $(N,\tilde{h} = \phi^4 h)$. For connection form we have

$$\tilde{\omega} = \partial\tilde{h}\cdot\tilde{h}^{-1} = \partial(\phi^4 h)\phi^{-4}h^{-1} = \omega + 4\,\partial\log\phi\cdot I$$

where $I = (\delta_{\alpha\beta})$, $\tilde{\omega}$ is the connection form of $(N,\tilde{h})$ and ω is the connection form of (N,h). For the curvature form we have

Received 12 Oct. 1981

$$\tilde{\Omega} = \overline{\partial}\tilde{\omega} = \overline{\partial}\omega + 4\overline{\partial}\partial\log\phi\cdot I = \Omega - 4\partial\overline{\partial}\log\phi\cdot I.$$

Since

$$\tilde{\Omega}_{\alpha}^{\beta} = \tilde{S}_{\alpha\gamma\overline{\delta}}^{\beta}\, dw^{\gamma}\wedge d\overline{w}^{\delta} ,$$

where $\{w^{\alpha}\}$ are the local coordinate systems, it follows that

$$\tilde{S}_{\alpha\gamma\overline{\delta}}^{\beta} = S_{\alpha\gamma\overline{\delta}}^{\beta} - 4\delta_{\alpha}^{\beta}\partial_{\gamma}\overline{\partial}_{\delta}\log\phi$$

and

(1) $$\tilde{S}_{\alpha\overline{\beta}\gamma\overline{\delta}} = \phi^{4}(S_{\alpha\overline{\beta}\gamma\overline{\delta}} - 4h_{\alpha\overline{\beta}}\partial_{\gamma}\overline{\partial}_{\delta}\log\phi),$$

where $\partial_{\gamma} = \frac{\partial}{\partial w^{\gamma}}$; $\overline{\partial}_{\delta} = \frac{\partial}{\partial\overline{w}^{\delta}}$. The formula (1) gives the relationship between the curvature tensors of $(N,\tilde{h})$ and (N,h).

Lemma 1. Let (M,g) be a complete Kähler manifold whose holomorphic sectional curvature is bounded from below by K_1 and whose sectional curvature is also bounded from below; let (N,h) be a complete Kähler manifold whose sectional curvature is bounded from above by $A^2 > 0$. Suppose that $B_{\rho_0}(Q)$ is a geodesic ball around Q with radius $\rho_0 < \frac{\pi}{2A}$ in (N,h) which does not meet the cut locus of Q. Let $f: M \longrightarrow N$ be a holomorphic map and $f(M) \subset B_{\rho_0}(Q)$. Then there is a positive constant $k > 0$ depending on A and ρ_0 such that

(2) $$f^{*}e^{4kA^{2}(\rho^{2}-\rho_0^{2})}\, ds_N^2 \le \frac{2K_1}{A\,(1-8kA\rho_0\operatorname{ctg} A\rho_0)}\, ds_M^2 ,$$

where $\rho(P) = \operatorname{dist}(Q,P)$, $P \in B(Q)$, and $1-8kA\rho_0\operatorname{ctg} A\rho_0 < 0$.

Proof. Consider the holomorphic bisectional curvature of (N,h). Let X and Y be real unit tangent vectors of (N,h) and $X_0 = \frac{1}{2}(X-\sqrt{-1}JX) = \xi^\alpha \frac{\partial}{\partial w^\alpha}$, $Y_0 = \frac{1}{2}(Y-\sqrt{-1}JY) = \eta^\beta \frac{\partial}{\partial w^\beta}$, where J is the complex structure. Then

$$\xi^\alpha \bar{\xi}^\beta \eta^\gamma \bar{\eta}^\delta S_{\alpha\bar{\beta}\gamma\bar{\delta}} = \tfrac{1}{4} S(JX, X, Y, JY)$$

$$= \tfrac{1}{4}[S(X,Y,Y,X) + S(X,JY,JY,X)]$$

$$\leq \frac{A^2}{4}[2 - \mathfrak{G}^2(X,Y) - \mathfrak{G}^2(X,JY)]$$

$$\leq \frac{A^2}{2},$$

where S is the curvature operator and

$$\mathfrak{G} = \frac{1}{\sqrt{2}} \begin{pmatrix} I^{(n)} & I \\ \sqrt{-1}\, I & -\sqrt{-1}\, I \end{pmatrix} \begin{pmatrix} h & 0 \\ 0 & \bar{h} \end{pmatrix} \frac{1}{\sqrt{2}}\, {}^t\overline{\begin{pmatrix} I & I \\ \sqrt{-1}\, I & -\sqrt{-1}\, I \end{pmatrix}}$$

is the Riemannian metric of M considered as a 2n-dimensional real manifold. The above inequality means that the holomorphic bisectional curvature of (N,h) is less than or equal to $A^2/2$.

Consider the Hermitian manifold $(B_{\rho_0}(Q), \tilde{h} = e^{4kA\rho^2} h)$ (where k is to be determined). For its curvature tensor we have from (1)

$$\tilde{S}_{\alpha\bar{\beta}\gamma\bar{\delta}} = e^{4kA\rho^2} (S_{\alpha\bar{\beta}\gamma\bar{\delta}} - 4kA^2 h_{\alpha\bar{\beta}} \partial_\gamma \partial_{\bar{\delta}} \rho^2).$$

For any (1,0)-type vectors $X_0 = \xi^\alpha \frac{\partial}{\partial w^\alpha}$ and $Y_0 = \eta^\alpha \frac{\partial}{\partial w^\alpha}$ we have

$$\xi^\alpha \bar{\xi}^\beta \eta^\gamma \bar{\eta}^\delta \tilde{S}_{\alpha\bar{\beta}\gamma\bar{\delta}} = e^{4kA^2\rho^2} \xi^\alpha \bar{\xi}^\beta \eta^\gamma \bar{\eta}^\delta (S_{\alpha\bar{\beta}\gamma\bar{\delta}} - 4kA^2 h_{\alpha\bar{\beta}} \partial_\gamma \bar{\partial}_\delta \rho^2)$$

$$\leq e^{4kA\rho^2} [\frac{A^2}{2} h(Y_0,Y_0) - kA^2 \mathcal{L}\rho^2 (Y_0,Y_0)] h(X_0,X_0),$$

where $\mathcal{L}\rho^4 = 4\frac{\partial^2\rho^2}{\partial w^\gamma \partial \bar{w}^\delta} dw^\gamma d\bar{w}^\delta$ is the Levi quadratic form. Using the comparison theorem (see [5]), we get

$$\xi^\alpha \bar{\xi}^\beta \eta^\gamma \bar{\eta}^\delta \tilde{S}_{\alpha\bar{\beta}\gamma\bar{\delta}} \leq \frac{A^2}{2} e^{-4kA^2\rho^2} (1-8kA\rho \operatorname{ctg} A\rho) \tilde{h}(X_0,X_0) \tilde{h}(Y_0,Y_0).$$

This means that the holomorphic bisectional curvature of $(B_{\rho_0}(Q),\tilde{h})$ is less than or equal to $\frac{A}{2} e^{-4kA\rho^2} (1 - 8kA\rho \operatorname{ctg} A\rho)$.

Let $\varphi(\rho) = 1 - 8kA\rho \operatorname{ctg} A\rho$. Then

$$\varphi'(\rho) = \frac{4kA}{\sin^2 A\rho}(2A\rho - \sin A\rho).$$

Hence, when $k > 0$, $\varphi' > 0$ for $\rho \in (0,\infty)$, φ is an increasing function of ρ. Since $\rho_0 < \frac{\pi}{2A}$, there is a ρ_1 such that $\rho_0 < \rho_1 < \frac{\pi}{2A}$. Set

$$(3) \qquad k = \frac{1}{8A\rho_1 \operatorname{ctg} A\rho_1} > 0 .$$

For k defined as above, let $\psi(\rho) = 8kA\rho \operatorname{ctg} A\rho$ for $\rho \in (0,\rho_1]$. We have

$$\psi'(\rho) = \frac{4kA}{\sin^2 A\rho}(\sin 2A\rho - 2A\rho) < 0$$

and $\psi(\rho_1) = 1$ so $\psi(\rho) \geq 1$ for $\rho \in (0,\rho_1]$. Therefore for $\rho \in (0,\rho_0]$, $\varphi(\rho) = 1-\psi(\rho) < 0$ is a negative-valued increasing function of ρ. Besides, we have

$$\frac{A^2}{2}e^{-4kA\rho^2}(1-8kA\rho ctgA\rho) \leq \frac{A^2}{2}e^{-4kA\rho_0^2}(1-8kA\rho ctgA\rho)$$

$$\leq \frac{A^2}{2}e^{-4kA\rho_0^2}(1-8kA\rho_0 ctgA\rho_0) < 0.$$

This implies that the holomorphic bisectional curvature of $(B_{\rho_0}(Q),\tilde{h})$ is bounded from above by

$$\frac{A^2}{2}e^{-4kA^2\rho_0^2}(1-8kA\rho_0 ctgA\rho_0) < 0.$$

From the Schwarz lemma in [3] we get

$$f^*d\tilde{s}^2_{B_{\rho_0}(Q)} \leq \frac{2K_1}{A^2e^{-4kA^2\rho_0^2}(1-8kA\rho_0 ctgA\rho_0)}\, ds^2_M.$$

Since

$$d\tilde{s}^2_{B_{\rho_0}(Q)} = e^{4kA\rho^2}\, ds^2_N\big|_{B_{\rho_0}(Q)},$$

it follows that (2) is valid. Q.E.D.

<u>Lemma 2</u>. Let (M,g) be a complete Kähler manifold whose holomorphic sectional curvature is bounded from below by K_1 and whose sectional curvature is also bounded from below. Let (N,h) be a complete Kähler manifold whose sectional curvature ≤ 0 and let $B_{\rho_0}(Q)$ be a geodesic ball around Q with radius $\rho_0 < \infty$ in N which does not meet the cut locus of Q. Let $f: M \longrightarrow N$ be a holomorphic map and $f(M) \subset B_{\rho_0}(Q)$. Then

(4) $$f^* e^{4(\rho^2-\rho_0^2)} ds_N^2 \le \frac{-K_1}{4} ds_M^2 .$$

Proof. The proof of the lemma is the same as that of lemma 1 except that here we take $\phi = e^{\rho^2}$. Q.E.D.

Remark. We can regard lemmas 1 and 2 as Schwarz lemmas of a class of holomorphic maps whose images are in $B_{\rho_0}(Q)$. Using elementary analysis, we can simplify inequalities (2) and (4) as follows:

(2') $$f^* ds_N^2 \le \frac{-K_1}{A} \rho_0 \operatorname{tg} A\rho_0 e^{1+\frac{1}{2}A\rho_0 \operatorname{tg} A\rho_0} ds_M^2 \quad \text{for} \quad A > 0.$$

(4') $$f^* ds_N^2 \le \frac{-K}{4} e^{4\rho_0^2} ds_M^2 \quad \text{for} \quad A = 0.$$

S. Hildebrandt, J. Jost and K.O. Widman have proved the following theorem (see [6]):

Theorem. Let (M,g) be a simple or compact Riemannian manifold and let (N,h) be a complete Riemannian manifold whose sectional curvature is bounded from above by A^2. Let $B_{\rho_0}(Q)$ be a geodesic ball around Q with radius $\rho_0 < \frac{\pi}{2A}$ in (N,h) which does not meet the cut locus of Q. Suppose that $f: M \longrightarrow N$ is a harmonic map and $f(M) \subset B_{\rho_0}(Q)$. Then f is constant.

From lemmas 1 and 2 we can obtain the following Liouville-type theorem:

Theorem 1. Let (M,g) be a complete Kähler manifold whose sectional curvature is bounded from below and whose holomorphic sectional curvature ≥ 0. Let (N,h) be a complete Kähler manifold whose sectional curvature is bounded from above by $A^2 \ge 0$, and let $B_{\rho_0}(Q)$ be a geodesic ball around Q with radius $\rho_0 < \frac{\pi}{2A}$ in N which does not meet the cut locus of Q. Let $f: M \longrightarrow N$ be a holomorphic map and $f(M) \subset B_{\rho_0}(Q)$. Then f is constant.

If we use other Schwarz lemmas, then we can get other Liouville-type theorems. For example, if we use the Schwarz lemma in [7], then we can get the following theorem:

Theorem 1'. Let (M,g) be a complete Kähler manifold whose Ricci curvature ≥ 0. Assume that the conditions concerning (N,h) and f are the same as those in theorem 1. Then f is constant.

Siu and Yau have obtained a condition under which a simply connected complete Kähler manifold is biholomorphic to $\mathbb{C}^n$. Greene and Wu have improved this result (see [5]) and proved that a simply connected complete Kähler manifold (N,h) whose curvature satisfies

$$-k(\rho) \leq \text{sectional curvature} \leq 0$$

(where $k: [0,\infty) \longrightarrow [0,\infty)$ with $\int_0^\infty sk(s)ds < \infty$) is biholomorphic to $\mathbb{C}^n$. Now naturally we are led to the question under what conditions is a manifold certainly not biholomorphic to $\mathbb{C}^n$. The following theorem answers this question.

Lemma 3. Let (N,h) be an n-dimensional simply connected complete Kähler manifold with a pole Q whose curvature satisfies

$$\text{sectional curvature} \geq -B^2$$

and

$$\text{Ricci curvature} \leq \frac{-nB}{2(1-\varepsilon)\sqrt{1+\rho^2}}, \quad 1 > \varepsilon > 0, \; B \geq \frac{1}{1-\varepsilon}, \quad \text{where}$$

$\rho(P) = \mathrm{dist}(Q,P)$. Then no open subset of N can be biholomorphic to $\mathbb{C}^n$.

<u>Proof</u>. Consider the Hermitian manifold $(N, \tilde{h} = \frac{h}{\sqrt{1+\rho^2}})$. We have

$$\tilde{S}_{\alpha\bar{\beta}\gamma\bar{\delta}} = (1+\rho^2)^{-\frac{1}{2}}[S_{\alpha\bar{\beta}\gamma\bar{\delta}} + \tfrac{1}{2}h_{\alpha\bar{\beta}}\, \partial_\gamma \bar{\partial}_\delta \log(1+\rho^2)],$$

$$\tilde{S}_{\gamma\bar{\delta}} = \tilde{h}^{\bar{\beta}\alpha}\tilde{S}_{\alpha\bar{\beta}\gamma\bar{\delta}} = S_{\gamma\bar{\delta}} + \tfrac{n}{2}\partial_\gamma\bar{\partial}_\delta \log(1+\rho^2),$$

and

$$\partial_\gamma \bar{\partial}_\delta \log(1+\rho^2) = \frac{1}{1+\rho^2}\partial_\gamma\bar{\partial}_\delta\, \rho^2 - \frac{1}{(1+\rho^2)^2}\, \partial_\gamma \rho^2\, \bar{\partial}_\delta \rho^2 .$$

So

$$\mathcal{L}\log(1+\rho^2) \leq \frac{1}{1+\rho^2}\,\mathcal{L}\rho^2 .$$

Since the sectional curvature $\geq -B^2$, using the comparison theorem (see [5]), we have

$$\mathcal{L}\rho^2 \leq (4B\rho\coth B\rho)h.$$

Hence

$$\mathcal{L}\log(1+\rho^2) \leq (\frac{4B\rho}{1+\rho^2}\coth B\rho)h = (\frac{4B\rho}{\sqrt{1+\rho^2}}\coth B\rho)\tilde{h}$$

and

$$(5) \qquad (\tilde{S}_{\gamma\bar{\delta}}) \leq n(\frac{B\rho\coth B\rho}{2\sqrt{1+\rho^2}} - \frac{B}{2(1-\varepsilon)})\tilde{h} .$$

Set

$$\varphi(\rho) = \frac{B\rho\coth B\rho}{2\sqrt{1+\rho^2}} .$$

Then

$$\varphi' = \frac{1}{8(1+\rho^2)^{3/2}\mathrm{sh}^2 B}(2B\mathrm{sh}2B\rho - 4B^2\rho - 4B^2\rho^3),$$

$$2B\mathrm{sh}2B\rho = \sum_{p=1}^{\infty} \frac{2B}{(2p-1)!}(2B\rho)^{2p-1},$$

and

$$(6) \qquad 2B\mathrm{sh}2B\rho - 4B^2\rho - 4B^2\rho^3 = \rho^3(\tfrac{8}{3}B^4 - 4B^2 + \sum_{p=3}^{\infty}\frac{(2B)^{2p}}{(2p-1)!}\rho^{2p-4}).$$

From (6) we can see that 1) if $B \geq \sqrt{\frac{3}{2}}$, then $2B\mathrm{sh}2B\rho - 4B^2\rho - 4B^2\rho^3 > 0$ for any $\rho \in (0,\infty)$ and, as a consequence, $\varphi' > 0$ and φ is an increasing function of ρ; 2) if $1 < B < \sqrt{\frac{3}{2}}$, then for sufficiently small ρ, $\varphi' < 0$ and there is only one zero of φ' which we denote by ρ_* so that when $\rho > \rho_*$, $\varphi' > 0$ and φ achieves its minimum at ρ_*. On the other hand,

$$\lim_{\rho\to\infty} \varphi = \frac{B}{2} > \frac{1}{2} = \varphi(0).$$

Hence we have

$$\varphi(\rho) \leq \frac{B}{2} \qquad \text{for} \qquad \rho \in [0,\infty).$$

Substituting the result into (5), we get

$$(7) \qquad (\tilde{S}_{\gamma\bar{\delta}}) \leq \frac{n}{2}(\frac{-\varepsilon B}{1-\varepsilon})\tilde{h} .$$

The inequality (7) implies that the Ricci curvature of $(N,\tilde{h})$

is bounded from above by $-\frac{n\varepsilon B}{2(1-\varepsilon)} < 0$. From the Schwarz lemma of volume element in [3] for any holomorphic map $f\colon \mathbb{C}^n \longrightarrow N$ we conclude that the rank of $f < n$. Q.E.D.

BIBLIOGRAPHY

[1] Hua Lo-keng, "Harmonic analysis of functions of severl complex variables in the classical domains", Translation of Mathematical Monographs, Vol. 6, Amer. Math. Soc. 1963.

[2] S.S. Chern, "On holomorphic mapping of Hermitian manifolds of the same dimension", in: Proc. Symp. Pure Math. 11, Amer. Math. Soc., Providence, R.I., 1968, pp. 157-170.

[3] Chen Zhihua, Shiu-yuen Cheng and Lu Qikeng, "On the Schwarz lemma for complete Kähler manifolds", Scientia Sinica, Vol. XXII No. 11, pp. 1238-1247.

[4] J. Eells and Liemaire, "A report on harmonic maps", Bull. London Math. Soc., 10 (1978), pp. 1-68.

[5] R.E. Greene and H. Wu, "Function theory on manifolds which possess a pole", Springer-Verlag, 1979.

[6] S. Hildebrandt, J. Jost and K.O. Widman, "Harmonic maps and minimal submanifolds", read before the First Conference of D.G. and P.D.E., in Beijing, 1980.

[7] Yau, S.T., "A general Schwarz lemma for Kähler manifolds", Amer. J. of Math., 100 (1978), pp. 197-203.

[8] Yang Hong-cang and Chen Zhi-hua,"Schwarz lemma for complete manifolds", Shuxue Xuebao (to appear).

Several Complex Variables
Proceedings of the 1981 Hangzhou Conference

The degree of strong nondegeneracy of the bisectional curvature of exceptional bounded symmetric domains

Zhong Jia-Qing

(Institute of Mathematics, Academia Sinica)

In [1],[2] Siu discovered the complex-analyticity of harmonic maps between two Kähler manifolds under some conditions and prove the strong rigidity of compact quotients of irreducible bounded symmetric domains of dimension at least two. Furthermore, he proposed the following conjecture:

Suppose $f: N \longrightarrow M$ is a harmonic map between compact Kähler manifolds and M is a compact quotient of an irreducible symmetric domain. Let r be the maximal rank of df (over $\mathbb{R}$). Then f is either holomorphic or antiholomorphic provided that r is appropriately large. In [3] Siu confirmed this conjecture for the four classical domains and indicated that the confirmation for the two exceptional domains depends on the computation of the degree of the strong nondegeneracy of the bisectional curvature in the two exceptional cases.

The aim of this paper is to give the computation of the degrees of strong nondegeneracy for the two exceptional cases needed for the confirmation of Siu's conjecture. The main result is the following:

<u>Theorem</u>. For the exceptional bounded symmetric domains D_V and D_{VI}, the degrees of strong nondegeneracy of bisectional

Received 15 Oct. 1981.

curvature are 6 and 11 respectively.

This work was finished during my visit at Stanford University in 1981. I am greatly indebted to Prof. Siu for his help and encouragement during that time.

Let M be a compact Kähler manifold and $x \in M$.

<u>Definition</u> (Siu [3]): The bisectional curvature of M is said to be strongly s-nondegenerate at x if the following holds: If k and ℓ are positive integers and if $\xi_{(1)}, \xi_{(2)}, \cdots, \xi_{(k)}$ (respectively $\eta_{(1)}, \eta_{(2)}, \cdots, \eta_{(\ell)}$) are $\mathbb{C}$-linearly independent tangent vectors of type (1,0) at x, such that

$$R_{\alpha\bar{\beta}\gamma\bar{\delta}} \; \xi^{\alpha}_{(u)} \bar{\xi}^{\beta}_{(u)} \eta^{\gamma}_{(\nu)} \bar{\eta}^{\delta}_{(\nu)} = 0, \qquad \begin{array}{l} 1 \leq u \leq k \\ 1 \leq \nu \leq \ell \end{array}$$

then $k+1 \leq s$, where $R_{\alpha\bar{\beta}\gamma\bar{\delta}}$ is the curvature tensor of M.

We first state briefly the facts about the curvature tensor of Hermitian symmetric domains [5].

Let G be a real, simple, compact and simply connected Lie group with trivial center and K be the identity component of the fixed point of an involutive automorphism of G such that the center of K is one-dimensional. Let g, k be the Lie algebras of G,K, and $g_{\mathbb{C}}, k_{\mathbb{C}}$ be their complexifications. Let $G_{\mathbb{C}}$ be the complex Lie group with Lie algebra $g_{\mathbb{C}}$. Let p be the orthogonal complement of k in g with respect to the Killing form of g. It is well-known that $g = k+p$ is the Cartan decomposition of g. Let $g_0 = k+\sqrt{-1}p$ and G_0 be the analytic subgroup of $G_{\mathbb{C}}$ corresponding to the $\mathbb{R}$-Lie algebra g_0. G_0 is a noncompact Lie group and K is its maximal compact subgroup. From the theory of symmetric spaces we know that the quotient G/K is a simply connected irreducible compact Hermitian manifold and its "dual" G_0/K is an irreducible bounded symmetric domain. Moreover, the curvature tensor of G_0/K is the curvature tensor of G/K with opposite sign:

$$\text{curvature of } G/K = (-1) \text{ curvature of } G_0/K.$$

Therefore instead of treating the case G_0/K we can deal with the curvature of G/K.

Let t be the Cartan subalgebra of k (and g) so that its complexification $t_{\mathbb{C}}$ is the Cartan subalgebra of $g_{\mathbb{C}}$. Let Δ denote the root system of g with respect to t. One can choose a partial order in Δ such that the center of k corresponds to a simple root.

Take the root space decomposition of $g_{\mathbb{C}}$:

$$g_{\mathbb{C}} = t_{\mathbb{C}} + \sum_{\varphi\in\Delta} g^{\varphi} .$$

We know that the center of k (which we denote by Z) is one-dimensional and $J = \mathrm{ad}\, Z$ is the complex structure of $M = G/K$.

For $\varphi \in \Delta$, let e_{φ} denote the root vector corresponding to φ. If $\varphi \in \Delta^{+}$, then $-\varphi \in \Delta^{-}$ and $e_{-\varphi} = \overline{e}_{\varphi}$. Take $M = G/K$. Let $o = \{K\}$. Then we have

$$T_0 M = p$$

$$T_0^{(1,0)} M = \bigoplus_{\varphi\in\psi} \mathbb{C} e_{\varphi} ,$$

where ψ is the set of noncompact roots. Recall that a root φ is a noncompact root iff $e_{\varphi} \in p_{\mathbb{C}}$ where $p_{\mathbb{C}}$ is the complexification of p. We know that $\forall \alpha,\beta \in \psi$, $[e_{\alpha}, e_{\beta}] = 0$.

Because $J = \mathrm{ad}\, Z|_{p_{\mathbb{C}}}$ is the complex structure, we have $J^2 = -1$. So $p_{\mathbb{C}}$ can be decomposed into eigenspaces according to eigenvalues $\pm i$. Denote by $p^{\pm}$ the eigenspaces with respect to $\pm i$. Then we have

$$g_{\mathbb{C}} = k_{\mathbb{C}} + p^{+} + p^{-}.$$

From the theory of symmetric spaces we know that p^{+} is spanned by all noncompact positive root vectors and p^{-} is spanned by all noncompact negative root vectors and the $\mathbb{R}$-basis of T_0M can be taken as $\{\mathrm{Re}\, e_\alpha, \mathrm{Im}\, e_\alpha | \alpha \in \psi\}$. Therefore $T_0^{(1,0)}M = \{ \sum_{\alpha \psi} \xi_\alpha e_\alpha | \xi_\alpha \in \mathbb{C}\}$.

The Killing form of g is negative definite since G is compact. The negative of the Killing form gives the invariant metric on M, which we denote by $\langle \cdot , \cdot \rangle_{\mathbb{R}}$. Extend it by $\mathbb{C}$-bilinearity to $g_{\mathbb{C}}$ and denote this extension also by $\langle \cdot , \cdot \rangle_{\mathbb{R}}$. Then the Hermitian metric on $T_0^{(1,0)}M$ is given by

$$\langle e_\alpha, e_\beta \rangle = \langle e_\alpha, \bar{e}_\beta \rangle_{\mathbb{R}}, \qquad \alpha, \beta \in \psi$$

The curvature tensor for the metric $\langle \cdot , \cdot \rangle_{\mathbb{R}}$ on M is

$$\langle R(X,Y)Y,X \rangle = \| [X,Y] \|^2, \qquad X,Y \in T_0M \cong p$$

where $\| \cdot \|^2 = \langle \cdot , \cdot \rangle_{\mathbb{R}}$ (see [4], p. 76).

Take $\xi^\alpha \in \mathbb{C}$. Let $X = 2\, \mathrm{Re} \sum \xi^\alpha e_\alpha$, $JX = 2\, \mathrm{Im} \sum \xi^\alpha e_\alpha$. Then it is easy to verify that

$$\sum R_{\alpha\bar{\beta}\gamma\bar{\delta}} \xi^\alpha \bar{\xi}^\beta \xi^\gamma \bar{\xi}^\delta = - \| [\sum \xi^\alpha e_\alpha , \overline{\sum \xi^\alpha e_\alpha}] \|^2$$

$$R_{\alpha\bar{\beta}\gamma\bar{\delta}} = -\langle [e_\alpha, e_{-\beta}], [e_\delta, e_{-\gamma}] \rangle$$

and the bisectional curvature for $\sum\xi^\alpha e_\alpha, \sum \eta^\alpha e_\alpha$ is given by

$$\sum R_{\alpha\bar\beta\gamma\bar\delta}\xi^\alpha\bar\xi^\beta\eta^\gamma\bar\eta^\delta = - \| [\sum \xi^\alpha e_\alpha, \overline{\sum\eta^\beta e_\beta}]\|^2 .$$

From the theory of symmetric spaces we know that one can find a maximal strong orthogonal basis Λ in the set ψ of noncompact positive roots so that $\alpha,\beta \in \Lambda \subset \psi \iff \alpha \pm \beta \notin \Delta$. If $\alpha,\beta \in \Lambda$, it follows that $[e_\alpha, e_{\pm\beta}] = 0$ and $\langle\alpha,\beta\rangle = 0$. The subalgebra $\sum_{\varphi\in\Lambda} \mathbb{C}e_\varphi$ is in fact a maximal Abelian Lie subalgebra in $p_{\mathbb{C}}$. The dimension of $\sum_{\varphi\in\Lambda} \mathbb{C}e_\varphi$ is called the rank of symmetric space M.

Set $a^+ = \sum_{\varphi\in\Lambda} \mathbb{R}e_\varphi$ and $a = \sum_{\varphi\in\Lambda} \mathbb{R}(e_\varphi+e_{-\varphi})$. a^+ is a real Abelian Lie algebra.

Proposition 1.

$$p^+ = (I - iJ)p, \qquad a^+ = (I - iJ)a. \tag{1}$$

Proof: For any $\varphi \in \Lambda$

$$(I-iJ)e_\varphi = e_\varphi - iJe_\varphi = e_\varphi - i(ie_\varphi) = 2e_\varphi$$
$$(I-iJ)e_{-\varphi} = e_{-\varphi} - iJe_{-\varphi} = e_{-\varphi} - i(-ie_\varphi) = 0$$
$$(I-iJ)(e_\varphi+e_{-\varphi}) = 2e_\varphi .$$

Proposition 2. $p^+ = \bigcup_{k\in K} \mathrm{Ad}(k)a^+.$ (2)

Proof: First we prove $p = \bigcup_{k\in K} \mathrm{Ad}(k)a$. Since Ad k is the adjoint representation and its Lie algebra is ad k (where k is the

Lie algebra of K), it suffices to prove $[k,a] = p$. It is trivial to see that $[k,a] \subset [k,p] \subset p$. If $[k,a] \subsetneq p$, then there exists $x \neq 0$, $x \in p$, such that $<[k,a],x> = 0$. But since a is a maximal strong orthogonal set in p, $0 = <[x,a],x> = -<a,[k,x]>$ implies $[k,x] = 0$ and $x = 0$, which is a contradiction. The proposition now follows from

$$p^+ = (I-iJ)p = (I-iJ) \bigcup_{k \in K} Ad(k)a$$

$$= \bigcup_{k \in K} Ad\ k\ (I-iJ)a = \bigcup_{k \in K} Ad(k)a^+$$

where we have used Proposition 1 and the fact that Ad k and J commute.

Now we are in a position to prove the main theorem. Because the process of proof is similar for D_V and D_{VI}, for simplicity we give the proof of theorem in detail for D_V and only sketch it for D_{VI}.

It is well known that the dual compact Hermitian symmetric manifold of D_V is $M = E_6/Spin(10) \times T^1$. Let x_i $(i = 1,..,6)$ denote the coordinates of $\mathbb{R}$. We regard the root systems of E_6 as the linear forms on $\mathbb{R}^6$. We list the simple roots, the positive roots Δ^+, the positive noncompact roots ψ, the set of maximal strong orthogonal roots Λ, and the rank as follows:

simple roots: $x_i - x_{i+1}$ $(1 \leq i \leq 5)$, $x_4+x_5+x_6$.

Δ^+ : x_i-x_j $(1\leq i<j\leq 6)$, $x_i+x_j+x_k$ $(1\leq i<j<k\leq 6)$.

$\sum_1^6 x_i$

Ψ : x_1-x_i $(2\leq i\leq 6)$, $x_1+x_i+x_j$ $(2\leq i<j\leq 6)$, $\sum_1^6 x_i$.

Λ : $x_1 - x_2$, $x_1 + x_2 + x_3$.

rank : 2.

In view of the above discussions, the theorem we want to prove can be stated as follows.

Theorem 1. For $M = E_6/Spin(10)\times T^1$, if $\xi_1,\ldots,\xi_k \in p^+$, $\eta_1,\cdots,\eta_\ell \in p^-$, ξ_i (respectively η_j) are $\mathbb{C}$-independent such that

$$[\xi_i,\eta_j] = 0, \qquad \forall\ 1 \leq i \leq k,\ 1 \leq j \leq \ell\ ,$$

then $k+\ell \leq 6$.

The proof is a consequence of the following steps.

Lemma 1. If $\xi \neq 0$, $\eta\neq 0$, $\xi \in p^+$, $\eta\in p^-$ such that $[\xi,\eta] = 0$, then ξ can be either transformed into $\{e_{x_1-x_2}\}$ or $\{e_{x_1+x_2+x_3}\}$ by ad K but it can never be transformed into $ae_{x_1-x_2} + be_{x_1+x_2+x_3}$, $a,b \neq 0$.

Proof: By proposition 2 it suffices to prove that, if $a,b \neq 0$, $[ae_{x_1-x_2}+be_{x_1+x_2+x_3},\eta] = 0$, $\eta\in p^-$, then $\eta = 0$. Set

$$\eta = \sum_{i=2}^{6} a_i e_{-(x_1-x_i)} + \sum_{2\le i<j\le 6} b_{ij} e_{-(x_1+x_i+x_j)} + c\, e_{-\sum_1^6 x_i} .$$

$$0 = [a e_{x_1-x_2} + b\, e_{x_1+x_2+x_3}, \eta]$$

$$= \sum_{i\ge 2} aa_i \{e_{x_i-x_2}\} + \sum_{2\le i<j\le 6} ab_{ij} \{e_{-(x_2+x_i+x_j)}\} + \sum_{2\le i<j\le 6} bb_{ij} \{e_{x_2+x_3-x_i-x_j}\}$$

$$+ \sum_{i\ge 2} ba_{ij} \{e_{x_2+x_3+x_i}\} + bc\{e_{-(x_4+x_5+x_6)}\} . \qquad (3)$$

So $c = 0$ and $a_i = 0$ $(i = 4,5,6)$. From the term $\sum ab_{ij}\, e_{-(x_2+x_i+x_j)}\}$, we have b_{ij} $(j > i > 2)$. It follows that

$$\eta = a_2 e_{-(x_1-x_2)} + a_3 e_{-(x_1-x_3)} + \sum_{j\ge 3}^{6} b_{2j} e_{-(x_1+x_2+x_j)} .$$

Thus (3) can be written as

$$0 = aa_2 (H_{x_1-x_2}) + a\, a_3\, e_{-(x_2-x_3)}\} + b\, b_{23} (H_{x_1+x_2+x_3}) + \sum_{j\ge 4}^{6} b b_{2j} \{e_{x_3-x_j}\},$$

from which we conclude that $a_3 = b_{2j} = 0$ $(4 \le j \le 6)$. Furthermore, $H_{x_1-x_2}$ and $H_{x_1+x_2+x_3}$ are independent, because x_1-x_2 is strongly orthogonal to $x_1+x_2+x_3$. Hence $a_2 = b_{23} = 0$, $\eta = 0$ and the lemma is proved.

For the subspace A of p^+, we set

$$A^{\perp} = \{\eta \mid \eta \in p^-,\ [\xi,\eta] = 0,\ \forall \xi \in A \} .$$

Lemma 2.

$$(e_{x_1-x_2})^{\perp} = e_{-(x_1+x_2+x_i)},\ i = 3,4,5,6; e_{-\Sigma x_i}\} . \tag{4}$$

$$\{(e_{x_1-x_2})^{\perp}\}^{\perp} = \{e_{x_1-x_2}\} . \tag{5}$$

$$(e_{x_1+x_2+x_3})^{\perp} = \{e_{-(x_1-x_2)}, e_{-(x_1-x_3)}, e_{-(x_1+x_4+x_5)}, e_{-(x_1+x_4+x_6)}, e_{-(x_1+x_5+x_6)}\}. \tag{6}$$

$$\{(e_{x_1+x_2+x_3})^{\perp}\}^{\perp} = \{e_{x_1+x_2+x_3}\} . \tag{7}$$

Proof: The verification of (4) and (6) is a direct and easy computation. Formula (5) follows from

$$\{e_{-(x_1+x_2+x_i)},\ 3 \le i \le 6, e_{-\Sigma x_j}\}^{\perp} = \bigcap_{i=3}^{6} (e_{-(x_1+x_2+x_i)})^{\perp} \cap (e_{-\Sigma x_j})^{\perp}$$

and

$$\{e_{-(x_1+x_2+x_i)}\}^{\perp} = \{e_{x_1-x_2}, e_{x_1-x_i},\ e_{x_1+x_k+x_\ell}\ (k,\ell \neq 1,2,i)\},\ (3 \le i \le 6)$$

$$\{e_{-\Sigma x_j}\}^{\perp} = \{e_{x_1-x_2}, e_{x_1-x_i}\ (i = 3,4,5,6)\} .$$

The proof of (7) is similar.

Corollary. For any $\xi \in p^{+}$, $\xi \neq 0$, $\dim\{\xi\}^{\perp} \le 5$.

Proof: By proposition 2, $\exists\, k \in K$ such that $\mathrm{Ad}\, k\, \xi \in a^{+}$. If $\mathrm{Ad}\, k\, \xi = c e_{x_1-x_2} + d e_{x_1+x_2+x_3}$, $c,d \neq 0$, then $\{\mathrm{Ad}(k)\xi\}^{\perp} = 0$

and it follows from Lemma 2 that either $\{\xi\}^{\perp} = 0$ or $\dim \{\xi\}^{\perp} = 5$.

Lemma 3. If ξ_1, ξ_2 are independent vectors in p^+, then $\dim \{\xi_1, \xi_2\}^{\perp} \leq 4$.

Proof: By proposition 2, without loss of generality we can assume $\xi_1 = \mathrm{Ad}\, k\, e_{x_1 - x_2}$. Set $F = \{e_{x_1-x_2}\}^{\perp}$. Because $[\mathrm{Ad}\, k\, \xi, \mathrm{Ad}\, k\, \eta] = \mathrm{Ad}\, k\, [\xi, \eta]$, we have $\mathrm{Ad}\, k^{-1}\{\xi\}^{\perp} = \{\mathrm{Ad}\, k^{-1}\xi\}^{\perp}$. So

$$\{\xi_1\}^{\perp} = \{\mathrm{Ad}\, k\, e_{x_1-x_2}\}^{\perp} = \mathrm{Ad}\, k\{e_{x_1-x_2}\}^{\perp} = \mathrm{Ad}\, k\, F.$$

But it is clear that $\{\xi_1, \xi_2\}^{\perp} \subseteq \{\xi_1\}^{\perp} = \mathrm{Ad}\, k\, F$. If $\{\xi_1, \xi_2\}^{\perp} = \mathrm{Ad}\, k\, F$, then we have

$$[\xi_1, \mathrm{Ad}\, k\, F] = [\xi_2, \mathrm{Ad}\, k\, F] = 0$$

and $\mathrm{Ad}\, k^{-1}\xi_i \in F^{\perp}$ $(i = 1,2)$. By lemma 2, $\dim F = 1$. So $\mathrm{Ad}\, k^{-1}\, \xi_1 = \lambda\, \mathrm{Ad}\, k^{-1}\xi_2$, $\xi_1 = \lambda \xi_2$, contradicting the assumptions. Hence $\{\xi_1, \xi_2\}^{\perp} \subsetneqq \mathrm{Ad}\, k\, F$ and it follows that

$$\dim \{\xi_1, \xi_2\}^{\perp} < \dim \mathrm{Ad}\, k\, F = \dim F = 5.$$

Lemma 4. If ξ_1, ξ_2, ξ_3 are independent vectors in p^+, then $\dim \{\xi_1, \xi_2, \xi_3\}^{\perp} \leq 3$.

Proof: Clearly $\{\xi_1, \xi_2, \xi_3\}^{\perp} = \{\xi_1\}^{\perp} \cap \{\xi_2\}^{\perp} \cap \{\xi_3\}^{\perp}$. From lemma 3, if $\xi_1 \notin \{\xi_2\}$, then $\{\xi_1\} \neq \{\xi_2\}^{\perp}$. So $\dim \{\xi\}^{\perp} \cap \{\xi\}^{\perp} \leq 4$. Furthermore, from $\xi_3 \notin \{\xi_1, \xi_2\}$ it follows that $\{\xi_1\}^{\perp} \cap \{\xi_2\}^{\perp} \not\subset \{\xi_3\}^{\perp}$. Therefore $\dim \{\xi_1, \xi_2, \xi_3\}^{\perp} = \dim \{\xi_1\}^{\perp} \cap \{\xi_2\}^{\perp} \cap \{\xi_3\}^{\perp} \leq 3$.

Proof of theorem 1: From $[\xi_i, \eta_j] = 0$, $1 \le i \le k$, $1 \le j \le \ell$, and $k \ge 1$, it follows that $\ell \le 5$ (Lemma 2). Because of the symmetry of the ξ_i, η_j, the only cases needed to verify are $k = 1$, $\ell \le 5$ (or $\ell = 1$, $k \le 5$); $k = 2$, $\ell \le 4$ (or $\ell = 2$, $k \le 4$); $k = 3$, $\ell \le 3$ (or $\ell = 3$, $k \le 3$).

For the case of $M = E_7/E_6 \times T^1$ (the compact dual of D_{VI}), we have the following list.

Simple roots: $x_i - x_{i+1}$ $(1 \le i \le 6)$, $x_5 + x_6 + x_7$.

Δ^+ : $x_i - x_j$ $(1 \le i < j \le 7)$, $x_i + x_j + x_k$ $(1 \le i < j < k \le 7)$, $d - x_i$ $(1 \le i \le 7)$, where $d = \sum_{i=1}^{7} x_i$.

ψ : $x_i - x_i$ $(2 \le i \le 7)$, $x_1 + x_i + x_j$ $(2 \le i < j \le 7)$, $d - x_i$ $(2 \le i \le 7)$.

Λ : $x_1 - x_2$, $x_1 + x_2 + x_3$, $d - x_3$.

rank : 3.

By direction computation we have

Lemma 5.

$$\dim\{e_{x_1 - x_2}\}^{\perp} = \dim\{e_{x_1 + x_2 + x_3}\}^{\perp} = \dim\{e_{d - x_3}\}^{\perp} = 10. \tag{8}$$

For example,

$$\{e_{x_1 - x_2}\}^{\perp} = \{e_{-(d - x_i)}\ (3 \le i \le 7),\ e_{-(x_1 + x_2 + x_j)}\ (3 \le j \le 7)\}.$$

Lemma 6. For any $\xi \in p^+$, $\dim \{\xi\}^\perp \leq 10$.

Proof: Without loss of generality we can assume $\xi = a\, e_{x_1-x_2} + b\, e_{x_1+x_2+x_3} + c e_{d-x_3}$. Take

$$\eta = \sum_{i\geq 2}^{7} a_i e_{-(x_1-x_i)} + \sum_{2\leq i<j\leq 7} b_{ij} e_{-(x_1+x_i+x_j)} + \sum_{i\geq 2}^{7} c_i e_{-(d-x_i)}.$$

From $[\xi,\eta] = 0$ we get

$$\begin{array}{lll} cc_i = 0 \ (i = 2,4,5,6,7), & ca_i = 0 \ (2\leq i\leq 7), & cb_{ij} = 0 \ (j>i\geq 4) \\ bb_{2j} = 0 \ (j \geq 4), & bb_{3j} = 0 \ (j \geq 4), \ ba_i = 0 \ (i \geq 4) & \\ bc_j = 0 \ (j \geq 4), & ab_{ij} = 0 \ (j > i \geq 4) & \\ bb_{23} + cc_3 = 0. & & \end{array} \tag{9}$$

From (9) we conclude the following.

If $a,c \neq 0$, then $\dim \{\xi\}^\perp \leq 5$

$a,b \neq 0$ then $\dim \{\xi\}^\perp \leq 4$

$b,c \neq 0$, then $\dim \{\xi\}^\perp \leq 3$.

In view of lemma 5, we have in general $\dim \{\xi\}^\perp \leq 10$.

Lemma 7. If $\xi_1,\xi_2 \in p^+$, then $\dim\{\xi_1,\xi_2\}^\perp \leq 9$.

Proof: Transform ξ_1 (or ξ_2) by Ad k into $a\, e_{x_1-x_2} + b\, e_{x_1+x_2+x_3} + c\, e_{d-x_3}$ in the case when two of the $\{a,b,c\} \neq 0$. From lemma 6 and $\{\xi_1,\xi_2\}^\perp \subset \{\xi_1\}^\perp$, we have

$$\dim\{\xi_1,\xi_2\}^\perp \leq \dim \{\xi_1\}^\perp \leq 5.$$

For the other cases by the same reason as in the proof of lemma 3 we have $\dim \{\xi_1, \xi_2\}^{\perp} \leq 9$.

The remainder of the proof of the theorem for D_{VI} is similar to that of theorem 1.

References

1. Yum-Tong Siu: The complex-analyticity of harmonic maps and the strong rigidity of compact Kahler manifolds. Ann. of Math. 112 (1980), 73-111.

2. Yum-Tong Siu: Strong rigidity of compact quotients of exceptional domains. Duke Math. J. 48 (1981), 857-871.

3. Yum-Tong Siu: Complex-analyticity of harmonic maps, Vanishing and Lefschetz Theorems. J.Diff.Geom.17(1982),55-138.

4. Cheeger, J. and Ebin, D.: Comparison theorems in Riemannian geometry. North-Holland, Amsterdam 1975.

5. Hergason, S.: Differential geometry and symmetric spaces. Academic Press, New York, 1962.

Section Three

Holomorphic Vector Bundles

Several Complex Variables
Proceedings of the 1981 Hangzhou Conference

Holomorphic vector bundles on tori

Otto Forster

We will give here a short sketch of the historical origin of the interest in line bundles on tori, which arose from the theory of elliptic integrals and doubly periodic functions through the notion of theta-functions. In the last section we give a short survey on the possibilities of constructing vector bundles of rank two.

1. Elliptic integrals and doubly periodic functions

In the last century an important role in the theory of analytic functions of one complex variable was played by the so-called elliptic integrals. Let us consider a particular example

$$\int \frac{dz}{\sqrt{P_3(z)}}$$

where $P_3(z)$ is a polynomial in z of degree 3 with 3 different zeroes $a_1, a_2, a_3 \in \mathbb{C}$. A first difficulty arises because $\sqrt{P_3(z)}$ is not univalent. Therefore we consider the Riemann surface R of $\sqrt{P_3(z)}$, which is a 2-sheeted covering $p: R \longrightarrow \mathbb{P}_1(\mathbb{C})$ of the Riemann sphere with branch points over a_1, a_2, a_3 and ∞. An easy calculus in local coordinates now shows that

$$\omega = \frac{dz}{\sqrt{P_3(z)}}$$

becomes a differential form everywhere holomorphic on R (such a differential form is called Abelian differential of the first kind). Therefore the integral $\int\omega$ is locally on R a holomorphic function. But if we want to consider the function

$$f(z) = \int_{z_0}^{z} \omega$$

globally on R, another difficulty arises. The integral depends on

Received 22 March, 1983

the path of integration chosen from z_0 to z. Of course the value of the integral depends only on the homotopy class of the curve form z_0 to z, but two curves form z_0 to z are not necessarily homotopic. The difference of two such curves is a closed curve and defines therefore an element of the homotopy group $\pi_1(R)$. This homotopy group is a free group with two generators c_1, c_2 which can be represented by curves running around the branch points as indicated in Fig. 1.

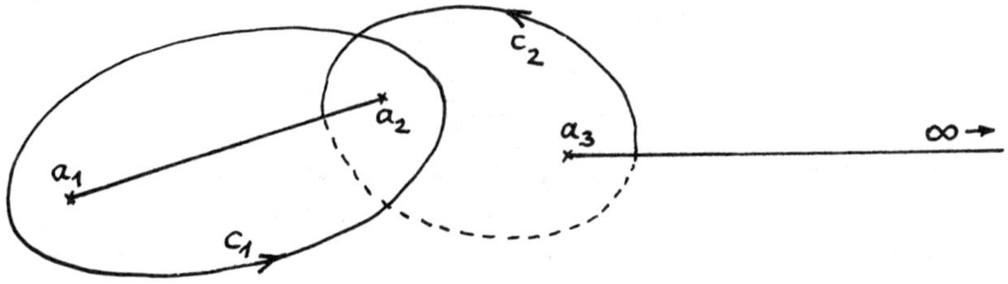

Fig. 1

The integrals of ω over the curves c_1, c_2

$$\gamma_j = \int_{c_j} \omega \quad , \quad j = 1,2 \quad ,$$

are so-called periods of ω and can be shown to be linearly independent over the real numbers. Therefore they generate a lattice

$$\Gamma := \mathbb{Z}\gamma_1 + \mathbb{Z}\gamma_2 = \{n_1\gamma_1 + n_2\gamma_2 : n_1, n_2 \in \mathbb{Z}\} \subset \mathbb{C} \ .$$

Now we can say that the integral $\int\omega$ is well defined modulo Γ; we have therefore a holomorphic map

$$R \ni z \overset{F}{\longmapsto} \int_{z_0}^{z} \omega \mod \Gamma \in \mathbb{C}/\Gamma =: X \ .$$

$X = \mathbb{C}/\Gamma$ is a torus, the points of which can be represented by the points of the fundamental parallelogram

$$P = \{s\gamma_1 + t\gamma_2 : s,t \in [0,1]\} \ ,$$

where points on the boundary have to be identified if they differ by a period vector, cf. Fig. 2 .

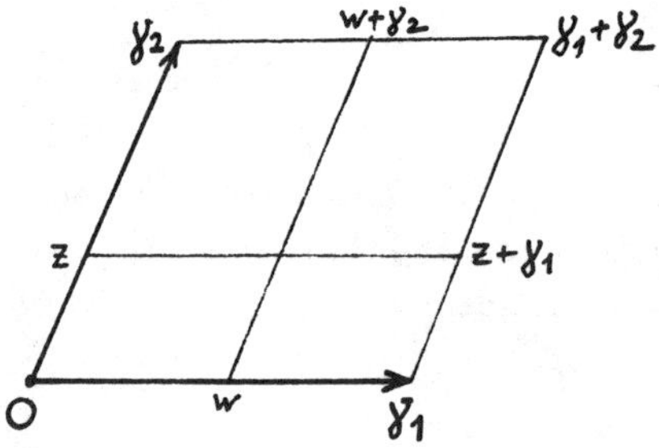

Fig. 2

It was the great discovery by Abel and Jacobi, that the map $F: R \longrightarrow \mathbb{C}/\Gamma$ is an isomorphism. Therefore the study of the elliptic integral is equivalent to the study of the inverse map $\Phi = F^{-1}: \mathbb{C}/\Gamma \longrightarrow R$. We compose this map with the projections $\pi: \mathbb{C} \longrightarrow \mathbb{C}/\Gamma$ and $p: R \longrightarrow \mathbb{P}_1(\mathbb{C})$ and get a holomorphic map (= meromorphic function)

$$f = P \circ \Phi \circ \pi: \mathbb{C} \xrightarrow{\pi} \mathbb{C}/\Gamma \xrightarrow{\Phi} R \xrightarrow{p} \mathbb{P}_1(\mathbb{C}) .$$

f is doubly periodic with respect to Γ, i.e.

(*) $\qquad f(z + g) = f(z)$ for all $z \in \mathbb{C}$ and $g \in \Gamma$.

Conversely, a meromorphic function on $\mathbb{C}$ satisfying (*) defines a meromorphic function on $\mathbb{C}/\Gamma$.

In the study of meromorphic functions it is often convenient to represent them as quotients of holomorphic functions. However, on a torus $X = \mathbb{C}/\Gamma$ this is not possible, since every holomorphic function on $\mathbb{C}/\Gamma$ (which corresponds to a doubly periodic function on $\mathbb{C}$) is constant. This leads us to a generalization of doubly periodic functions, the so-called theta-functions.

2. Theta-functions and line bundles

We define theta-functions immediately for several complex variables. Let $\Gamma \subset \mathbb{C}^n$ be a lattice of rank 2n, i.e.

$$\Gamma = \mathbb{Z}\gamma_1 + \ldots + \mathbb{Z}\gamma_{2n} ,$$

where $\gamma_1,\ldots,\gamma_{2n}$ are vectors in $\mathbb{C}^n$, linearly independent over $\mathbb{R}$. The quotient $X = \mathbb{C}^n/\Gamma$ is then an n-dimensional complex torus. A holomorphic function

$$f: \mathbb{C}^n \longrightarrow \mathbb{C}$$

is called a theta-function with respect to Γ, if it satisfies the following relations:

(1) $\qquad f(z + g) = \mu_g(z)f(z) \quad$ for all $z \in \mathbb{C}^n$ and $g \in \Gamma$,

where the "theta-factors" $\mu_g: \mathbb{C}^n \longrightarrow \mathbb{C}^*$ are functions of the form

(2) $\qquad \mu_g(z) = e^{L_g(z)}$

with affine linear functions $L_g(z) = \sum_{k=1}^{n} a_{gk}z_k + b_g$.
For $f \not\equiv 0$, it follows from (1), that the factors μ_g satisfy the relations

(3) $\qquad \mu_{g+g'}(z) = \mu_g(z+g')\mu_{g'}(z) \quad$ for all $z \in \mathbb{C}^n$, $g,g' \in \Gamma$.

<u>Example.</u> Let n=1 and $\Gamma \subset \mathbb{C}$ be the lattice $\Gamma = \mathbb{Z} + \mathbb{Z}\tau$, $\mathrm{Im}(\tau) > 0$. (Every lattice in $\mathbb{C}$ can be normalized in this way.) The series

$$\theta(z) = \sum_{n\in\mathbb{Z}} e^{i\pi n^2\tau}e^{2\pi inz}$$

converges (very rapidly) for all $z \in \mathbb{C}$. It is easy to verify that θ is a theta-function with respect to Γ. It can be shown that in the case of one complex variable every theta-function is, up to a factor of the form e^{az^2+bz+c}, a product of finitely many translates $\theta(z-z_1),\ldots,\theta(z-z_m)$ of this standard theta-function θ .

Let us return to the general case. If f_1 and f_2 are two theta-functions with the same system of factors (μ_g), and $f_2 \not\equiv 0$, the quotient $F = f_1/f_2$ is periodic with respect to Γ and defines therefore a meromorphic function on the torus $\mathbb{C}^n/\Gamma$.

In general (if $\mu_g \not\equiv 1$) a theta-function itself is not periodic with respect to Γ, hence does not define a function on $\mathbb{C}^n/\Gamma$. Nevertheless we want to identify a theta-function with a function theoretic object on the torus $\mathbb{C}^n/\Gamma$, namely a holomorphic section of a line bundle. Line bundles are special cases of vector bundles.

Definition. A vector bundle of rank r over a complex manifold X is a complex manifold E together with a holomorphic map $p: E \longrightarrow X$ and structures of r-dimensional complex vector spaces on every fibre $E_x = p^{-1}(x)$, $x \in X$, such that the following holds: For every $x \in X$ there exists an open neighborhood $U \subset X$ and a biholomorphic map $h: p^{-1}(U) \longrightarrow U \times \mathbb{C}^n$, which induces vector space isomorphisms

$$h_x: E_x \xrightarrow{\sim} \{x\} \times \mathbb{C}^n \cong \mathbb{C}^n$$

for all $x \in U$.
A holomorphic section of E is a holomorphic map $s: X \longrightarrow E$ with $p \circ s = id_X$, i.e. $s(x) \in E_x$ for every $x \in X$.

A line bundle E is a vector bundle of rank 1. In this case all fibres E_x are 1-dimensional vector spaces, i.e. isomorphic to $\mathbb{C}$. However the isomorphism $E_x \xrightarrow{\sim} \mathbb{C}$ is not uniquely determined, only up to a factor $\lambda \in \mathbb{C}^*$. Therefore a holomorphic section $s: X \longrightarrow E$ cannot be interpretated as a holomorphic function on X. But if $s_1, s_2: X \longrightarrow E$ are two holormophic sections of the same line bundle E, $s_2 \not\equiv 0$, then the quotient $f = s_1/s_2$ is a well-defined meromorphic function on X, since the indeterminacy cancels out. Conversely one can show that every meromorphic function f on a complex manifold X can be written as $f = s_1/s_2$, where s_1, s_2 are holomorphic sections of a suitable line bundle E on X.

We return to the case of a torus $X = \mathbb{C}^n/\Gamma$. Let there be given a system of theta-factors, i.e. holomorphic functions $\mu_g: \mathbb{C}^n \longrightarrow \mathbb{C}^*$, $g \in \Gamma$, of the form (2), satisfying the relations (3). We want to associate to this system a line bundle E_μ on X. This is done as follows: We define on $\mathbb{C}^n \times \mathbb{C}$ an equivalence relation: $(z,v) \sim (z',v')$ if there exists a $g \in \Gamma$ such that

$$z' = z + g \quad \text{and} \quad v' = \mu_g(z)v .$$

Set $E_\mu := \mathbb{C}^n \times \mathbb{C}/\sim$. The projection $pr: \mathbb{C}^n \times \mathbb{C} \longrightarrow \mathbb{C}^n$ induces a map $p: E_\mu \longrightarrow X$. All fibres are (not canonically) isomorphic to $\mathbb{C}$ and E_μ becomes a line bundle over X. By construction the holormphic sections of E are in one-to-one correspondence with holomorphic functions $f: \mathbb{C}^n \longrightarrow \mathbb{C}$ satisfying (1), i.e. theta-functions.

Now a classical theorem of Appell-Humbert can be reformulated as follows (cf. [3]):

Every line bundle E over an n-dimensional torus $X = \mathbb{C}^n/\Gamma$ is isomorphic to a line bundle E_μ constructed as above from a system of theta-factors $(\mu_g)_{g\in\Gamma}$.

This implies in particular that every meromorphic function on $\mathbb{C}^n/\Gamma$ can be represented as a quotient of two theta-functions.

3. Vector bundles on tori

In this last section we want to give examples of vector bundles of rank $r > 1$ on tori. For simplicity we consider only the case $r = 2$.

a) If L,M are two line bundles on X, then the direct sum $L \oplus M$ is a vector bundle of rank 2 on X. By a theorem of Grothendieck (cf. [4], § 2.1), every vector bundle over the Riemann sphere $\mathbb{P}_1(\mathbb{C})$ is a direct sum of line bundles. However on tori this is no longer true.

b) More generally one can consider extensions of line bundles by line bundles, i.e. exact sequences

$$0 \longrightarrow L \longrightarrow E \longrightarrow M \longrightarrow 0 ,$$

where L and M are line bundles. On a 1-dimensional torus $X = \mathbb{C}/\Gamma$ every vector bundle of rank 2 is such an extension. In this way Atiyah [1] studied vector bundles on 1-dimensional tori.

c) On higher-dimensional tori the construction principle of b) does not suffice. One has to generalize once more and consider extensions

$$0 \longrightarrow L \longrightarrow E \longrightarrow M \otimes I_Z \longrightarrow 0 ,$$

where L,M are line bundles and I_Z is the ideal sheaf of a 2-codimensional locally complete intersection $Z \subset X$. In fact every holomorphic vector bundle of rank 2 over a projective algebraic manifold X arises in this way. Serre [5] has given a theory of such extensions.

d) If the torus $X = \mathbb{C}^n/\Gamma$ is not algebraic, a vector bundle of rank 2 is not necessarily an extension as in c). Counter-examples are given in [2]. These counter-examples are deformations of certain vector bundles which are extensions.

Bibliography

[1] M. Atiyah: Vector bundles on elliptic curves. Proc. London Math. Soc. 7 (1957), 414-452.

[2] G. Elencwajg and O. Forster: Vector bundles on manifolds without divisors and a theorem on deformations. Ann. Inst. Fourier, Grenoble 32, 4 (1982), 25-51.

[3] D. Mumford: Abelian varieties. Oxford Univ. Press 1970.

[4] C. Okonek, M. Schneider and H. Spindler: Vector bundles on complex projective spaces. Progress in Math. 3, Birkhäuser 1980.

[5] J.-P. Serre: Sur les modules projectifs, Séminaire Dubreil-Pisot 1960/1961, Exposé 2.

Otto Forster
Mathematisches Institut der LMU
Theresienstraße 39

D-8000 München 2
Federal Republic of Germany

Several Complex Variables
Proceedings of the 1981 Hangzhou Conference

SUBMANIFOLDS OF PROJECTIVE SPACE WITH SEMI-STABLE NORMAL BUNDLE

Michael Schneider
Bayreuth

Concerning the classification of smooth subvarieties Y of complex-projective space $\mathbb{P}_n$ one has the following conjectures of Hartshorne [10]:

<u>SHC</u> Y is a complete intersection if $\dim Y > \frac{2}{3}n$

<u>WHC</u> Y is linearly normal if $\dim Y > \frac{2}{3}(n-1)$.

The strong conjecture is still unsolved but the much weaker WHC has recently been settled by Zak (cf.[6]). Hartshorne was led in part to his conjectures by the following theorem of Barth and Van de Ven [4], [5], [1].

<u>Theorem</u> Let $Y \subset \mathbb{P}_n$ be a smooth subvariety of degree d. If $n > N(d)$, then Y is a complete intersection.

Here $N(d)$ is a polynomial in d. For $\operatorname{codim} Y = 2$ for instance

(*) $N(d) = 4d-6$.

The object of this note is to improve the bound of Barth, Van de Ven by entirely different and elementary methods (at least if Y has semi-stable normal bundle). Our method uses the fact that the normal bundle of Y is positve and therefore certain polynomials in the Chern classes are positive too.

I would like to thank Robert Switzer for calculating for me on a computer.

Received 1 December, 1981

§ 1. Positivity of Chern classes

If E is a complex vector bundle on a space X one has the total Chern class $c(E)$ with components $c_i(E) \in H^{2i}(X,Z)$ and the total Segre class $s(E) = c(E)^{-1}$ with components $s_i(E) \in H^{2i}(X,Z)$.

We set $\quad \tilde{c}_i(E) = s_i(E^*)$.

If $$c(E) = \prod_{\nu=1}^{r} (1+\delta_\nu)$$

is the formal decomposition of $c(E)$ one has

$$\tilde{c}_i(E) = \sum_{\nu_1+\ldots+\nu_r=i} \delta_1^{\nu_1}\ldots\delta_r^{\nu_r} .$$

For rank $E = 2$ one gets for example

$$\tilde{c}_1 = c_1,\ \tilde{c}_2 = c_1^2 - c_2\ ,\ \tilde{c}_3 = c_1(c_1^2-2c_2),$$
$$\tilde{c}_4 = c_1^2\ (c_1^2 - 3c_2) + c_2^2\ ,\ \tilde{c}_5 = c_1(c_1^2 - c_2)(c_1^2 - 3c_2) .$$

A holomorphic vector bundle E on a compact complex manifold X is called positive if the dual bundle E^* is negative in the sense of Grauert [8], i.e. the zero section of E^* can be collapsed to a point. This is equivalent to the ampleness of E in the sense of algebraic geometry i.e. $\mathcal{O}_{\mathbb{P}(E)}(1)$ is an ample line bundle on $\mathbb{P}(E)$ (= hyperplanes in the fibres of E). If E is positive, X is necessarily projective algebraic [8].

The following proposition is well known and easy to prove using the Nakai-Moishezon criterion of ampleness of a line bundle (cf.[7]).

<u>Proposition 1.1.</u> Let X be a compact complex manifold of dimension n and let E be a positive holomorphic vector bundle on X. Then

$$\tilde{c}_n(E)[X] > o .$$

As an important consequence we get the

<u>Corollary 1.2.</u> Let E be a holomorphic vector bundle of rank r on $\mathbb{P}_n$ having a holomorphic section σ whose zero set $Y = \{\sigma = o\}$ is smooth of codimension r. Then one has

$$\tilde{c}_k(E) > o \quad \text{for} \quad k \leq n - r .$$

<u>Proof.</u> By assumption (Koszul-complex!) E restricts to the normal bundle of Y

$$E|Y \simeq N_{Y/\mathbb{P}_n} .$$

$N_{Y/\mathbb{P}_n}$ is positive (being a quotient of $T_{\mathbb{P}_n}|Y$). Hence by the proposition

$$\tilde{c}_{n-r}(E|Y)[Y] > o .$$

But one has

$$\tilde{c}_{n-r}(E|Y)[Y] = \deg(Y)\tilde{c}_{n-r}(E) .$$

Hence

$$\tilde{c}_{n-r}(E) > o .$$

Now take a general hyperplane $H \subset \mathbb{P}_n$. Then

$$Z = H \cap Y$$

is smooth of dimension $n - r - 1$ and

$$E|Z \simeq (N_{Y/\mathbb{P}_n})|Z$$

is positive. As before we conclude $\tilde{c}_{n-r-1}(E) > o$. Continuing this way we obtain the desired result.

§ 2. Splitting vector bundles

In this section we show how to use the positivity of the classes $\tilde{c}_i(E)$ to estimate $c_2(E)$ and to get some splitting results.

If E is a vector bundle of rank 2 with

$$c_1(E)^2 - 4c_2(E) \leq o$$

we write

$$c_1(E) = \delta + \bar{\delta}$$

$$c_2(E) = |\delta|^2$$

$$\delta = re^{i\varphi} \ , \ r \geq o \ , \ -\pi \leq \varphi < \pi .$$

Proposition 2.1. Let E be a holomorphic vector bundle of rank 2 on $\mathbb{P}_n$ admitting a holomorphic section with smooth 2-codimensional zero locus. If $c_1(E)^2 - 4c_2(E) < o$ one has

$$|\varphi| < \frac{\pi}{n-1}$$

Proof. We have

$$\tilde{c}_k(E) = \sum_{\nu=o}^{k} \delta^{k-\nu}\bar{\delta}^{\nu} = r^k \sum_{\nu=o}^{k} e^{i(k-2\nu)\varphi} .$$

By Corollary 1.1 the classes $\tilde{c}_k(E)$ are positive for $k \leq n - 2$. This implies

$$\sum_{\nu=o}^{k} e^{i(k-2\nu)\varphi} > o \ , \ k \leq n - 2 .$$

One easily verifies

$$\sum_{\nu=o}^{k} e^{i(k-2\nu)\varphi} = \frac{\sin(k+1)\varphi}{\sin\varphi} .$$

Suppose we know $|\varphi| < \frac{\pi}{m}$ and $\tilde{c}_m(E) > o$. This gives

$$\frac{\sin(m+1)\varphi}{\sin\varphi} > o \ .$$

If $\varphi > o$ we have $\sin(m+1)\varphi > o$, hence $(m+1)\varphi < \pi$ since $(m+1)\varphi < 2\pi$. For $\varphi < o$ we see in the same way that $(m+1)\varphi > -\pi$. This shows

$$|\varphi| < \frac{\pi}{m+1} \ .$$

Induction on m gives the result.

The Chern classes of a topological vector bundle E of rank r on $\mathbb{P}_n$ are not arbitrary. They have to obey the Schwarzenberger conditions [11]:

$$\sum_{i=1}^{r} \binom{m+\delta_i}{m} \in \mathbb{Z} \quad \text{for} \quad m \leq n \ .$$

Denote by

$$F : \mathbb{N} \to \mathbb{N}$$

the following function

$$F(n) = \min_E \{m \in \mathbb{N} \ : \ m = 4c_2(E) - c_1(E)^2\}$$

where E is any topological rank 2 vector bundle on $\mathbb{P}_n$. F is an increasing function of n . Exploiting the Schwarzenberger conditions and a computer one gets the following estimates for $F(n)$:

$$F(n) \geq S(n)$$

n	S(n)	n	S(n)	n	S(n)
4	12	9	119	14	2639
5	12	10	119	15	2999
6	71	11	119	16	2999
7	71	12	1679	17	3576
8	119	13	1679	18	5712

It would be desireable to have an estimate of $S(n)$ for all n, but this leads to difficult number-theoretic questions. One might hope that $S(n) \geq n^2$ for $n \geq 6$.

Theorem 2.2. Let E be a holomorphic vector bundle of rank 2 on $\mathbb{P}_n$ admitting a holomorphic section with smooth 2-codimensional zero-locus. If $c_1(E)^2 - 4c_2(E) < o$ then

$$c_2(E) > \frac{1}{4} \frac{F(n)}{\sin^2(\frac{\pi}{n-1})} .$$

Proof. As above we write $c_1(E) = \delta + \bar{\delta}$, $c_2(E) = |\delta|^2$, $\delta = re^{i\varphi}$, $r > o$, $-\pi \leq \varphi < \pi$. By definition and 2.1 we get

$$F(n) \leq 4c_2(E) - c_1(E)^2 = 4r^2\sin^2\varphi < 4r^2\sin^2(\frac{\pi}{n-1}) .$$

Observing $c_2(E) = r^2$ gives the result.

Corollary 2.3. Let E be a semi-stable holomorphic vector bundle of rank 2 on $\mathbb{P}_n$ having a section with smooth 2-codimensional zero set satisfying

$$c_2(E) \leq \frac{1}{4} \frac{F(n)}{\sin^2(\frac{\pi}{n-1})} .$$

Then E is of the form

$$E = \mathcal{O}(k) \oplus \mathcal{O}(k) .$$

Proof. The semi-stability of E implies [2]

$$c_1(E)^2 - 4c_2(E) \leq o .$$

The case $c_1(E)^2 - 4c_2(E) < o$ is excluded by 2.2.
The remaining possibility $c_1(E)^2 - 4c_2(E) = o$ is settled by the following

Lemma 2.4. Let E be a semi-stable holomorphic vector bundle of rank 2 on $\mathbb{P}_n$ with $c_1(E)^2 = 4c_2(E)$. Then

$$E \simeq \mathcal{O}(\frac{c_1}{2}) \oplus \mathcal{O}(\frac{c_1}{2}).$$

Proof. By twisting we may assume $c_1(E) = o$. This implies $c_2(E) = o$. Moreover E has to have a non-trivial section (otherwise E would be stable which is incompatible with $c_2(E) = o$ by [2]).

Thus we get an exact sequence

$$o \to \mathcal{O} \to E \to \mathfrak{J}_Z \to o$$

with $Z \subset \mathbb{P}_n$ a locally complete intersection of codimension at least 2. But

$$\deg Z = c_2(E) = o.$$

Hence $Z = \emptyset$, $\mathfrak{J}_Z = \mathcal{O}$ and

$$E \simeq \mathcal{O} \oplus \mathcal{O} .$$

§ 3. Complete Intersections

In this final section the splitting results of § 2 are translated into more geometric form.

Theorem 3.1. Let $Y \subset \mathbb{P}_n$, $n \geq 6$, be a smooth subvariety of degree d with stable normal bundle. Then

$$d > \frac{1}{4} \quad \frac{F(n)}{4\sin^2(\frac{\pi}{n-1})} .$$

Proof. By Barth, Larsen [3] we know that $\det N_{A/\mathbb{P}_n}$ extends for $n \geq 6$ to a line bundle on $\mathbb{P}_n$. This implies (cf.[12]) the extendability of $N_{Y/\mathbb{P}_n}$, i.e. there is a holomorphic vector bundle E of rank 2 on $\mathbb{P}_n$ having a holomorphic section whose zero-locus is Y. Observing $c_2(E) = \deg(Y)$ and $c_1(E)^2 - 4c_2(E) < o$ by stability of E we conclude by 2.2.

Corollary 3.2. Let $Y \subset \mathbb{P}_n$, $n \geq 6$, be a smooth subvariety of codimension 2 and degree d having a semistable normal bundle. If

$$d \leq \frac{1}{4} \frac{F(n)}{4\sin^2(\frac{\pi}{n-1})}$$

then Y is a complete intersection.

Proof. As in the proof of 3.1 we extend N_Y to a vector bundle E on $\mathbb{P}_n$. By 2.3 we have

$$E \simeq \mathcal{O}(k) \oplus \mathcal{O}(k).$$

But this implies that Y is a complete intersection.

A weaker form of this corollary improves the bound (*) of Barth, Van de Ven.

Theorem 3.3. Let $Y \subset \mathbb{P}_n$, $n \geq 6$, be a non-singular 2-codimensional subvariety with semi-stable normal bundle. If

$$n \geq 2\sqrt{\deg(Y)} + 1,$$

then Y is a complete intersection.

Proof. Use 3.2 and the estimate for $F(n)$ as shown in the table.

The strong conjecture of Hartshorne reads in the case of codimension 2 as:

"Y is a complete intersection if $n \geq 7$" .

From 3.2 one gets for $n = 6$ however the following

Corollary 3.4. Let $Y \subset \mathbb{P}_6$ be a smooth 2-codimensional subvariety with semi-stable normal bundle. If

$\deg(Y) \leq 51$

then Y is a complete intersection.

Concluding remarks. 1) By a "conjecture" of Grauert and myself (cf. [9],[13]) all holomorphic rank-2 vector bundles E on $\mathbb{P}_n$, $n \geq 5$, which are not stable are direct sums of line bundles. This would imply that we could drop in our assumptions the semi-stability.

2) Similar results as in § 2 and § 3 can be proved for codimension 2 submanifolds of Grassmannians improving the results of Barth, Van de Ven in [5].

Bibliography

[1] Barth, W.: Submanifolds of low codimension in projective space. Proc. I. C. M. Vancouver, 409 - 413 (1975).

[2] Barth, W.: Some properties of stable rank-2 vector bundles on $\mathbb{P}_n$. Math. Ann. 226, 125 - 150 (1977).

[3] Barth, W., Larsen, M.E.: On the homotopy groups of complex projective algebraic manifolds. Math.Scand. 30, 88 - 94 (1972).

[4] Barth, W., Van de Ven, A.: A decomposability criterion for algebraic 2-bundles on projective spaces. Inventiones math. 25, 91 - 106 (1974).

[5] Barth, W., Van de Ven, A.: On the geometry in codimension 2 of Grassmann manifolds. In Classification of algebraic varieties and compact complex manifolds, Lecture Notes in Math. 412, 1 - 35, Springer (1974).

[6] Fulton, W., Laszarsfeld, R.: Connectivity and its applications in algebraic geometry. Preprint, Brown University (1980).

[7] Gieseker, D.: p-ample bundles and their Chern classes. Nagoya Math. J. 43, 91 - 116 (1971).

[8] Grauert, H.: Über Modifikationen und exzeptionelle analytische Mengen. Math. Ann. 146, 331 - 368 (1962).

[9] Grauert, H., Schneider, M.: Komplexe Unterräume und holomorphe Vektorraumbündel vom Rang zwei. Math. Ann. 30, 75 - 90 (1977).

[10] Hartshorne, R.: Varieties of small codimension in projective space. BAMS 80, 1017 - 1032 (1974).

[11] Hirzebruch, F.: Topological methods in algebraic geometry. Springer (1966).

[12] Okonek, C., Schneider, M., Spindler, H.: Vector bundles on complex projective spaces. Progress in Mathematics n° 3, Birkhäuser (1980).

[13] Schneider, M.: Holomorphic vector bundles on $\mathbb{P}_n$. Sém. Bourbaki 1978/79, exposé 520. Lecture Notes in Mathematics n° 770, Springer (1980).

Michael Schneider
Mathematisches Institut der
Universität Bayreuth
Postfach 3008
D-8580 Bayreuth

Several Complex Variables
Proceedings of the 1981 Hangzhou Conference

PARAMETERS FOR INSTANTON BUNDLES AND SMOOTHNESS OF M(O,2)

Günther Trautmann
FB Mathematik der Universität
D-6750 Kaiserslautern
West-Germany

1. Notations. Let $z_o,\ldots,z_n$ denote homogeneous coordinates of the complex projective space $\mathbb{P}_n(\mathbb{C})$, and let $\mathcal{O}(d)$ be the line bundle on this space determined by the cocycle $g_{ij} = (z_j z_i^{-1})^d$, where $d \in \mathbb{Z}$ is the first Chern class. By $p\mathcal{O}(d)$ we denote the p-fold direct sum of $\mathcal{O}(d)$. It is well known that the space $\mathrm{Hom}(\mathbb{P}_n; p\mathcal{O}(d), q\mathcal{O}(e))$ of global homomorphisms identifies with the space of pxq matrices of homogeneous polynomials of degree e-d in the coordinates $z_o,\ldots,z_n$. We use the following convention: Given such a matrix h, the corresponding homomorphism is described with respect to canonical local trivializations of the bundles over $\{z_i \neq 0\}$ by yssigning to a row of p elements the row $f \circ (hz_i^{d-e})$ of q elements.

Received 1 Dec. 1981.

Let now k be a natural number. A k-instanton monad is by definition a complex

$$k\mathcal{O}(-1) \xrightarrow[m]{} (2k+2)\mathcal{O} \xrightarrow[n]{} k\mathcal{O}(1)$$

of homomorphisms of bundles over $\mathbb{P}_3(\mathbb{C})$ (m and n are matrices of linear forms) such that

(1.1) m is a bundle monomorphism (subbundle)

(1.2) n is a bundle epimorphism

(1.3) $m \circ n = 0$ (or $\mathrm{Im}(m) \subset \mathrm{Ker}(n)$).

If these conditions are satisfied, $E = \mathrm{Ker}(n)/\mathrm{Im}(m)$ is a holomorphic (algebraic) vector bundle of rank 2 with Chern classes $c_1E = 0$, $c_2E = k$, and satisfies $\Gamma(\mathbb{P}_3,E) = 0$ and $H^1(\mathbb{P}_3,E(-2)) = 0$. Here we use the abbreviation $E(d) = E\otimes\mathcal{O}(d)$. Bundles with these properties are called mathematical k instanton bundles. It is shown in [1] that any k-instanton bundle can be constructed by a k-instanton monad. Let $M_I(k)$ be the set of isomorphism classes of k-instanton bundles. We shall consider a parametrization of $M_I(k)$ by matrices of 2-forms.

2. Let us consider a symmetric ($a^{\mu\nu} = a^{\nu\mu}$) k×k matrix $A = (a^{\mu\nu})$ of 2-forms $a^{\mu\nu} \in \Lambda^2\mathbb{C}^4$. By

$$\begin{pmatrix} x^1 \\ \vdots \\ x^k \end{pmatrix} \longrightarrow \begin{pmatrix} \Sigma a^{1\lambda} \wedge x^\lambda \\ \vdots \\ \Sigma a^{k\lambda} \wedge x^\lambda \end{pmatrix} =: \begin{pmatrix} a^{11} \dots a^{1k} \\ \vdots \quad\quad \vdots \\ a^{k1} \dots a^{kk} \end{pmatrix} \wedge \begin{pmatrix} x^1 \\ \vdots \\ x^k \end{pmatrix},$$

where each x^λ denotes a column vector of $\mathbb{C}^4$, a linear operator

$$\underbrace{\mathbb{C}^4\times\ldots\times\mathbb{C}^4}_{k} \xrightarrow[A\wedge]{} \underbrace{\wedge^3\mathbb{C}^4\times\ldots\times\wedge^3\mathbb{C}^4}_{k}$$

is defined. Let us denote by KA a matrix

$$\begin{pmatrix} b^{11} & \ldots & b^{1\ell} \\ \vdots & & \vdots \\ b^{k1} & \ldots & b^{k\ell} \end{pmatrix}$$

of column vectors $b^{\kappa\lambda}$ of $\mathbb{C}^4$, whose ℓ columns are a basis of the null space of $A\wedge$. This matrix defines an operator $(KA)\wedge$ as before, and we can consider again a kernel matrix $K^2A = K(KA)\wedge$. Continuing in this way we obtain a sequence of matrices KA, K^2A, $K^3A,\ldots$, the entries of which are column vectors of $\mathbb{C}^4$. It is called a kernel sequence of A. Note that the rank of $K^\mu A$ does not depend on the construction.

Let $\mathfrak{M}(k)$ be the space of all symmetric $k\times k$ matrices A of 2-forms in $\wedge^2\mathbb{C}^4$ as before, satisfying:

(2.1) $\operatorname{rank}(A\wedge) = 2k+2$

(2.2) $K^pA = 0$ for some p.

The group $GL(k,\mathbb{C})$ operates on $\mathfrak{M}(k)$ by SAS^t, where for $A = (a^{\mu\nu}) \in \mathfrak{M}(k)$ and $S = (s^{\mu\nu}) \in GL(k,\mathbb{C})$ SAS^t is the matrix of the 2-forms $\sum\limits_{\lambda,\kappa} s^{\mu\lambda}a^{\lambda\kappa}s^{\nu\kappa}$.

We define now a map $\mathfrak{M}(k) \to M_I(k)$ as follows. Let $e_0,\ldots,e_3$ be a basis of $\mathbb{C}^4$, write $a^{\mu\nu}$ as

$$a^{\mu\nu} = \sum_{i<j} a_{ij} e_i \wedge e_j ,$$

and define the 4×4 matrix

$$A^{\mu\nu} := \begin{pmatrix} -a_{12} & a_{o2} & -a_{o1} & 0 \\ -a_{13} & a_{o3} & 0 & -a_{o1} \\ -a_{23} & 0 & a_{o3} & -a_{o2} \\ 0 & -a_{23} & a_{13} & -a_{12} \end{pmatrix} ,$$

which represents the operator $a^{\mu\nu}\wedge: \mathbb{C}^4 \to \Lambda^3\mathbb{C}^4$. Let then $\tilde{A}$ be the $4k\times 4k$ matrix

$$\tilde{A} = \begin{pmatrix} A^{11} & \dots & A^{1k} \\ \vdots & & \vdots \\ A^{k1} & \dots & A^{kk} \end{pmatrix} .$$

Choose a $(2k+2)\times 4k$ matrix N of rank $2k+2$ satisfying $N\circ(KA) = 0$. (Here KA is considered a $4k\times\ell$ matrix with $\ell=2k-2$, which has rank ℓ by definition. The lines of N are a basis of the left null space of KA.) After choosing KA and N there is a unique $4k\times(2k+2)$ matrix M with $M\circ N = \tilde{A}$. Now denote by Z_3^k resp. Z_o^k the k-fold direct sum of

$$Z_3 = (-z_3\ z_2\ -z_1\ z_o) \text{ resp. } Z_o = (z_o\ z_1\ z_2\ z_3)^t$$

such that Z_3^k is a $k\times 4k$ and Z_o^k is a $4k\times k$ matrix. Finally we define the $k\times(2k+2)$ matrix m and the $(2k+2)\times k$ matrix n of linear forms by

$$m = Z_3^k\circ M \quad\text{and}\quad n = N\circ Z_o^k \quad .$$

It can now be verified that

(i) $$k\mathcal{O}(-1) \xrightarrow[m]{} (2k+2)\mathcal{O} \xrightarrow[n]{} k\mathcal{O}(1)$$

is a k-instanton monad,

(ii) the isomorphism class $[E(A)]$ of the bundle $E(A) = \mathrm{Ker}(n)/\mathrm{Im}(m)$ is independent of the choice of KA and N.

(iii) $[E(A)] = [E(A')]$ if and only if $A' = SAS^t$ for some $S \in GL(k,\mathbb{C})$.

Remark: The space $\mathfrak{M}(k)$ is in between the space $\mathfrak{Mon}(k)$ of self-dual k-instanton monads and $M_I(k)$. There is a canonical morphism $\mathfrak{Mon}(k) \to \mathfrak{M}(k)$ which is a fibre bundle with fibre $Sp(k+1,\mathbb{C})$, as is proved in [2]. Here we have constructed a local section of this fibering in order to obtain E(A). One can construct E(A) from A without using monads, [2], [5].

3. Some properties of the bundle E(A) can be read off directly from the matrix $A \in \mathfrak{M}(k)$. If we denote by $h^1E(d)=\dim_{\mathbb{C}} H^1(\mathbb{P}_3, E(d))$ for the bundle E = E(A), it can be proved that

$$\begin{aligned} h^1E(-1) &= k \\ h^1E(o) &= 4h^1E(-1) - \operatorname{rk}(A\wedge) = 2k-2 \\ h^1E(d) &= 4h^1E(d-1) - \operatorname{rk}(K^dA)\wedge, \text{ for } d \geq 0. \end{aligned}$$

Moreover if $p_{01},\ldots,p_{23}$ are the Plücker coordinates of a line $L \subset \mathbb{P}_3$, we can consider the linear forms

$$\delta_L^{\mu\nu} = a_{01}p_{23} - a_{02}p_{13} + a_{12}p_{03} + a_{03}p_{12} - a_{13}p_{02} + a_{23}p_{01} ,$$

defined by $a^{\mu\nu} = \Sigma a_{ij} e_i \wedge e_j$. It turns out that $E|L = \mathcal{O}_L(-d) \oplus \mathcal{O}_L(d)$ if and only if

$$\operatorname{rank}(\delta_L^{\mu\nu}) = k-d .$$

The space $\mathfrak{M}(k)$ should also be helpful in proving that $M_I(k)$ has the structure of a complex manifold, which is only known for $k \leq 4$. In section 4 a simple proof in the case k=2 is given using $\mathfrak{M}(2)$. Note that the case k=1 is trivial since by the above description $M_I(1)$ identifies with $\mathbb{P}_5 \setminus G_{2,4}$, where $G_{2,4} \hookrightarrow \mathbb{P}_5$ is the Grassmannian of lines of $\mathbb{P}_3$ embedded as a nonsingular quadric in $\mathbb{P}_5$ by Plücker coordinates.

4. Smoothness of $\mathfrak{M}(2)$. Let $A \in \mathfrak{M}(2)$ and write KA in the form

$$\begin{pmatrix} x & x' \\ y & y' \end{pmatrix} .$$

It can be shown that in the case k=2 condition (2.2) is equivalent with $K^2A = 0$, i.e. $(KA)\wedge$ is injective. This again is equivalent to x,y,x',y' being a basis of $\mathbb{C}^4$. Now let

$$\mathfrak{M}(2) \xrightarrow[\pi]{} G_{2,8}$$

be the map which assigns to A the 2-dimensional subspace of $\mathbb{C}^8$ spanned by the columns $\binom{x}{y}$, $\binom{x'}{y'}$ of KA.
Let $p_{ij} = x_i x_j' - x_j x_i'$ and $q_{ij} = y_i y_j' - y_j y_i'$. The vectors x,y,x',y' are linear independent if and only if

$$p_{o1}q_{23}-p_{o2}q_{13}+p_{o3}q_{12}+p_{12}q_{o3}-p_{13}q_{o2}+p_{23}q_{o1} \neq 0.$$

This condition defines a Zariski-open set $G^*_{2,8}$ of $G_{2,8}$.
Let F be the set of $A \in \mathfrak{M}(2)$ such that

$$A\wedge \begin{pmatrix} e_o & e_1 \\ e_2 & e_3 \end{pmatrix} = 0.$$

It is easily checked that F identifies with $\mathbb{C}^5 \setminus H$, where H is a cubic hypersurface. Using the unique linear transformation which transforms x,x',y,y' into the basis e_o, e_1, e_2, e_3 it can be checked easily that π is a fibre bundle with fibre F, which is trivial over the subsets $\{q_{ij} \neq 0\}$ of $G^*_{2,8}$. By this $\mathfrak{M}(2)$ is seen to be a complex manifold of dimension 17. Since the group $GL(k,\mathbb{C})/\{\pm 1\}$ acts free on $\mathfrak{M}(k)$, it follows from wellknown theorems on quotients, [4], that $M(0,2) = M_I(2) = \mathfrak{M}(2)/GL(2,\mathbb{C})$ is a manifold of dimension 13. A different approach to M(0,2) was given in [3].

References

[1] W. Barth - K. Hulek, Monads and moduli of vector bundles, Manuscripta math. 25, 323-347 (1978)

[2] W. Böhmer, Monaden und Matrizen für Vektorbündel über $\mathbb{P}_n$, Dissertation Kaiserslautern 1981

[3] R. Hartshorne, Stable vector bundles and instantons, Comm. Math. Phys. 59, 1-15 (1978)

[4] H. Holmann, Komplexe Räume mit komplexen Transformationsgruppen, Math. Ann. 150, 327-360 (1963)

[5] G. Trautmann, Zur Berechnung von Yang-Mills Potentialen durch holomorphe Vektorbündel, Proc. Nice Conference 1979, Progr. in Math. 7 (1980).

Section Four

Kernels and Integral Formulae

Several Complex Variables
Proceedings of the 1981 Hangzhou Conference

THE INTEGRAL REPRESENTATION FOR POLYHEDRAL DOMAINS OF $\mathbb{C}^n$

Chen Shu-jin

(Xiamen University)

By a polyhedral domain in $\mathbb{C}^n$ we mean a bounded domain D in $\mathbb{C}^n$ which satisfies the following two conditions.

1) The boundary ∂D of D is homeomorphic to the polyhedron $|\dot{S}^{2n}|$ of the boundary complex $\dot{S}^{2n}$ of the standard 2n-dimensional simplex S^{2n} of the 2n-dimensional Euclidean space. We denote by $\sigma_{j_1 \cdots j_k}$ a subset of ∂D which corresponds to a (2n-k)-dimensional simplex $S^{(2n-k)}$ of $\dot{S}^{2n}$ under the homeomorphism.

2) For some differentiable functions $w_j = w_j(z) = u_j(x,y) + \sqrt{-1}\, v_j(x,y)$ on some bounded domain R in $\mathbb{C}^n$ and for some bounded domain R_j in the w_j-plane with piecewise smooth boundary $(j = 1,\cdots,N)$, D is a component of $\{z \in R \mid w_j(z) \in R_j,\ j = 1,\cdots,N\}$ such that the topological closure $\overline{D}$ of D is contained in R. Without loss of generality we can assume that all the domains R_j are needed to define D.

When $w_j = w_j(z)$ $(j = 1,\cdots,N)$ are analytic functions in R, the polyhedral domain D is called an analytic polyhedral domain.

<u>Definition</u>. By a function of class A we mean a function $F(\zeta,z)$, $\zeta \in \partial D$, $z \in \overline{D}$, of the form

---

Received 16 Nov. 1981

$$F(\zeta,z) = \sum_{\ell=1}^{n} (\zeta_\ell - z_\ell)\phi_\ell(\zeta,z),$$

where $\phi_\ell(\zeta,z)$ is real-analytic, such that $F(\zeta,z) \neq 0$ whenever $\zeta \in \partial D$, $z \in \bar{D}$, and $\zeta \neq z$. We use the notation $F \in A$ to mean that F is a function of class A.

A set of C^2 functions $N_j = N_j(\zeta,z)$, $\zeta \in \partial D$, $z \in \bar{D}$, $j = 1,\cdots,n$, is said to be of class B (in notations, $N_j \in B$) if $\sum_{j=1}^{n} (\zeta_j - z_j)N_j(\zeta,z) \neq 0$ for $\zeta \neq z$, $\zeta \in \partial D$, and $z \in \bar{D}$.

For $F_{j_m} = \sum_{\ell=1}^{n} (\zeta_\ell - z_\ell)\phi_{j_m\ell} \in A$ $(m = 1,\cdots,k)$ and $N_j \in B$ we use the following notations:

$$N = (N_1,N_2,\cdots,N_n),\ N_{\bar{\beta}_j} = (N_{1\bar{\beta}_j}, N_{2\bar{\beta}_j},\cdots,N_{n\bar{\beta}_j})$$

$$= \left(\frac{\partial N_1}{\partial \bar{\xi}_{\beta_j}}, \frac{\partial N_2}{\partial \bar{\xi}_{\beta_j}},\cdots,\frac{\partial N_n}{\partial \bar{\xi}_{\beta_j}}\right),$$

$$H_{j_m} = (H_{j_m1}, H_{j_m2},\cdots,H_{j_mn}),\ H_{j_m\ell} = \frac{\phi_{j_m\ell}}{F_{j_m}},$$

$$M = \sum_{j=1}^{n} (\xi_j - z_j)N_j, \qquad G = \sum_{\ell,\beta=1}^{n} (\xi_\ell - z_\ell)N_{\ell\bar{\beta}}\, d\bar{\xi}_\beta,$$

$$\det{}_{(n)}(R_1,\cdots,R_\ell, E_{\bar{1}},\cdots,E_{\overline{n-\ell}}) = \begin{vmatrix} R_{11}\cdots R_{\ell 1} & E_{1\bar{1}}\cdots E_{1\overline{n-\ell}} \\ \vdots \quad\ \vdots & \vdots \quad\ \vdots \\ R_{1n}\cdots R_{\ell n} & E_{n\bar{1}}\cdots E_{n\overline{n-\ell}} \end{vmatrix}.$$

We obtain the following theorems.

Theorem 1. If D is a polyhedral domain and the functions $F_{j_m}(\xi,z) \in A$, $N_j(\xi,z) \in B$, then for any analytic function f(z) on $\bar{D}$ we have the following integral representation

$$f(z) = \frac{\varepsilon}{(2\pi i)^n} \sum_{j_1<\cdots<j_k} \int_{\sigma_{j_1\cdots j_k}} \frac{f(\xi)}{M^{n-k+1}} \sum_{\rho=1}^{k} (-1)^{k-\rho} \sum_{\beta_1,\cdots,\beta_{n-k}=1}^{n}$$

$$\det{}_{(n)}(H_{j_1},\cdots,[H_{j_\rho}],\cdots,H_{j_k},N,N_{\bar{\beta}_1},\cdots,N_{\bar{\beta}_{n-k}})d\bar{\xi}_{\beta_1}\wedge\cdots\wedge d\bar{\xi}_{\beta_{n-k}}\wedge\omega(\xi),$$

where $\omega(\xi) = d\xi_1 \wedge d\xi_2 \wedge \cdots \wedge d\xi_n$ and $\varepsilon = \pm 1$ according to the choice of the orientation of ∂D.

This integral representation gives the relations between the value of analytic function in the domain and its value on boundary faces of real dimension between n and 2n-1.

Theorem 2. If D is a polyhedral domain, u(z) is a differentiable function on $\bar{D}$, $F_{j_m}(\xi,z) \in A$, and $N_j(\xi,z) \in B$, then we have the following Leray-Stokes formula:

$$u(z) = \frac{\varepsilon}{(2\pi i)^n} \sum_{j_1<\cdots<j_n} \int_{\sigma_{j_1\cdots j_k}} u(\xi)\det{}_{(n)}(H_{j_1},\cdots,H_{j_n})\omega(\xi) -$$

$$- \frac{\varepsilon}{(2\pi i)^n} \sum_{k=1}^{n-1} \sum_{j_1<\cdots<j_k} \int_{\sigma_{j_1\cdots j_k}} \bar{\partial}u(\xi) \wedge \sum_{\beta_1,\cdots,\beta_{n-1}=1}^{n} \det{}_{(n)}(H_{j_1},\cdots,H_{j_{k-1}},$$

$$\frac{N}{M^{n-k+1}} N_{\overline{\beta}_1}, \cdots, N_{\overline{\beta}_{n-k}}) d\overline{\xi}_{\beta_1} \wedge \cdots \wedge d\overline{\xi}_{\beta_{n-k}} \wedge \omega(\xi) + \frac{\varepsilon(n-1)!}{(2\pi i)^n} \int_{\partial D \times [0,1]} \overline{\partial} u(\xi) \wedge \omega^*(\eta) \wedge \omega(\xi)$$

$$- \frac{\varepsilon(n-1)!}{(2\pi i)^n} \int_D \overline{\partial} u(\xi) \wedge \omega^*\left(\frac{\overline{\xi}-\overline{z}}{|\xi-z|^2}\right) \wedge \omega(\xi),$$

where

$$\eta_j = \lambda \frac{\overline{\xi}_j - \overline{z}_j}{|\xi-z|^2} + (1-\lambda) \frac{N_j(\xi,z)}{M(\xi,z)}, \qquad 0 \le \lambda \le 1,$$

$$\omega^*(\eta) = \sum_{j=1}^{n} (-1)^{j-1} \eta_j d\eta_1 \wedge d\eta_2 \wedge \cdots \wedge d\eta_{j-1} \wedge d\eta_{j+1} \wedge \cdots \wedge d\eta_n.$$

Theorem 1 was published in Acta Math. Sinica (Chinese) 24 (1981), No. 4, 537-543.

The proof of Theorem 2 depends on the following two lemmas.

<u>Lemma 1</u>. If $F_{j_m}(\xi,z) \in A$, $N_j(\xi,z) \in B$, then for any differentiable function $u(z)$ on $\overline{D}$, we have

$$\frac{\varepsilon}{(2\pi i)^n} \sum_{j_1<\cdots<j_k} \int_{\sigma_{j_1 \cdots j_k}} u(\xi) \sum_{\rho=1}^{k} (-1)^{k+\rho} \sum_{\beta_1, \ldots, \beta_{n-k}=1}^{n} \det{}_{(n)}(H_{j_1}, \cdots,$$

$$[H_{j_\rho}], \cdots, H_{j_k}, \frac{N}{M^{n-k+1}}, N_{\overline{\beta}_1}, \cdots, N_{\overline{\beta}_{n-k}}) d\overline{\xi}_{\beta_1} \wedge \cdots \wedge d\overline{\xi}_{\beta_{n-k}} \wedge \omega(\xi) =$$

$$= \frac{\varepsilon}{(2\pi i)^n} \sum_{j_1<\cdots<j_{k-1}} \int_{\sigma_{j_1 \cdots j_{k-1}}} u(\xi) \sum_{\rho=1}^{k-1} (-1)^{k+\rho-1} \sum_{\beta_1, \ldots, \beta_{n-k+1}=1}^{n} \det{}_{(n)}(H_{j_1},$$

$$\cdots, [H_{j_\rho}], \cdots, H_{j_{k-1}}, \frac{N}{M^{n-k+2}}, N_{\overline{\beta}_1}, \cdots, N_{\overline{\beta}_{n-k+1}}) d\overline{\xi}_{\beta_1} \wedge \cdots \wedge d\overline{\xi}_{\beta_{n-k+1}} \wedge$$

$$\wedge \omega(\xi) + \frac{\varepsilon}{(2\pi i)^n} \sum_{j_1<\cdots<j_{k-1}} \int_{\sigma_{j_1 \cdots j_{k-1}}} \overline{\partial} u(\xi) \wedge \sum_{\beta_1, \ldots, \beta_{n-k}=1}^{n} \det{}_{(n)}(H_{j_1},$$

$$\ldots, H_{j_{k-1}}, \frac{N}{M^{n-k+1}}, N_{\overline{\beta}_1}, \cdots, N_{\overline{\beta}_{n-k}}) d\overline{\xi}_{\beta_1} \wedge \cdots \wedge d\overline{\xi}_{\beta_{n-k}} \wedge \omega(\xi).$$

<u>Lemma 2</u>. If $u(z)$ is a differentiable function on $\overline{D}$ and $N_j(\xi,z) \in B$, then

$$\frac{\varepsilon}{(2\pi i)^n} \int_{\partial D} u(\xi) \sum_{\beta_1,\cdots,\beta_{n-1}=1}^{n} \frac{1}{M^n} \det_{(n)}(N, N_{\overline{\beta}_1}, \cdots, N_{\overline{\beta}_{n-1}}) d\overline{\xi}_{\beta_1} \wedge \cdots$$

$$\wedge\, d\overline{\xi}_{\beta_{j-1}} \wedge \omega(\xi) = \frac{\varepsilon(n-1)!}{(2\pi i)^n} \int_{\partial D} u(\xi)\omega^*(\tfrac{N}{M}) \wedge \omega(\xi) = u(z) - \frac{\varepsilon(n-1)!}{(2\pi i)^n} \cdot$$

$$\int_{\partial D\times[0,1]} \overline{\partial}\, u(\xi) \wedge \omega^*(\eta) \wedge \omega(\xi) + \frac{\varepsilon(n-1)!}{(2\pi i)^n} \int_D \overline{\partial} u(\xi) \wedge \omega^*(\tfrac{\overline{\xi}-\overline{z}}{|\xi-z|^2}) \wedge \omega(\xi),$$

where

$$\eta_j = \lambda \frac{\overline{\xi}_j - \overline{z}_j}{|\xi-z|^2} + (1-\lambda)\frac{N_j(\xi,z)}{M(\xi,z)}, \qquad 0 \le \lambda \le 1,$$

$$\omega^*(\eta) = \sum_{j=1}^{n} (-1)^{j-1} \eta_j d\eta_1 \wedge d\eta_1 \wedge d\eta_2 \wedge \cdots \wedge d\eta_{j-1} \wedge d\eta_{j+1} \wedge \cdots \wedge d\eta_n .$$

Several Complex Variables
Proceedings of the 1981 Hangzhou Conference

REMOVABLE SINGULARITIES FOR HOLOMORPHIC FUNCTIONS WHICH SATISFY THE AREA-BMO CONDITION

I.R. Graham*
Dept. of Math., University of Toronto
Toronto, Canada

This is a report on some joint work with Professor J.A. Cima concerning removable singularities theorems. The general situation is as follows: We are given a bounded domain Ω in $\mathbb{C}^n$, a complex-analytic subvariety V of Ω, and a holomorphic function f on $\Omega - V$. We seek to determine conditions on f and possibly on V such that f extends holomorphically to Ω and the extended function belongs to a specified class of functions. For example, in [3] we Proved

Theorem 1: Let B_n be the unit ball in $\mathbb{C}^n$ and let V be an analytic subvariety of B_n. Suppose f is holomorphic on $B_n - V$ and there exists a harmonic function u on $B_n - V$ such that $|f|^p \le u$ on $B_n - V$ for some $p > 0$. Then f extends to $\tilde{f} \in H^p(B_m)$.

No conditions on V are needed for this result. Cegrell [2] has recently obtained a generalization in which V is replaced by a closed subset of capacity zero (with respect to a suitable capacity).

Cima and the author have now studied removable singularities for the class of holomorphic functions which satisfy the area BMO condition. In one variable and on strongly pseudo-convex domains this class coincides with the Bloch class. Definitions follow:

Definition 1: Let Ω be a domain in $\mathbb{R}^n$ and let $f \in L^1_{loc}(\Omega)$. Then $f \in BMO(\Omega)$ if

* Partially supported by the National Sciences and Engineering Research Council of Canada.

Received Nov. 1981

$$\sup_B \frac{1}{|B|} \int_B |f(x) - f_B| \, d\lambda(x) < \infty$$

where the supremum is taken over all balls $B \subset \Omega$. Here f_B denotes the average value of f on B, $|B|$ denotes the volume of B, and $d\lambda$ denotes Lebesgue measure.

An important fact is that if f is harmonic then

(1) $$f \in BMO(\Omega) \iff |\nabla f(x)| = O\left((\text{dist}(x, \partial\Omega))^{-1}\right).$$

<u>Definition 2:</u> Let f be holomorphic on the unit disc $D \subset \mathbb{C}$. f belongs to the Bloch class $\mathcal{B}(D)$ if

$$\sup_{z\in D} (1 - |z|^2)|f'(z)| < \infty$$

From the fact just noted it follows that $\mathcal{B}(D)$ coincides with the class of holomorphic functions on D which satisfy the area BMO condition. Note that this is *not* the space $BMOA(D)$ of holomorphic functions in (say) $H^2(D)$ with BMO boundary values. Functions in $\mathcal{B}(D)$ need not have boundary values except in a distributional sense. (However they grow only like $-C \log(1 - |z|)$). References for Bloch functions in one variable are [1] and [8]. In [8] Pommerenke showed that if $f \in BMOA(D)$ then f satisfies the gradient condition (1). Hence f belongs to $\mathcal{B}(D)$; or, equivalently, to the area BMO class. He also showed that if $f \in \mathcal{B}(D)$ and f is univalent then $f \in BMOA(D)$. (He actually proved a stronger result.)

<u>Definition 3.</u> Let Ω be a bounded domain in $\mathbb{C}^n$. Let $H_z(\xi, \eta)$ denote the Bergman metric tensor. A holomorphic function f belongs to the Bloch class $\mathcal{B}(D)$ if

$$\sup_{\substack{z\in\Omega \\ \xi\in\mathbb{C}^n}} \frac{|\nabla f(z) \cdot \xi|}{(H_z(\xi,\xi))^{\frac{1}{2}}} < \infty .$$

If Ω is strongly pseudoconvex then $f \in \mathcal{B}(\Omega)$ iff f satisfies the gradient condition (1). Hence in this case $\mathcal{B}(\Omega)$

coincides with the class $BMO(\Omega)$. References for Bloch functions in several variables are Hahn [6, 7] and Timoney [9].

Our theorem on removable singularities involves a geometric condition on the variety which is motivated by the sparseness condition $\left|\frac{z_i - z_j}{1 - z_i\bar{z}_j}\right| \geq \delta > 0$ for a sequence of points $\{z_j\}_{j=1}^{\infty}$ on the disc.

Definition 4: Let V be a subvariety of a domain $\Omega \subset\subset \mathbb{C}^n$. V satisfies the A covering condition if the following conditions are satisfied:

(a) There exist polydiscs P_α with polyradii $r_\alpha = (r_1(\alpha), \ldots, r_n(\alpha))$ such that

$$\bar{P}_\alpha \subset \Omega \quad \text{and} \quad V \subset \cup P_\alpha .$$

(b) There are positive constants c_1 and c_2 such that

$$c_1 r_j(\alpha) \leq \operatorname{dist}(P_\alpha, \partial\Omega) \leq c_2 r_j(\alpha), \qquad j = 1, \ldots, n.$$

(c) There is a constant $c_3 > 0$ such that

$$\operatorname{dist}(\partial_0 P_\alpha, V) \geq c_3 \operatorname{dist}(P_\alpha, \partial\Omega), \quad \text{all } \alpha .$$

($\partial_0 P_\alpha$ denotes the distinguished boundary of P_α.)

(d) There is a constant $c_4 > 0$ such that for any $w \in V$ there exists α with $w \in P_\alpha$ and

$$\operatorname{dist}(w, \partial P_\alpha) \geq c_4 \operatorname{dist}(P_\alpha, \partial\Omega).$$

For example, if $V = \{z \in B_n \mid z_1 \in V_1\}$ where V_1 is a sparse subset of the disc D then V satisfies the A covering condition. If V is a subvariety of a bounded domain Ω which extends across $\partial\Omega$ and is smooth near $\partial\Omega$ then V satisfies the A covering condition.

Theorem 2 (BMO version): Suppose V is a subvariety of $\Omega \subset\subset \mathbb{C}^n$ which satisfies the A covering condition. Suppose f is holomorphic on $\Omega - V$ and $f \in BMO(\Omega - V)$. Then f extends holomorphically to $\tilde{f}$ on Ω and $\tilde{f} \in BMO(\Omega)$.

In view of the remark following Definition 1 this is equivalent to

Theorem 2 (Gradient version): Suppose V and Ω are as above. Suppose f is holomorphic on $\Omega - V$ and

$$\|\nabla f(z)\| \leq C\left[\min\left(\operatorname{dist}(z, \partial\Omega), \operatorname{dist}(z, V)\right)\right]^{-1}.$$

Then f extends to a holomorphic function $\tilde{f}$ on Ω such that

$$\|\nabla\tilde{f}(z)\| \leq C' \operatorname{dist}(z, \partial\Omega))^{-1}.$$

Details of the proof are given in [3]. The idea is as follows: We work with the gradient version of the theorem. It is easy to show that f extends holomorphically to Ω without assuming the Λ covering property for V. The main difficulty is to estimate $\|\nabla\tilde{f}\|$. (In Theorem 1 on the other hand, the main difficulty is to show that f has a holomorphic extension.) On $\Omega - \cup P_\alpha$ this is straightforward, while on P_α we use the maximum principle and the following fact:

Lemma: If ω_1, ω_2 are in P_α then there are positive constants k_1 and k_2 which are independent of α such that

$$k_1 \leq \frac{\operatorname{dist}(\omega_1, \partial\Omega)}{\operatorname{dist}(\omega_2, \partial\Omega)} \leq k_2 .$$

We shall now make some remarks on the one-variable case of Theorem 2. It is easy to show that sparseness of a sequence $V = \{z_j\}_{j=1}^{\infty} \subset D$ is equivalent to the following : there exists $\delta' > 0$ such that the closed discs $D_j = \{z \in \mathbb{C} \mid |z - z_j| \leq \delta'(1 - |z_j|)$ are contained in D and disjoint. Thus sparse sequences are removable for holomorphic BMO functions since the Λ covering condition is clearly satisfied.

In general the Λ covering condition in one variable reads as follows: A discrete sequence of points in a domain $\Omega \subset\subset \mathbb{C}$

satisfies the A covering condition if there exist two sequences of discs $\{D_j\}_{j=1}^{\infty}$ and $\{E_j\}_{j=1}^{\infty}$ and a constant c, $0 < c < 1$ such that

(a) D_j and E_j are concentric, $j = 1,2,3,\ldots$

(b) radius of $D_j = c(\text{radius of } E_j)$

(c) $\bar{E}_j \subset \Omega$

(d) $E_j \cap E_k = \phi$, $j \neq k$

(e) $V \subset \bigcup_{j=1}^{\infty} D_j$.

The A covering condition in one variable may provide a necessary and sufficient condition for a discrete set of points in the disc to be removable for holomorphic BMO functions. Some modification would be necessary for an arbitrary domain in $\mathbb{C}$. Clearly any discrete sequence which is bounded away from $\partial\Omega$ is removable for BMO functions, because one has "room" to estimate $|\tilde{f}'(z)|$ near $\partial\Omega$. An example of R. Timoney given in [4] shows that some geometric condition on the removable set is needed.

Questions:

(1) Does an analytic subvariety V of a domain $\Omega \subset\subset \mathbb{C}^n$ which extends across $\partial\Omega$ (without being smooth near $\partial\Omega$) have the A covering property?

(2) Is an assumption on the size of V, e.g. finite volume, sufficient to guarantee that the A covering property is satisfied?

Bibliography

(1) J.M. Anderson, J. Clunie, and C. Pommerenke, "On Bloch functions and normal functions," J. Reine Amgew. Math., 270 (1974), 12-37.

(2) U. Cegrell, "Removable singularity sets for analytic functions having modulus with bounded Laplace mass," Prepring, McGill University and Uppsala Universitet.

(3) J.A. Cima and I.R. Graham, "On the extension of holomorphic functions with growth conditions across analytic subvarieties," Mich. Math. J. 28 (1981), 241-256.

(4) J.A. Cima and I.R. Graham, "Removable singularities for Bloch and BMO functions," Preprint, University of North Carolina at Chapel Hill and University of Toronto.

(5) I.R. Graham, "Zero sets and extension theorems for the H^p and Nevanlinna classes on the unit ball and polydisc in $\mathbb{C}^n$," to appear in the Proceedings of the Beijing Symposium on Differential Geometry and Partial Differential Equations, Science Press, China and Van Nostrand Reinhold.

(6) K.T. Hahn, "Holomorphic mappings of the hyperbolic space into the complex Euclidean space and the Bloch theorem," Can. J. Math. 27 (1975), 446-458.

(7) K.T. Hahn, "Quantitative Bloch's theorem for certain classes of holomorphic mappings of the ball into $P_n\mathbb{C}$," J. Reine Angew. Math. 283 (1976), 99-109.

(8) C. Pommerenke, "Schlichte Funktionen und analytische Funktionen von beschränkler mittlerer Oszillation," Comment. Math. Helv. 52 (1977), 591-602.

(9) R.M. Timoney, "Bloch functions in several complex variables, I," Bull. London Math. Soc. 12 (1980), 241-267.

Several Complex Variables
Proceedings of the 1981 Hangzhou Conference

SINGULAR INTEGRALS IN SEVERAL COMPLEX VARIABLES

Sheng Kung

(University of Science and Technology of China;
Institue of Applied Mathematics of Academic Sinica)

Ji-Huai Shi

(University of Science and Technology of China)

(I)

Let Ω be a smooth, bounded, strictly pseudo-convex domain in $\mathbb{C}^n$. Let $H(w,z)$ be the Henkin-Ramirez kernel and $E(w,z)+C(w,z)$ be the Stein-Kerzman kernel. Since both $H(w,z)d\sigma_z$ and $E(w,z)d\sigma_z$ are Cauchy-Fantappie forms, they may be written as

$$\frac{c_n}{g^n}\,\omega dz_1\wedge\cdots\wedge dz_n$$

where

$$c_n = (-1)^{\frac{n(n-1)}{2}}(n-1)!(2\pi i)^{-n}, \qquad g(w,z) = \sum_{i=1}^{n}(z_i-w_i)g_i(w,z)$$

$$\omega = \sum(-1)^{j-1}g_j\bar\partial g_1\wedge\cdots\wedge\widehat{\bar\partial g_j}\wedge\cdots\wedge\bar\partial g_n\ .$$

Alt in 1974, Kerzman and Stein in 1978 proved respectively the following Plemelj formulas of the Cauchy integrals defined by the Henkin-Ramirez kernel and the Stein-Kerzman kernel

Received 16 Nov. 1981

$$\lim_{w\to w_0} \int_{z\in b\Omega} H(w,z)u(z)d\sigma_z = \frac{1}{2}u(w_0) + \text{V.P.}\int_{z\in b\Omega} H(w_0,z)u(z)d\sigma_z$$

where $H(w,z)$ is either the Henkin-Ramirez kernel or the Stein-Kerzman kernel, $u \in C^\infty$, $w_0 \in b\Omega$, $w \in \Omega$, $d\sigma_z$ is the element of area on $b\Omega$, V.P. $\int_{b\Omega}$ is defined as $\lim_{\varepsilon\to 0} \int_{z\in b\Omega - B(w_0,\varepsilon)}$,

and

$$B(w_0,\varepsilon) = \{z \in b\Omega,\ |g(w_0,z)| < \varepsilon\}.$$

We generalize the above Plemelj formula and obtain the following results:

If we replace $B(w_0,\varepsilon)$ by

$$B_e(w_0,\varepsilon) = \{z \in b\Omega,\ \alpha^2(\text{Re } g)^2 + \beta^2(\text{Im } g)^2 < \varepsilon^2,\ \alpha \geq 0,\ \beta \geq 0,\ \alpha+\beta \neq 0\},$$

then the Plemelj formula becomes

$$\lim_{w\to w_0} \int_{z\in b\Omega} H(w,z)u(z)d\sigma_z = \frac{1}{2}\left(\frac{2\beta}{\alpha+\beta}\right)^{n-1} u(w_0) + \text{V.P.}\int_{b\Omega} H(w_0,z)u(z)d\sigma_z,$$

where V.P. $\int$ is defined as $\lim_{\varepsilon\to 0} \int_{z\in b\Omega - B_e(w_0,\varepsilon)}$.

When $\alpha = \beta$, this is the theorem of Alt and Stein-Kerzman.

If we replace $B(w_0,\varepsilon)$ by

$$B_R(w_0,\varepsilon) = \{z \in b\Omega,\ |\text{Re } g| \leq \alpha\varepsilon,\ |\text{Im } g| \leq \beta\varepsilon,\ \alpha > 0, \beta > 0\},$$

then the Plemelj formula becomes

$$\lim_{w\to w_0} \int_{z\in b\Omega} H(w,z)u(z)d\sigma_z = a\,u(w_0) + \text{V.P.}\int_{b\Omega} H(w_0,z)u(z)d\sigma_z$$

where

$$a = \frac{2^{n-1}}{\pi}\left\{\frac{\pi}{2} - h_n(\operatorname{arctg}\frac{\beta}{\alpha})\right\}, \qquad h_n(x) = \int_0^x \cos^{n-2}t\,\frac{\sin(n-1)t}{\sin t}\,dt$$

and V.P. $\int$ is defined as $\lim_{\varepsilon\to 0}\int_{z\in b\Omega - B_R(w_o,\varepsilon)}$.

It is worth noting that in the case of

$$\tilde{B}(w_0,\varepsilon) = \{z \in b\Omega, |\text{Re } g| < \varepsilon\}$$

we have

$$\lim_{w\to w_0}\int_{z\in b\Omega} H(w,z)u(z)d\sigma_z = \text{V.P.}\int_{b\Omega} H(w_0,z)u(z)d\sigma_z$$

where V.P.$\int = \lim_{\Sigma\to 0}\int_{b\Omega-\tilde{B}}$. In other words we can represent the limit value of the Cauchy integral by certain Cauchy principal value in the case of several complex variables, which is impossible to do in the case of one complex variable.

This interesting phenomenon happens if the domain is one of the classical domains and the kernel is the Cauchy-Szegö kernel, but it does not happen if the domain is a smooth orientable manifold and the kernel is the Bochner-Martinelli kernel.

(II)

Suppose $z = (z_1, \cdots, z_n)$, $z\bar{z}' < 1$ and $f(u)$ is an integrable function on the sphere $u\bar{u}' = 1$. Then the Cauchy integral of $f(u)$ is

$$F(z) = \frac{1}{\omega_{2n-1}} \int_{u\bar{u}'=1} \frac{f(u)\dot{u}}{(1-z\bar{u})^n}$$

where ω_{2n-1} is the area of sphere $u\bar{u}' = 1$ and $\dot{u}$ is the element of area.

We will give the limiting value of the derivative of the Cauchy integral $F(z)$ as z approaches the sphere.

If $f = f_1 + if_2$ is a complex function defined in $u\bar{u}' \leq 1$ and f_1, f_2 have the third-order partial derivatives respectively, then for an arbitrary point v on the sphere, the limit

$$\lim_{\varepsilon\to 0} \frac{1}{\omega_{2n-1}} \int_{\sigma_\varepsilon(v)} \frac{\bar{u}_k[f(u)-f(v)]}{(1-v\bar{u}')^{n+1}} \dot{u} \qquad (k = 1,2,\cdots,n)$$

exists, where $\sigma_\varepsilon(v) = \{u \mid u\bar{u}'=1,\ \alpha^2(1-|v\bar{u}'|^2)^2 + 4\beta^2(\operatorname{Im} v\bar{u}')^2 > \varepsilon^2\}$.

The above limit value is called the Hadamard principal value of the singular integral

$$\frac{1}{\omega_{2n-1}} \int_{u\bar{u}'=1} \frac{\bar{u}_k f(u)}{(1-v\bar{u}')^{n+1}} \dot{u}$$

and is denoted by

$$P \frac{1}{\omega_{2n-1}} \int_{u\bar{u}'=1} \frac{\bar{u}_k f(u)}{(1-v\bar{u}')^{n+1}} \dot{u} = \lim_{\varepsilon\to 0} \frac{1}{\omega_{2n-1}} \int_{\sigma_\varepsilon(v)} \frac{\bar{u}_k[f(u)-f(v)]}{(1-v\bar{u}')^{n+1}} \dot{u} .$$

When z approaches a point v on the sphere, we have the following formula:

$$\lim_{z\to v} \frac{\partial F}{\partial z} = P \frac{n}{\omega_{2n-1}} \int_{u\bar{u}'=1} \frac{\bar{u}f(u)}{(1-v\bar{u}')^{n+1}} \dot{u} + \frac{1}{2}\left(\frac{2\beta}{\alpha+\beta}\right)^{n-1}\Big\{\frac{\partial f(v)}{\partial u}\left[\frac{2\beta}{\alpha+\beta} I - n\frac{\beta-\alpha}{\beta+\alpha} v'\bar{v}\right]$$

$$- n\frac{\partial f(v)}{\partial \bar{u}} v'\bar{v} + \frac{2\beta}{\alpha+\beta}\bar{v}\left[\mathrm{tr}\left(\frac{\partial^2 f(v)}{\partial u \partial \bar{u}}\right) - v\frac{\partial^2 f(v)}{\partial u \partial \bar{u}}\bar{v}'\right]\Big\}$$

where $v = (v_1, \cdots, v_n)$, $\frac{\partial F}{\partial z} = \left(\frac{\partial F}{\partial z_1}, \cdots, \frac{\partial F}{\partial z_n}\right)$, $\frac{\partial f}{\partial u} = \left(\frac{\partial f}{\partial u_1}, \cdots, \frac{\partial f}{\partial u_n}\right)$,

$$\frac{\partial^2 f}{\partial u \partial \bar{u}} = \begin{pmatrix} \frac{\partial^2 f}{\partial u_1 \partial \bar{u}_1}, & \cdots, & \frac{\partial^2 f}{\partial u_1 \partial \bar{u}_n} \\ & \cdots\cdots & \\ & \cdots\cdots & \\ \frac{\partial^2 f}{\partial u_n \partial \bar{u}_1}, & \cdots, & \frac{\partial^2 f}{\partial u_n \partial \bar{u}_n} \end{pmatrix} .$$

If $\alpha = \beta$, we can obtain the simpler formula

$$\lim_{z\to v} \frac{\partial F}{\partial z} = P \frac{n}{\omega_{2n-1}} \int_{u\bar{u}'=1} \frac{\bar{u}\, f(u)}{(1-v\bar{u}')^{n+1}} \dot{u} + \frac{1}{2}\left\{\frac{\partial f(v)}{\partial u} - n\frac{\partial f(v)}{\partial \bar{u}}\bar{v}'\bar{v} + \right.$$

$$\left. \bar{v}\left[\mathrm{tr}\left(\frac{\partial^2 f(v)}{\partial u \partial \bar{u}}\right) - v\frac{\partial^2 f(v)}{\partial u \partial \bar{u}}\bar{v}'\right]\right\} .$$

Several Complex Variables
Proceedings of the 1981 Hangzhou Conference

INTEGRAL FORMULAE IN COMPLEX ANALYSIS

Ingo Lieb

0. Introduction

This is a brief introduction to the use of integral representations for differential forms, with particular emphasis on the elementary aspects of the theory. The results and methods are due to many authors; the solution of Levi's problem by the Kerzman-Stein formula was pointed out to me by M. Range.

1. The Bochner-Martinelli-Koppelman formula

Consider in $\mathbb{C}^n \times \mathbb{C}^n$, with coordinates ζ and z, the double differential forms

$$\beta(\zeta,z) = \sum_{j=1}^{n} \frac{\bar{\zeta}_j - \bar{z}_j}{|\zeta-z|^2} \, d\zeta_j \tag{1}$$

$$B_{nq}(\zeta,z) = c_{nq} \, \beta \wedge \overset{q}{\wedge} \bar{\partial}_z \beta \wedge \overset{n-q-1}{\wedge} \bar{\partial}_\zeta \beta \ , \tag{2}$$

where $|.|$ is the euclidean norm, $\overset{\ell}{\wedge}$ stands for exterior powers, and

$$c_{nq} = (-1)^{n(n-1)/2} \binom{n-1}{q} \left(\frac{1}{2\pi i}\right)^n . \tag{3}$$

The forms $B_{nq}(\zeta,z)$, of type $(n,n-q-1;0,q)$ in (ζ,z) are called the Bochner-Martinelli kernels for $(0,q)$-forms, $q = 0,\dots,n-1$. They have a singularity of order $|\zeta-z|^{2n-1}$ on the diagonal. With

$$B_{n,-1} = B_{n,n} = 0 \quad , \tag{4}$$

Received 1 December, 1981

we have the Bochner-Martinelli-Koppelman formula:

Proposition 1. 1) For $q = 0,\ldots,n$:

(5) $$\bar\partial_z B_{n,q-1} = (-1)^q \bar\partial_\zeta B_{nq} .$$

2) If D is a bounded domain in $\mathbb{C}^n$ with a piecewise smooth boundary and $f \in C^1_{0q}(\bar D)$ a $(0,q)$-form on $\bar D$ with continuous first derivatives, then for any $z \in D$:

(6) $$f(z) = \int_{\partial D} f(\zeta) \wedge B_{nq}(\zeta,z) - \int_D \bar\partial f(\zeta) \wedge B_{nq}(\zeta,z) - \bar\partial_z \int_D f(\zeta) \wedge B_{n,q-1}(\zeta,z)$$

For a simple new proof compare [9]. Bochner [1] proved the case $q = 0$ to obtain a new proof of Hartog's Kugelsatz:

Theorem 1. Let K be a compact subset of a domain D in $\mathbb{C}^n$, $n > 1$, such that $D - K$ is connected. Then every holomorphic function u on $D - K$ extends holomorphically to all of D.

Proof. Choose two domains D_1 and D_2 with piecewise smooth boundary and $K \subset D_1 \subset\subset D_2 \subset\subset D$. A candidate for the extension is

$$U(z) = \int_{\partial D_2} u(\zeta) B_{n0}(\zeta,z) \quad , \quad z \in D_2 .$$

Since - by (5) -

$$\bar\partial U(z) = - \int_{\partial D_2} u(\zeta) \bar\partial_\zeta B_{n1}(\zeta,z) = 0 ,$$

U is holomorphic. Moreover,

$$v(z) = \int_{\partial D_1} u(\zeta) B_{n0}(\zeta,z)$$

is holomorphic on the unbounded component of $\mathbb{C}^n - \bar D_1$, approaches 0 for $|\omega| \to \infty$, and defines entire holomorphic functions of the variable z_2 on all complex lines $z_1 = c$ for $|c|$ suitably large. So v vanishes there, and, as

$$u(z) = \int_{\partial D_2 - \partial D_1} u(\zeta) B_{n0}(\zeta, z) \quad , \qquad z \in D_2 - \bar{D}_1 \quad ,$$

u coincides with U on some component of $D_2 - \bar{D}_1$.

2. The Cauchy-Fantappié (CF) formula

The calculus of CF-forms, which we present here following Koppelman [7], provides the formal frame within which integral formulae adapted to special situations can be constructed by suitably "deforming" the BM-formula.

Let $W \subset \mathbb{C}^n \times \mathbb{C}^n$ be an open set and

$$(7) \qquad P_j : W \to \mathbb{C} \quad , \quad j = 1, \ldots, n$$

be n smooth functions. We set

$$(8) \qquad F(\zeta, z) = \sum_{j=1}^{n} P_j(\zeta, z)(\zeta_j - z_j)$$

and make the crucial

Assumption E. F has no zeros on W.

We then introduce the double differential forms

$$(9) \qquad \alpha(\zeta, z) = \sum_{j=1}^{n} \frac{P_j(\zeta, z)}{F(\zeta, z)} d\zeta_j$$

$$(10) \qquad \alpha_q(\zeta, z) = c_{nq}\, \alpha \wedge \overset{q}{\wedge}\, \bar{\partial}_z \alpha \overset{n-q-1}{\wedge} \bar{\partial}_\zeta \alpha \ ,$$

where c_{nq} is given by (3), and call α_q the Cauchy-Fantappiè kernel for (0,q)-forms associated to the map $P = (P_1,\dots,P_n)$. If necessary, we write $\alpha_q = \alpha_q^P$. Note that

$$(11) \qquad B_{nq} = \alpha_q^{\overline{\zeta}-\overline{z}} \quad .$$

Again, $\alpha_{-1} = \alpha_n = 0$ by definition. The main properties of these kernels are listed as

Proposition 2. If α_q^P, α_q^Q are two CF-forms on W, then there are double differential forms $A_q = A_q^{P,Q}$ and $C_{q-1}^{P,Q} = C_{q-1}$ given by explicit formulas in terms of P and Q, such that

$$(12) \qquad \alpha_q^P - \alpha_q^Q = \overline{\partial}_\zeta A_q^{P,Q} + \overline{\partial}_z C_{q-1}^{P,Q} \quad .$$

For the details cf. [5] or [8] .

Now suppose that W is a neighbourhood of $\partial D \times D$, where $D \subset\subset \mathbb{C}^n$ has a piecewise smooth boundary, and that $P: W \to \mathbb{C}^n$ satisfies (E). Combining Stokes' formula with propositions 1 and 2 we obtain

Proposition 3. For $f \in C^1_{0q}(\overline{D})$ and $z \in D$,

$$(13) \quad f(z) = \int_{\partial D} f(\zeta) \wedge \alpha_q^P(\zeta,z) + (-1)^{q+1} \int_{\partial D} \overline{\partial} f(\zeta) \wedge A^{P,\overline{\zeta}-\overline{z}}(\zeta,z)$$

$$- \int_D \overline{\partial} f(\zeta) \wedge B_{nq}(\zeta,z) + \overline{\partial}_z \left[\int_{\partial D} f(\zeta) \wedge C_{q-1}^{P,\overline{\zeta}-\overline{z}}(\zeta,z) - \int_D f(\zeta) \wedge B_{nq-1}(\zeta,z) \right]$$

3. Convex domains and shells

The use of proposition 3 depends on the possibility of finding maps $P: W(\partial D \times D) \to \mathbb{C}^n$ satisfying (E) such that the first boundary integral in (13) vanishes or is at least a smoothing operator. The existence of such a map reflects, to some extent, the geometry of the boundary of D. The easiest case is the case of convex domains.

So let

$$(14) \qquad D = \{\zeta : r(\zeta) < 0\} \subset\subset \mathbb{C}^n$$

be a convex domain with a smooth boundary. Setting

$$(15) \qquad P_j(\zeta,z) = \frac{\partial r}{\partial \zeta_j}(\zeta)$$

we see that (E) is satisfied: this simply reflects the fact that all tangent planes to the boundary stay outside D. The corresponding CF-Kernels

$$(16) \qquad K_q(\zeta,z) = \alpha_q^P(\zeta,z)$$

satisfy

(H) $\quad K_o(\zeta,z)$ is holomorphic in z

(N) $\quad K_q(\zeta,z) = 0$ for $q \geq 1$.

If $f \in C^1_{0q}(\bar{D})$ with $\bar{\partial} f = 0$, we have, by (13):

$$(17) \qquad f = \bar{\partial} u$$

with

$$(18) \qquad u(z) = \int_{\partial D} f(\zeta) \wedge C_{q-1}^{P,\bar{\zeta}-\bar{z}}(\zeta,z) - \int_D f(\zeta) \wedge B_{n,q-1}(\zeta,z) \quad .$$

An easy exhaustion argument combined with Dolbeault's lemma now yields

Theorem 2. For D convex, $H^q(D,\mathcal{O}) = 0$, $q \geq 1$.

$\mathcal{O}$ is the sheaf of germs of holomorphic functions.

Let now D be a shell, i.e. $D = D_1 - \overline{D}_2$, where $D_1 \supset\supset D_2$ are smooth convex domains given by inequalities $r_1 < 0$, $r_2 < 0$. Setting

$$(19) \qquad P_j(\zeta,z) = \begin{cases} \dfrac{\partial r_1}{\partial \zeta_j}(\zeta) & \text{on } \partial D_1 \times D \\ \dfrac{\partial r_2}{\partial z_j}(z) & \text{on } \partial D_2 \times D \end{cases},$$

we again obtain a map

$$(20) \qquad P\colon W(\partial D \times D) \to \mathbb{C}^n$$

satisfying (F); the corresponding kernels (16) have the properties

(H) $\quad K_o(\zeta,z)$ is holomorphic in z

(N) 1) $K_o(\zeta,z) \equiv 0$ on $\partial D_2 \times D$

2) $K_q(\zeta,z) \equiv 0$ for $1 \leq q \leq n-1$.

The above argument then gives

Proposition 4. 1) $H^q(D,\mathcal{O}) = 0$ for $1 \leq q \leq n-2$.
2) $\mathcal{O}(D)$ extends to $\mathcal{O}(D_1)$.

To see 2), we take u holomorphic on $\overline{D}$ (without loss of generality); then, by (13), (H) and N1,

$$(21) \qquad U(z) = \int_{\partial D_1} u(\zeta) \wedge K_o(\zeta,z)$$

extends u.

Proposition 4 gives a general version of the Kugelsatz, namely

Theorem 3. The cohomology groups with compact support vanish:

$$H_c^q(\mathbb{C}^n,\mathcal{O}) = 0 \quad , \quad 1 \leq q \leq n-1 \ .$$

Proof. Let $f \in C^1_{0q,c}(\mathbb{C}^n)$, $\bar\partial f = 0$, $q \geq 2$. Choose balls D_1 and D_2 with

(22) $\quad \operatorname{supp} f \subset D_1 \subset\subset D_2$

and - by theorem 2 - a (0,q-1)-form u_2 on D_2 with $\bar\partial u_2 = f$. Since

(23) $\quad \bar\partial u_2 = 0$ on $D_2 - \bar D_1$,

there is - by proposition 4 - a form $v \in C^1_{0q-2}(D_2)$ with

(24) $\quad \bar\partial v = u$

on a shell $D_2 - \overline{D_1'}$, where $D_1' \supset\supset D_1$. So

(25) $\quad u = u_2 - \bar\partial v$

has compact support in D_2 and satisfies

(26) $\quad \bar\partial u = f$.

To solve (26) for $q = 1$, we use part 2 of proposition 2 as above.

The kernels we have been using here were introduced, among others, by Henkin [3] and Hortmann [4].

4. Strictly pseudoconvex domains and Levi's problem

Let us recall that a domain $D \subset\subset \mathbb{C}^n$ is strictly pseudoconvex if ∂D is smooth of class C^2 and, moreover, if for each boundary point a there is a biholomorphic map $F: U \to V$ from a neighbourhood U of a such that $F(U \cap \partial D)$ is a strictly euclidean convex hypersurface and $F(D \cap U)$ is convex. D can be given by (14), where r is strictly plurisubharmonic near ∂D, and $dr \neq 0$.

We now define

$$(27) \qquad \hat{P}_j(\zeta,z) = \frac{\partial r}{\partial \zeta_j}(\zeta) - \frac{1}{2}\sum_{k=1}^{n} \frac{\partial^2 r}{\partial \zeta_j \partial \zeta_k}(\zeta)(\zeta_k - z_k)$$

$$(28) \qquad \hat{F}(\zeta,z) = \Sigma\, \hat{P}_j(\zeta,z)(\zeta_j - z_j) \ ;$$

the local convexity of D (after suitable coordinate changes) is then expressed in the fundamental inequality

$$(29) \qquad \mathrm{Re}\, \hat{F}(\zeta,z) \geq \gamma(r(\zeta) - r(z) + |\zeta - z|^2) \quad ,$$

where $\gamma > 0$ and $|\zeta - z|$ is small enough. Consequently, choosing a patching function $\varphi(\zeta,z)$ which is $\equiv 1$ near the diagonal $\zeta = z$ and setting

$$(30) \qquad P_j(\zeta,z) = \varphi(\zeta,z)\hat{P}_j(\zeta,z) + (1-\varphi(\zeta,z))(\bar{\zeta}_j - \bar{z}_j) \quad ,$$

we obtain a map P on $W(\partial D \times D)$ which satisfies (E). Let us call the associated kernels

$$(31) \qquad E_q(\zeta,z) = \alpha_q^P(\zeta,z) \quad ;$$

they were - for $q = 0$ - introduced by Kerzman and Stein [6]. Note that

(N) $\quad E_q(\zeta,z) \equiv 0 \quad , \quad q \geq 1$

near the diagonal; so the kernels $E_q(\zeta,z)$ are smooth on $\overline{D} \times \overline{D}$. Let us define

(32) $$E_q f = \int_{\partial D} f(\zeta) \wedge E_q(\zeta,z)$$

(33) $$C_{q-1}f = \int_{\partial D} f(\zeta) \wedge C_{q-1}(\zeta,z) - \int_D f(\zeta) \wedge B_{n,q-1}(\zeta,z)$$

with $C_{q-1}(\zeta,z) = C_{q-1}^{P,\overline{\zeta}-\overline{z}}$; (13) can now be rewritten as

(34) $$f = E_q f + \overline{\partial} C_{q-1} f \quad , \quad f \in C^1_{0q}(\overline{D}) \quad , \quad \overline{\partial} f = 0 \ .$$

<u>Proposition 5</u>. 1) <u>The operators</u>

$$E_q\colon C^1_{0q}(\overline{D}) \to C^1_{0q}(\overline{D}) \quad , \quad q \geq 1$$

<u>are compact</u>.

2) <u>There is a constant</u> γ <u>such that</u>

(35) $$|C_{q-1}f| \leq \gamma |f| .$$

Here, $|.|$ means the sup-norm; in 1) the spaces carry the C^1-sup-norm. - Part 1 follows from the smoothness of E_q; part 2 was proved for instance in [8].

Now consider the spaces

$$Z^q = \{f \in C^1_{0q}(\overline{D}) : \overline{\partial} f = 0\}$$
$$B^q = \{f \in Z^q : f = \overline{\partial} u,\ u \in C^1_{0q-1}(D) \cap L^\infty(D)\}$$
$$H^q(\overline{D}) = Z^q / B^q \quad .$$

Proposition 5.1 yields finite codimension for the operator

id - E_q, formula (34) shows that $\mathrm{Im}(\mathrm{id}-E_q) \subset B^q$; consequently

Proposition 6. *The spaces $H^q(\bar{D})$ are finite-dimensional for $q \geq 1$, D strictly pseudoconvex*.

This solves Levi's problem. Indeed, if $a \in \partial D$, there is a function $u \in C^1(\bar{D}-\{a\})$, holomorphic near a, with $u(z) \to \infty$ for $z \to a$. Because of $\dim H^1(\bar{D}) < \infty$ there are numbers $c_1,\dots,c_k$, $c_k \neq 0$, and a function $v \in C^1(D) \cap L^\infty$ such that

$$(36) \qquad \bar{\partial}\left(\sum_{\kappa=1}^{k}\right) c_\kappa u^\kappa = \bar{\partial} v \quad .$$

Therefore

$$(37) \qquad h = \Sigma\, c_\kappa u_\kappa - v$$

is holomorphic on D, $h(z) \to \infty$ for $z \to a$, and we have

Theorem 4. *A strictly pseudoconvex domain is holomorphically convex*.

This solution to Levi's problem is due to Range [10]; similar solutions can be found in Henkin [3] and Harvey-Polking [2].

References

[1] BOCHNER, S.: Analytic and meromorphic continuation by means of Green's formula. Ann. Math. 44 (1943), 652-673.

[2] HARVEY, R./J. POLKING: Fundamental solutions in complex analysis I. Duke Math. J. 46 (1979), 253-300.

[3] HENKIN, G.M.: The Lewy equation and analysis on pseudoconvex manifolds. Usp. Mat. Nauk 32 (1977), 57-118.

[4] HORTMANN, M.: Über die Lösbarkeit der $\bar{\partial}$-Gleichung mit Hilfe von L^p-, C^k- und $\mathcal{D}'$ stetigen Integraloperatoren. Math. Ann. 223 (1976), 139-156.

[5] JAMBON, M.: L'équation différentielle de Cauchy-Riemann sur un domaine strictement pseudoconvexe. Solutions bornées, 18 (1972), 304-337.

[6] KERZMAN, N./E. STEIN: The Szegö kernel in terms of Cauchy-Fantappié kernels. Duke Math. J. 45 (1978), 197-224.

[7] KOPPELMAN, W.: The Cauchy integral for differential forms. Bull. Am. Math. Soc. 73 (1967), 554-556.

[8] LIEB, I.: Die Cauchy-Riemannschen Differentialgleichungen auf streng pseudokonvexen Gebieten. Math. Ann. 190 (1970), 6-44.

[9] LIEB, I./M. RANGE: On integral representations and a priori Lipschitz estimates for the canonical solution of $\bar{\partial}$. To appear in Math. Ann.

[10] RANGE, M.: An elementary integral solution operator for the Cauchy-Riemann equations on pseudoconvex domains in $\mathbb{C}^n$. Trans. Am. Math. Soc. 274 (1982), 809-816.

Mathematisches Institut
der Universität
SFB 40 "Theoretische Mathematik"
Wegelerstr. 10

D-5300 Bonn 1

Several Complex Variables
Proceedings of the 1981 Hangzhou Conference

ON THE REPRESENTATIVE DOMAIN

Qi-keng Lu

(Institute of Mathematics, Academia Sinica)

Professor Stefan Bergman [1] introduced the idea of Repräsentantenbereich of a bounded domain $\mathfrak{D}$ in $\mathbb{C}^n$. However the strict definition of a representative domain is not very clear as noted in [2]. It seems that he called the image $f(\mathfrak{D})$ of the mapping f:

$$(1) \qquad z \longmapsto \frac{\partial \log \frac{K(z,\bar{t})}{K(t,\bar{t})}}{\partial \bar{t}^{\beta}} T^{\bar{\beta}\alpha}(t,\bar{t})$$

the representative domain of $\mathfrak{D}$. Here we use the summation convention and denote by $K(z,\bar{t})$ the Bergman kernel of $\mathfrak{D}$ and by $T^{\bar{\beta}\alpha}(t,\bar{t})$ the elements of the inverse matrix of the Bergman metric tensor

$$T_{\alpha\bar{\beta}}(t,\bar{t}) = \frac{\partial^2 \log K(t,\bar{t})}{\partial t^{\alpha} \partial \bar{t}^{\beta}} .$$

We don't know whether the mapping of (1) is one-to-one or the image of the mapping is really a domain in $\mathbb{C}^n$. Especially we don't know whether the Bergman kernel function $K(z,\bar{t})$ does not possess zeroes in $(z,t) \in \mathfrak{D}\times\mathfrak{D}$ so that (1) can be well defined. Some authors called the last question the L-conjecture [3-6] and the domain, the kernel of which does not possess zero, is

Received 15 Oct. 1981.

called the L-domain. Since there do exist bounded domains the kernel of which really possesses zeros, it is important to have a good definition of representative domain and study its properties.

Let $\mathfrak{D}$ be a bounded domain in $\mathbb{C}^n$ and $K(z,\bar{t})$ the Bergman kernel of $\mathfrak{D}$. Denote by

$$T(z,\bar{z}) = (T_{\alpha\bar{\beta}}(z,\bar{z})) = \left(\frac{\partial^2 \log K(z,\bar{z})}{\partial z^\alpha \partial \bar{z}^\beta}\right)$$

the $n \times n$ matrix formed from the Bergman metric tensor $T_{\alpha\bar{\beta}}(z,\bar{z})$. For any point $t_0 \in \mathfrak{D}$, there is a neighbourhood V_{t_0} of $\mathfrak{D}$ such that $T(z,\bar{t})$ is holomorphic in $z \in V_{t_0}$ and anti-holomorphic in $t \in V_{t_0}$.

We noted in [2] that if the mapping defined by (1) is one-to-one, then the matrix of the Bergman metric tensor $T_1(w,0)$ of the image domain is a constant matrix. This suggests the following definition of representative domains.

DEFINITION. A bounded domain $\mathfrak{D}$ in $\mathbb{C}^n$ is called a representative domain if there is a point $t \in \mathfrak{D}$ such that the matrix of the Bergman metric tensor $T(z,\bar{t})$ is independent of $z \in \mathfrak{D}$. The point t is called the centre of the representative domain.

Examples.

Obviously any bounded circular domain containing its centre is a representative domain with the same centre.

According to the results of Xu Yichao [7] any bounded homogeneous domain possesses a representative domain, i.e., there is a biholomorphic mapping carrying a bounded homogeneous domain onto a representative domain.

A normalized representative domain is a representative domain with the origin as the centre and with

$$T(z,0) = \lambda I,$$

where is a positive constant and I is the identity matrix.

Evidently every representative domain can be normalized after an affine transformation.

By definition, if $\mathfrak{D}$ is a representative domain with centre t, then

$$\frac{\partial^2 \log K(z,\bar{t})}{\partial z^\alpha \partial \bar{t}^\beta} = T_{\alpha\bar{\beta}}(t,\bar{t}).$$

Hence

$$(2) \qquad \frac{\partial \log K(z,t)}{\partial \bar{t}^\beta} = T_{\alpha\bar{\beta}}(t,\bar{t})(z^\alpha - t^\alpha) + \frac{\partial \log K(t,\bar{t})}{\partial \bar{t}^\beta}.$$

We have

<u>Theorem 1</u>. If $\mathfrak{D}$ is a representative domain with centre at t, then

$$\frac{\partial^{m+1} \log K(z,\bar{t})}{\partial z^{\alpha_1} \cdots \partial z^{\alpha_m} \partial \bar{t}^\beta} = 0$$

when $m > 1$ and $\alpha_1, \cdots, \alpha_m = 1, \cdots, n$; especially

$$\frac{\partial^{m+1} \log K(t,\bar{t})}{\partial t^{\alpha_1} \cdots \partial t^{\alpha_m} \partial \bar{t}^\beta} = 0 \qquad \text{for } m > 1.$$

Theorem 2. Let $\mathfrak{D}$ be a bounded domain of $\mathbb{C}^n$ and $\mathfrak{D}_1$ be a representative domain of $\mathbb{C}^n$ with centre at S. If $f: \mathfrak{D} \longrightarrow \mathfrak{D}_1$ is a biholomorphic mapping of $\mathfrak{D}$ onto $\mathfrak{D}_1$ and $f(t) = S$, $t \in \mathfrak{D}$, then

(i) the matrix of the Bergman metric tensor $T(z,\bar{t})$ of $\mathfrak{D}$ is holomorphic and non-singular in $\mathfrak{D}$, and

(ii) the Jacobian matrix

$$\frac{\partial f}{\partial z} = \begin{pmatrix} \frac{\partial f^1}{\partial z^1}, & \cdots, & \frac{\partial f^n}{\partial z^1} \\ \cdots & \cdots & \cdots \\ \frac{\partial f^1}{\partial z^n}, & \cdots, & \frac{\partial f^n}{\partial z^n} \end{pmatrix}$$

of the mapping f satisfies

$$\frac{\partial f}{\partial z} = T(z,\bar{t})T^{-1}(t,\bar{t})A,$$

where $A = (\frac{\partial f}{\partial z})_{z=t}$ is a constant matrix satisfying

$$AT_1(s,\bar{s})\bar{A}' = T(t,\bar{t}),$$

$\bar{A}$ is the complex conjugate matrix of A, A' is the transpose of A, and $T_1(s,\bar{s})$ is the matrix of the Bergman metric tensor of $\mathfrak{D}_1$.

Proof. When $w = f(z)$, $z \in \mathfrak{D}$, it is well known that

$$T(z,\bar{z}) = \frac{\partial f}{\partial z} T_1(w,\bar{w}) \overline{\frac{\partial f}{\partial z}'} .$$

Since the elements of both $T(z,\bar{z})$ and $T_1(w,\bar{w})$ are real analytic, we know that when z lies in the sufficiently small neighbourhood of t,

$$(3) \qquad T(z,\bar{t}) = \frac{\partial f}{\partial z} T_1(w,\bar{s}) \overline{\left(\frac{\partial f}{\partial z}\right)}'_{z=t}$$

where $s = f(t)$. Since $\mathfrak{D}_1$ is a representative domain with centre s, we have

$$T_1(w,\bar{s}) = T_1(s,\bar{s}).$$

Applying the equality

$$(4) \qquad T(t,\bar{t}) = \left(\frac{\partial f}{\partial z}\right)_{z=t} T_1(s,\bar{s}) \overline{\left(\frac{\partial f}{\partial z}\right)}'_{z=t}$$

and letting $A = \left(\frac{\partial t}{\partial z}\right)_{z=t}$, we obtain

$$T(z,\bar{t}) = \frac{\partial f}{\partial z} T(s,\bar{s}) \bar{A}' = \frac{\partial f}{\partial z} A^{-1} T(t,\bar{t}).$$

This shows that $T(z,\bar{t})$ is holomorphic with respect to $z \in \mathfrak{D}$ and non-singular in $\mathfrak{D}$, and

$$\frac{\partial f}{\partial z} = T(z,\bar{t}) T^{-1}(t,\bar{t}) A.$$

The theorem is proved.

<u>Corollary 1</u>. If $f: \mathfrak{D} \longrightarrow \mathfrak{D}_1$ is a holomorphic isomorphism of a bounded domain $\mathfrak{D}$ in $\mathbb{C}^n$ onto a representative domain $\mathfrak{D}_1$ with centre s such that $s = f(t)$, $t \in \mathfrak{D}$, then the mapping

functions $f(z) = (f^1(z),\dots,f^n(z))$ satisfy the following equations

$$\frac{\partial^2 f^\alpha(z)}{\partial z^\beta\,\partial z^\nu} - \Gamma^\lambda_{\beta\nu}(z,\bar{t})\,\frac{\partial^\alpha(z)}{\partial z^\lambda} = 0;$$

and the mapping function $\varphi(z) = (\varphi^1(z),\cdots,\varphi^n(z))$ of the inverse mapping φ of f satisfies

$$\frac{\partial^2 \varphi^\alpha(w)}{\partial w^\beta\,\partial w^\nu} - \Gamma^\alpha_{\lambda\mu}(\varphi,\bar{t})\,\frac{\partial\varphi^\lambda}{\partial w^\beta}\,\frac{\partial\varphi^\mu}{\partial w^\nu} = 0,$$

where $\Gamma^\alpha_{\beta\nu}(z,\bar{t}) = T^{\bar{\lambda}\alpha}(z,\bar{t})\dfrac{\partial T_{\beta\bar{\lambda}}(z,t)}{\partial z^\nu}$ and $(T^{\bar{\lambda}\alpha}(z,\bar{t})) = T^{-1}(z,\bar{t})$.

In fact, by (ii) of Theorem 2 we have

$$\frac{\partial f^\alpha}{\partial z^\nu} = T_{\nu\bar{\lambda}}(z,\bar{t})\,B^{\bar{\lambda}\alpha},$$

where

$$B = (B^{\lambda\alpha}) = T^{-1}(t,\bar{t})A.$$

Obviously

$$\begin{aligned}\frac{\partial^2 f^\alpha}{\partial z^\beta\,\partial z^\nu} &= \frac{\partial T_{\nu\bar{\lambda}}(z,\bar{t})}{\partial z^\beta}\,B^{\bar{\lambda}\alpha}\\ &= \frac{\partial T_{\nu\bar{\mu}}(z,\bar{t})}{\partial z^\beta}\,T^{\bar{\mu}\nu}(z,\bar{t})\,T_{\nu\bar{\lambda}}(z,\bar{t})\,B^{\bar{\lambda}\alpha}\\ &= \Gamma^\sigma_{\beta\nu}(z,\bar{t})\,\frac{\partial f^\alpha}{\partial z^\sigma}.\end{aligned}$$

Moreover, according to (ii) of Theorem 2 the inverse matrix of $\frac{\partial f}{\partial z}$ is

$$\frac{\partial\varphi(w)}{\partial w} = B^{-1}T^{-1}(z,\bar{t})$$

or

$$\frac{\partial\varphi^{\alpha}(w)}{\partial w^{\beta}} = B_{\beta\bar{\lambda}}T^{\bar{\lambda}\alpha}(z,\bar{t}).$$

Hence

$$\frac{\partial^2\varphi^{\alpha}}{\partial w^{\beta}\,\partial w^{\nu}} = B_{\beta\bar{\lambda}}\,\frac{\partial T^{\bar{\lambda}\alpha}(z,\bar{t})}{\partial z^{\mu}}\,\frac{\partial\varphi^{\mu}}{\partial w^{\nu}}$$

$$= -B_{\beta\bar{\lambda}}T^{\bar{\lambda}\gamma}(z,\bar{t})\,\frac{\partial T_{\gamma\bar{\sigma}}(\bar{z},t)}{\partial z^{\mu}}\,T^{\bar{\sigma}\alpha}(z,\bar{t})\frac{\partial\varphi^{\mu}}{\partial w^{\nu}}$$

$$= -\,\frac{\partial\varphi^{\gamma}}{\partial z^{\beta}}\,\Gamma^{\alpha}_{\gamma\mu}(z,\bar{t})\frac{\partial\varphi^{\mu}}{\partial z^{\nu}}\quad .$$

<u>Corollary 2</u>. If $\mathfrak{D}$ and $\mathfrak{D}_1$ are both representative domains of $\mathbb{C}^n$, then any holomorphic isomorphism $f\colon \mathfrak{D} \longrightarrow \mathfrak{D}_1$ which maps the centre of $\mathfrak{D}$ to that of $\mathfrak{D}_1$ is an affine transformation. Moreover, if $\mathfrak{D} = \mathfrak{D}_1$ and $\mathfrak{D}$ is normalized, then f is a unitary transformation.

In fact, if $\mathfrak{D}$ is a representative domain with centre t, then $T(z,\bar{t}) = T(t,\bar{t})$. According to (ii) of Theorem 2, we have

$$\frac{\partial f}{\partial z} = A.$$

Hence

$$f = zA + b,$$

where $z = (z^1, \cdots, z^n)$. If $\mathfrak{D} = \mathfrak{D}_1$ and $\mathfrak{D}$ is a normalized representative domain, then $t = 0$ and $b = 0$. According to (4) we have

$$A\bar{A}' = I,$$

since $T(0,0) = \lambda I$ by definition. This shows that f is unitary.

Theorem 3. Let $\mathfrak{D}$ be a bounded domain and $\mathfrak{D}_1$ be a representative domain in $\mathbb{C}^n$ with centre s. If $f: \mathfrak{D} \longrightarrow \mathfrak{D}_1$ is a holomorphic isomorphism, then f is of the form

$$f(z) = s + [\frac{\partial}{\partial \bar{t}} \log \frac{K(z,\bar{t})}{K(t,\bar{t})}] T^{-1}(t,\bar{t})A$$

where $s = f(t)$, $A = (\frac{\partial f}{\partial z})_{z=t}$, and $\frac{\partial}{\partial \bar{t}} = (\frac{\partial}{\partial \bar{t}^1}, \cdots, \frac{\partial}{\partial \bar{t}^n})$.
Moreover, $K(z,\bar{t})$ has no zero when $z \in \mathfrak{D}$.

Proof: According to Theorem 2, we have

$$dz \frac{\partial f}{\partial z} = dz\ T(z,t)T^{-1}(t,\bar{t})\ A, \quad \text{where} \quad dz = (dz^1, \cdots, dz^n).$$

Since $dz \frac{\partial f}{\partial z} = df$ and $dz\ T(z,\bar{t}) = d \frac{\partial \log K(z,\bar{t})}{\partial \bar{t}}$, the above formula becomes

$$df = d[\frac{\partial \log K(z,\bar{t})}{\partial \bar{t}}]T^{-1}(t,\bar{t})A \quad .$$

Since f is univalent in $\mathfrak{D}$, we obtain by integration

$$f(z)-f(t) = [\frac{\partial}{\partial \bar{t}} \log \frac{K(z,\bar{t})}{K(t,\bar{t})}]T^{-1}(t,\bar{t})A.$$

Now it remains to prove that $K(z,\bar{t})$ possesses no zero when $z \in \mathfrak{D}$.

Suppose that there is a point $z_0 \in \mathfrak{D}$ such that $K(z_0,\bar{t}) = 0$. Since the function $K(\xi) = K(\xi^1,\cdots,\xi^n,\xi^{n+1},\cdots,\xi^{2n})$ is holomorphic in $\mathfrak{D}\times\mathfrak{D}^*$ (where $\mathfrak{D}^*$ is the image of $\mathfrak{D}$ under the mapping: $z \longmapsto \bar{z}$) and since $K(\xi_0) = 0$ when

$$\xi_0^\alpha = z_0^\alpha, \ \xi_0^{n+\alpha} = \bar{t}^\alpha \qquad (\alpha = 1,\cdots,n),$$

we can without loss of generality assume

$$K(\xi_0^1,\cdots,\xi_0^{j-1},\xi^j,\xi_0^{j+1},\cdots,\xi_0^{2n}) \not\equiv 0$$

for all $j = 1,...,2n$ after we can make a non-singular linear transformation

$$\eta^j-\xi_0^j = \sum_{k=1}^{2n} a_k^j(\xi^k-\xi_0^k)$$

if necessary.

By Weierstrass Preparation Theorem

$$K(\xi) = [(\xi^j-\xi_0^j)^{k_j} + \varphi_1(\xi^1,\cdots,\xi^{j-1},\xi^{j+1},\ldots,\xi^{2n})(\xi^j-\xi_0^j)^{k_j-1}$$

$$+\cdots+ \varphi_{k_j}(\xi^1,\cdots,\xi^{j-1},\xi^{j+1},\cdots,\xi^{2n})]\psi_j(\xi),$$

where $k_j \geq 1$ and $\psi_j(\xi)$ does not vanish at some neighbourhood of ξ_0 and

$$\varphi_\iota(\xi_0^1,\cdots,\xi_0^{j-1},\xi_0^{j+1},\cdots,\xi_0^{2n}) = 0, \qquad \iota = 1,\cdots,k_j.$$

Let

$$F_j(\xi) = \frac{\partial \log K(\xi)}{\partial \xi^j}$$

$$= \frac{k_j(\xi^j-\xi_0^j)^{k_j-1}+(k_j-1)\varphi_1(\xi^1,\cdots,\xi^{j-1},\xi^{j+1},\cdots,\xi^{2n})(\xi^j-\xi_0^j)^{k_j-2}+\cdots}{(\xi^j-\xi_0^j)^{k_j}+\varphi_1(\xi^1,\cdots,\xi^{j-1},\xi^{j+1},\cdots,\xi^{2n})(\xi^j-\xi_0^j)^{k_j-1}+\cdots} +$$

$$+ \frac{\partial \log \psi_j(\xi)}{\partial \xi^j}, \qquad j = n+1,\cdots,2n.$$

Then

$$F_j(\xi_0^1,\cdots,\xi_0^{j-1},\xi^j,\xi_0^{j+1},\cdots,\xi^{2n})$$

$$= \frac{1}{\xi^j-\xi_0^j} + \left[\frac{\partial \log \psi_j(\xi)}{\partial \xi^j}\right]_{\xi^k=\xi_0^k}, \qquad k = 1,\cdots,j-1,j+1,\cdots,2n,$$

cannot be analytic at $\xi^j = \xi_0^j$.

In particular, this shows that the functions $F_j(\xi^1,\cdots,\xi^n,\xi_0^{n+1},\cdots,\xi_0^{2n})$ are not analytic at $\xi^1 = \xi_1^0,\cdots,\xi^n = \xi_0^n$. However,

$$[F_{n+1}(z^1,\cdots,z^n,\xi_0^{n+1},\cdots,\xi_0^{2n}),\cdots,F_{2n}(z^1,\cdots,z^n,\xi_0^{n+1},\cdots,\xi_0^{2n})]$$

$$= [f(z)-f(t)]A^{-1}T(t,\bar{t}) + \frac{\partial \log K(t,\bar{t})}{\partial t}$$

is analytic in $z = (z^1,\cdots,z^n)$, in particular at the point $z^\alpha = \xi_0^\alpha$ $(\alpha=1,\cdots,n)$. This is a contradiction. The theorem is proved.

This theorem shows that whenever one has the existence of a holomorphic isomorphism $f\colon \mathcal{D} \longrightarrow \mathcal{D}_1$, the mapping functions can be constructed from the kernel function of $\mathcal{D}$. For example, if $\mathcal{D}$ is a simply connected bounded domain in $\mathbb{C}$, by Riemann mapping Theorem, there is a holomorphic isomorphism $f\colon \mathcal{D} \longrightarrow \mathcal{D}_1$, where $\mathcal{D}_1$ is a unit disc. $\mathcal{D}_1$ is a normalized representative domain with the origin as centre. Moreover, the matrix $T(t,\bar{t})$ of the Bergmann metric tensor is now equal to $cK(t,\bar{t})$, where c is a positive constant. We have

<u>Corollary 3</u>. If $\mathcal{D}$ is a simply connected bounded domain in $\mathbb{C}$, then

$$f(z) = \frac{1}{\sqrt{cK(t,\bar{t})}} \frac{\partial}{\partial \bar{t}} \log \frac{K(z,\bar{t})}{K(t,\bar{t})}$$

is the function which maps $\mathcal{D}$ onto the unit disc conformally such that $f(t) = 0$ and $f'(t) > 0$.

Moreover, applying the result of [2], we have

<u>Corollary 4</u>. If $\mathcal{D}$ is a bounded domain with complete Bergman metric and constant unitary curvature, then the holomorphic mapping defined by

$$f(z) = \frac{\partial \log \frac{K(z,\bar{t})}{K(t,\bar{t})}}{\partial \bar{t}} T^{-\frac{1}{2}}(t,\bar{t})$$

is one-to-one and maps $\mathcal{D}$ onto a ball such that $f(t) = 0$ and $\frac{\partial f(t)}{\partial t}$ is positive definite. Here for any positive Hermitian matrix T, $T^{\frac{1}{2}}$ means the unique positive definite Hermitian matrix such that $T^{\frac{1}{2}}T^{\frac{1}{2}} = T$.

Finally we remark that the definition of representative domains introduced in this paper agrees with the original idea of S. Bergman, as is seen from the following

Theorem 4. Let both $\mathfrak{D}$ and $\mathfrak{D}_1$ be bounded domains in $\mathbb{C}^n$ and $f: \mathfrak{D} \longrightarrow \mathfrak{D}_1$ be a holomorphic isomorphism. If the mapping functions of f is defined by

$$f(z) = s + [\frac{\partial}{\partial \bar{t}} \log \frac{K(z,\bar{t})}{K(t,\bar{t})}]T^{-1}(t,\bar{t})A$$

where A is a constant matrix, then $\mathfrak{D}_1$ is a representative domain with centre s.

Proof. It is only necessary to prove

$$T_1(w,\bar{s}) = \text{const. matrix.}$$

The method used is the same as in the proof of Lemma in [2]. Since $A = (\frac{\partial f}{\partial z})_{z=t}$ and

$$\frac{\partial f(z)}{\partial z} = T(z,\bar{t})T^{-1}(t,\bar{t})A$$

when z is in a sufficiently small neighbourhood of t, we have by (3)

$$\begin{aligned} T_1(w,\bar{s}) &= (\frac{\partial f}{\partial z})^{-1}T(z,\bar{t})\bar{A}'^{-1} \\ &= A^{-1}T(t,\bar{t})T^{-1}(z,\bar{t})T(z,t)\bar{A}'^{-1} \\ &= A^{-1}T(t,\bar{t})\bar{A}'^{-1} = \text{const. matrix.} \end{aligned}$$

The theorem is proved.

References

[1] Bergman, S., Über die Existenz von Repräsentantenbereichen in Theorie der Abbildung durch Paare von Funktionen zweier komplexen Veränderlichen. Math. Ann. 102 (1929),430-446.

[2] Lu, Qi-keng, On the Kähler manifold of constant unitary curvature, Acta Mathematica Sinica, 16 (1966), 269-281.

[3] Skwarzcynski, M., The invariant distance in the theory of pseudoconformal mappings and the Lu Qi-keng conjecture, Proc. Amer. Math. Soc. 22 (1969), 305-310.

[4] Rosenthal, P.L., On the zeros of the Bergman function in doubly-connected domains, Proc. Amer. Math. Soc. 21 (1969), 33-35.

[5] Matsura, S., On the Lu Qi-keng conjecture and the Bergman representative domains, Pacific J. Math., 49 (1973),407-16.

[6] Suita, N., and Yamada, A., On the Lu Qi-keng conjecture, Proc. Amer. Math. Soc. 59 (1976), 222-224.

[7] Xu Yichao, The canonical realization of complex homogeneous bounded domains (preprint).

Several Complex Variables
Proceedings of the 1981 Hangzhou Conference

A REMARK ON POISSON KERNELS

Yin Weiping

(Dept. of Math., Univ. of Science & Technology of China)

It is well known that for any symmetric domain D in $\mathbb{C}^n$ Prof. Hua Lao-Keng (L.K. Hua) has computed the Cauchy kernel H(Z,U) [1]. He and Prof. Lu Qi-Keng [2] defined the Poisson kernel P(Z,U) in terms of H(Z,U) by

$$P(Z,U) = \frac{|H(Z,U)|^2}{H(Z,\overline{Z})} \quad ,$$

where U belongs to the Silov boundary of D and proved that the Poisson kernel P(Z,U) was annihilated by the Laplace-Beltrami operator of D with respect to the Bergman metric. For some nonsymmetric homogeneous Siegel domains, Prof. Lu Ru-Qian [3] in 1964 has shown that the Poisson kernels were not annihilated by the Laplace-Beltrami operator and pointed out that perhaps this fact was the characteristic property of nonsymmetric homogeneous domains. In this note I want to discuss the following question: If D is a nonsymmetric homogeneous Siegel domain and Aut(D) denotes the group of analytic automorphisms of D, does there exist another differential operator Δ invariant under Aut(D) such that the Poisson kernel can be annihilated by Δ?

The invariant differential operators of bounded homogeneous domains form a ring in the usual sense. This ring has a finite basis. In 1980 Prof. Zhong Jiaqing [4] has obtained a formula

Received 16 Nov. 1981

for the dimension of the invariant differential operator ring.

Our aim here is to find an example on a nonsymmetric homogeneous Siegel domain D such that the Poisson kernel is annihilated by one of the invariant differential operators under Aut(D).

Consider the domain

$$D = \left\{ Z \,\middle|\, \frac{1}{2i}(Z-\bar{Z}') > 0, \qquad Z = \begin{pmatrix} z_{11} & z_{12} & z_{13} \\ z_{12} & z_{22} & 0 \\ z_{13} & 0 & z_{33} \end{pmatrix} \right\}.$$

It is well known that D is a nonsymmetric homogeneous Siegel domain of first type [5]. A basis of the invariant differential operator ring at the point iI consists of

$$\frac{\partial^2}{\partial z_{11}\partial \bar{z}_{11}},\ \frac{\partial^2}{\partial z_{12}\partial \bar{z}_{12}},\ \frac{\partial^2}{\partial z_{13}\partial \bar{z}_{13}},\ \frac{\partial^2}{\partial z_{22}\partial \bar{z}_{22}},\ \frac{\partial^2}{\partial z_{33}\partial \bar{z}_{33}},\ \frac{\partial^2}{\partial z_{11}\partial z_{11}},\ \frac{\partial^2}{\partial \bar{z}_{11}\partial \bar{z}_{11}}.$$

The Cauchy kernel of D is

$$H(Z,X) = C_1 \frac{(z_{22}-x_{22})(z_{33}-x_{33})}{\det(Z-X)^2}$$

where C_1 is a constant and

$$X = \begin{pmatrix} x_{11} & x_{12} & x_{13} \\ x_{12} & x_{22} & 0 \\ x_{13} & 0 & x_{33} \end{pmatrix}$$

is a real matrix which belongs to Silov boundary of D. From this we obtain the Poisson kernel P(Z,X) of D

$$P(Z,X) = \frac{|H(Z,X)|^2}{H(Z,\bar{Z})} = C \frac{\det(Z-\bar{Z})^2 \, |z_{22}-x_{22}|^4 |z_{33}-x_{33}|^2}{|\det(Z-X)|^4 (z_{22}-\bar{z}_{22})(z_{33}-\bar{z}_{33})} \quad .$$

Let

$$\Delta = \frac{\partial^2}{\partial z_{11}\partial \bar{z}_{11}} + \frac{1}{4}\left(\frac{\partial^2}{\partial z_{12}\partial \bar{z}_{12}} + \frac{\partial^2}{\partial z_{13}\partial \bar{z}_{13}}\right).$$

We have

$$\Delta P_{Z=iI} = 0 \; .$$

The general form of Δ is given by

$$\Delta(Z) = a(Z)\left[\frac{z_{11}\bar{z}_{11}}{2i}\frac{\partial^2}{\partial z_{11}\partial \bar{z}_{11}} + \frac{z_{22}-\bar{z}_{22}}{8i}\frac{\partial^2}{\partial z_{12}\partial \bar{z}_{12}} + \frac{z_{33}-\bar{z}_{33}}{8i}\frac{\partial^2}{\partial z_{13}\partial \bar{z}_{13}} + \frac{z_{12}-\bar{z}_{12}}{4i}\left(\frac{\partial^2}{\partial z_{11}\partial \bar{z}_{12}} + \frac{\partial^2}{\partial z_{12}\partial \bar{z}_{11}}\right) + \frac{z_{13}-\bar{z}_{13}}{4i}\left(\frac{\partial^2}{\partial z_{11}\partial \bar{z}_{13}} + \frac{\partial^2}{\partial z_{13}\partial \bar{z}_{11}}\right)\right],$$

where

$$a(Z) = \frac{z_{11}-\bar{z}_{11}}{2i} - \frac{(z_{12}-\bar{z}_{12})^2}{2i(z_{22}-\bar{z}_{22})} - \frac{(z_{13}-\bar{z}_{13})^2}{2i(z_{33}-\bar{z}_{33})} \quad .$$

We have proved that $\Delta(Z)$ is an invariant differential operator under Aut(D) and

$$\Delta(Z)P(Z,X) = 0.$$

Let

$$P_*(Z_1X) = \det(Z-\bar{Z})^2(|\det(Z-X)|^4)^{-1},$$

$$R = \left\{ Z \,\middle|\, \frac{1}{2i}(Z-\bar{Z}') > 0, \qquad Z = \begin{pmatrix} z_{11} & z_{12} & z_{13} \\ z_{12} & z_{22} & z_{23} \\ z_{13} & z_{23} & z_{33} \end{pmatrix} \right\} \; .$$

Then R is a symmetric domain and the Poisson kernel of R restricted to D is equal to $P_*(Z,X)$. We have

$$\left(\frac{\partial^2 P_*}{\partial z_{11}\partial \bar{z}_{11}} + \frac{\partial^2 P_*}{\partial z_{22}\partial \bar{z}_{22}} - \frac{\partial^2 P_*}{\partial z_{33}\partial \bar{z}_{33}} + \frac{1}{2}\frac{\partial^2 P_*}{\partial z_{12}\partial \bar{z}_{12}}\right)_{Z=iI} = 0,$$

$$\left(\frac{\partial^2 P_*}{\partial z_{11}\partial \bar{z}_{11}} + \frac{\partial^2 P_*}{\partial z_{33}\partial \bar{z}_{33}} - \frac{\partial^2 P_*}{\partial z_{22}\partial \bar{z}_{22}} + \frac{1}{2}\frac{\partial^2 P_*}{\partial z_{13}\partial \bar{z}_{13}}\right)_{Z=iI} = 0,$$

$$\left(\frac{\partial^2 P_*}{\partial z_{11}\partial \bar{z}_{11}} + 2\left(\frac{\partial^2 P_*}{\partial z_{33}\partial \bar{z}_{33}} - \frac{\partial^2 P_*}{\partial z_{22}\partial \bar{z}_{22}}\right) - \frac{1}{4}\frac{\partial^2 P_*}{\partial z_{12}\partial \bar{z}_{12}} + \frac{3}{4}\frac{\partial^2 P_*}{\partial z_{13}\partial \bar{z}_{13}}\right)_{Z=iI} = 0.$$

This note is an abstract of my paper in "Kexue Tongbao"(Chinese) Vol. 26, No. 10, pp. 581-583 (1981).

Bibliography

[1] Hua Loo-Keng (L,K. Hua), Harmonic analysis of functions of several complex variables in the classical domains, Science Press, Peking, 1958. English translation, AMS, Providence, 1963.

[2] Hua Loo-Keng and Lu Qi-Keng, Harmonic functions on the classical domains, Acta Math. Sinica 8 (1958), 531-549, and 9 (1959), 295-314.

[3] Lu Ru-Qian, Harmonic functions in a class of nonsymmetric transitive domains, Acta Math. Sinica, 15 (1965), 614-650.

[4] Zhong Jiaqing, Dimensions of the ring of invariant operators on bounded homogeneous domains, Chinese Annals of Math. 1 (1980), 261-272.

[5] Zhong Jiaqing & Yin Weiping, Some types of nonsymmetric homogeneous domains, Acta Math. Sinica 24(1981), 587-613.

Several Complex Variables
Proceedings of the 1981 Hangzhou Conference

SOME APPLICATIONS OF BOCHNER-MARTINELLI INTEGRAL REPRESENTATION

Zhong Tong-de

(Xiamen University)

I. INTRODUCTION

In the space of $\mathbb{C}^n$ there is a well-known integral representation of Bochner-Martinelli [1][2]:

Theorem 1.1. Let D be a bounded domain in the space $\mathbb{C}^n$ of complex variables $z_1,\cdots,z_n$ whose boundary ∂D is a 2n-1 dimensional smooth orientable manifold. If $f(z)$ is a function holomorphic in D and continuous on ∂D (denoted by $f(z) \in A(D)$), then

$$f(z) = \int_{\partial D} f(\zeta)K(\zeta,z), \qquad z \in D, \tag{1.1}$$

where

$$K(\zeta,z) = \frac{(n-1)!}{(2\pi i)^n}\frac{1}{|\zeta-z|^{2n}}\sum_{k=1}^{n}(\bar{\zeta}_k-\bar{z}_k)d\bar{\zeta}_1\wedge d\zeta_1\wedge\cdots\wedge[d\bar{\zeta}_k]\wedge d\zeta_k\wedge\cdots \wedge d\bar{\zeta}_n\wedge d\zeta_n, \quad (n>1) \tag{1.2}$$

$$|\zeta-z| = \sqrt{\sum_{k=1}^{n}|\zeta_k-z_k|^2}\ . \tag{1.3}$$

This is an extension of the Cauchy formula of one complex variable. In the higher-dimensional case, the kernel $K(\zeta,z)$ is only a complex harmonic function of z (i.e., it satisfies the Laplace equation) and in general is not a holomorphic function of z. It is a

Received 16 Nov. 1981

closed exterior differential form of type (n,n-1) in $\mathbb{C}^n \setminus \{z\}$. Many known extensions of the Cauchy formula stemmed from it [3]. G.M. Henkin in his well known paper [4] discussed some applications of the integral representation of strictly pseudoconvex domain. In this paper we give several applications of the B-M integral.

II. SOME AUXILIARY LEMMAS

Lemma 2.1. For any $z \in \bar{D}$ and arbitrary δ $(0 < \delta \leq \gamma_0)$, the inequality

$$\int_{\partial D \setminus S_{2,\delta}} |K(\zeta,z)| \leq \frac{1}{2} + \gamma_1 \delta$$

holds, where $S_{2,\delta}$ is a hypersphere with z as center and radius δ, γ_0 and γ_1 are constants independent of z and δ.

Proof: see [5], Th. 1.

Lemma 2.2. For any $z \in \bar{D}$ and arbitrary δ $(0 < \delta \leq \gamma_0)$, the inequality

$$\int_{(S_{2,\delta}) \cap \partial D} |\zeta - z|^{\alpha} |K(\zeta,z)| \leq \gamma_2 \delta^{\alpha}, \qquad 0 < \alpha \leq 1 \tag{2.2}$$

holds, where the constant γ_2 is independent of z and δ.

To prove this lemma, it is only necessary to apply the finite covering theorem in addition to the proof of formula (2.1) in [6].

Now suppose $f(z) \in A(D)$ and $g(\zeta)$ is a function satisfying Lipschitz condition on ∂D. Consider the function

$$f_g = \int_{\partial D} f(\zeta) g(\zeta) K(\zeta,z). \tag{2.3}$$

Since for all $\zeta \in \partial D$ the kernel $K(\zeta,z)$ is complex harmonic with respect to $z \in \bar{D}\setminus\{\zeta\}$, the function $f_g(z)$ has the following properties.

Lemma 2.3. 1) $f_g(z)$ is complex harmonic at $z \in D$; 2) $f_g(z)$ is complex harmonic at $z \in \partial D$ if in a neighbourhood of $z \in \partial D$, $g(\zeta) \equiv 0$.

For an arbitrary point $z \in \partial D$, the integral (2.3) is in general divergent. Nevertheless we have the following

Lemma 2.4. The function $f_g(z)$ may be extended to a continuous function on the closed domain $\bar{D}$ if at the point $z \in \partial D$ we set

$$f_g(z) = f(z)g(z) + \int_{\partial D} f(\zeta)[g(\zeta)-g(z)]K(\zeta,z). \tag{2.4}$$

oreover, $|f_g(z)| = \sup_{z\in D}|f_g(z)|$ has the following estimate in the space $H(D)$ (of all functions complex harmonic in D and continuous on ∂D)

$$\|f_g(z)\| \leq \gamma_3 M\|f\|(\gamma_4 + \frac{M}{L}), \tag{2.5}$$

where

$$M = \max_{\zeta\in\partial D} |g(\zeta)|, L = \max_{\zeta_1\zeta_2\in\partial D} \frac{|g(\zeta_1)-g(\zeta_2)|}{|\zeta_1-\zeta_2|},$$

γ_3,γ_4 are constants independent of f and g.

Proof. For fixed $z \in D$, we have to prove that $f_g(z)$ is continuous at z. By lemma 2.2, the integral on the right of (2.4) exists. Now we fix δ $(0 < \delta \leq \gamma_0$; γ_0 is the constant in lemma 2.1). If for arbitrary $\omega \in D$ which satisfies $|z-\omega| < \rho < \delta$, we have the estimate

$$|f_g(z)-f_g(\omega)| \leq \gamma_4 g, \tag{2.6}$$

where γ_4 is a constant independent of ε and ω, then the lemma is proved.

For this purpose we derive some estimates which we need. We assume that the function $g(\zeta)$ may be continuously extended from the boundary ∂D to the whole domain D without increasing its modulus of continuity.

Given a positive number $\varepsilon > 0$. By lemma 2.2 there is a positive number $\delta > 0$ such that for any $\omega \in \overline{D}$

$$\int_{(S_{\omega,3\delta}) \cap \partial D} |g(\zeta)-g(\omega)||K(\zeta,\omega)| \leq \varepsilon . \tag{2.7}$$

Let K_δ be the set of points of $\omega \in \overline{D}$ and $\overline{\zeta} \in \partial D$ which satisfy $|\omega-\zeta| \geq \delta$. Then the function

$$H(\zeta,\omega) = [g(\zeta)-g(\omega)]K(\zeta,\omega)/dS_\zeta$$

is continuous in the compact set K_δ, where dS_ζ is the volume element of ∂D. Therefore we may select positive numbers $\delta > \rho > 0$ such that for any point ω (whose distance from the point z is smaller than ρ) the inequality

$$|H(\zeta,z)-H(\zeta,\omega)| < \varepsilon \tag{2.8}$$

holds for all ζ which satisfies $|\zeta - z| \geq 2\delta$ and

$$|f(z)g(z)-f(\omega)g(\omega)| < \varepsilon. \tag{2.9}$$

In the following we utilize the integral representation (1.1) and equalities (2.7), (2.8) and (2.9) to prove the estimate (2.6). In fact we have

$$\begin{aligned}
|f_g(z)-f_g(\omega)| &= \Big|f(z)g(z) + \int_{\partial D} f(\zeta)[g(\zeta)-g(z)]\,K(\zeta,z) \\
&\quad - \int_{\partial D} f(\zeta)g(\zeta)K(\zeta,\omega)\Big| = |f(z)g(z)-f(\omega)g(\omega)| \\
&\quad + \Big|\int_{\partial D} f(\zeta)\,[g(\zeta)-g(z)]K(\zeta,z) \\
&\quad - \int_{\partial D} f(\zeta)\,[g(\zeta)-g(\omega)]K(\zeta,\omega)\Big| \leq |f(z)g(z)-f(\omega)g(\omega)| \\
&\quad + \int_{\partial D\setminus S_{z,2\delta}} |f(\zeta)|\,|H(\zeta,z)-H(\zeta,\omega)|\,dS_\zeta \\
&\quad + \int_{(S_{z,2\delta})\cap\partial D} |f(\zeta)|\,|H(\zeta,z)|\,d\zeta_\zeta \\
&\quad + \int_{(S_{w,3\delta})\cap\partial D} |f(\zeta)|\,|H(\zeta,\omega)|\,dS_\zeta \\
&\leq \varepsilon+\varepsilon \int_{\partial D\setminus S_{z,2\delta}} |f(\zeta)|\,dS_\zeta + \varepsilon\|f\| + \varepsilon\|f\| = \gamma_4\varepsilon.
\end{aligned}$$

Hence the function $f_g(z)$ is complex harmonic in D and continuous on ∂D. That is, $f \in H(D)$.

Now we estimate $\|f_g(z)\|$. Assume $z \in \partial D$. For arbitrary δ $(0 < \delta \le \gamma_0)$

$$|f_g(z)| \le M\|f\| + \|f\| \int_{\partial D} |g(\zeta)-g(z)|\,|K(\zeta,\omega)|,$$

utilizing lemma 2.1 and lemma 2.2, we have

$$|f_g(z)| \le M\|f\| + 2M\|f\|(\tfrac{1}{2} + \gamma_1\delta) + \gamma_5 L\|f\|\delta \ .$$

Now set $\delta = \frac{M}{L}$ if $\frac{M}{L} \le \gamma_0$; and set $\delta = \gamma_0$ if $\frac{M}{L} \ge \gamma_0$. In the first case we have the estimate

$$|f_g(z)| \le \gamma_3 M\|f\|(\gamma_4 + \tfrac{M}{L}) \ ,$$

and in the second case we have the estimate

$$|f_g(z)| \le \gamma_6 M\|f\| .$$

The Lemma is proved.

III. MAIN THEOREMS

By lemmas 2.3 and 2.4 we have immediately the following

Theorem 3.1. If $f(z) \in A(D)$ and $g(\zeta)$ is a function defined on ∂D and satisfies Lipschitz condition on ∂D, then the function

$$f_g(z) = \int_{\partial D} f(\zeta)g(\zeta)K(\zeta,z)$$

has a definite meaning for the point $z \in D$, and may be extended to a continuous function on the closed domain $\overline{D}$. Moreover, the extended function has the following properties:

1) $f_g(z) \in H(D)$;

2) $f_g(z)$ is complex harmonic at the point on the boundary if in a neighbourhood of this point $g(\zeta) \equiv 0$;

3) $\|f_g(z)\| \leq \gamma_3 M \|f\| (\gamma_4 + \frac{M}{L})$,

where

$$\|f\| = \sup_{z\in D} |f(z)|, \quad M = \max_{\zeta\in\partial D} |g(\zeta)|, \quad L = \max_{\zeta_1,\zeta_2\in\partial D} \frac{|g(\zeta_1)-g(\zeta_2)|}{|\zeta_1-\zeta_2|},$$

γ_3, γ_4 are constants independent of the functions f and g.

By theorem 3.1 we have the following theorem of partition of singular point.

Theorem 3.2. Suppose $f(z) \in A(D)$. Then for any arbitrary positive number $\delta > 0$ there exist closed balls S_k $(k = 1,2,\cdots,N(\delta))$ with radius not greater than δ which cover the boundary ∂D and there exist functions

$f_k(z)$ $(k = 1,2,\cdots,N(\delta))$ such that

1) $f(z) = \sum_{k=1}^{N(\delta)} f_k(z)$;

2) for arbitrary k $(1 \le k \le N(\delta))$ the function $f_k(z)$ is complex harmonic at the point $z \in \bar{D} \setminus S_k$; and

3) for arbitrary k $(1 \le k \le N(\delta))$ one has the estimate

$$\|f_k\| \le \gamma_3 \|f\| (\gamma_4 + \frac{\gamma_5}{\delta}) ,$$

where the constants $\gamma_3, \gamma_4, \gamma_5$ depend neither on f nor on δ.

Proof. By the well-known theorem of partition of unity, we may construct a non-negative real function system $\{g_k(\delta)\}$, where $\zeta \in \partial D$, $\delta > 0$, $k = 1,2,\cdots,N(\delta)$, such that (see [4] page 629 and [7] appendix A):

1) For arbitrary positive number $\delta > 0$, $\sum_{k=1}^{N(\delta)} g_k^\delta(\zeta) \equiv 1$ on ∂D;

2) For arbitrary k and δ, the function $g_k^\delta(\zeta)$ satisfies the Lipschitz condition with constant γ/δ, that is

$$|g_k^\delta(\zeta_1) - g_k^\delta(\zeta_2)| \le \frac{\gamma}{\delta} |\zeta_1 - \zeta_2| ,$$

where the constant γ is independent of k and δ;

3) For every k and δ the function $g_k^\delta(\zeta)$ is supported on ∂D and its support is included in a ball with radius δ.

Hence for an arbitrary function $f(z) \in A(D)$, we have

$$f(z) = \int_{\partial D} f(\zeta)K(\zeta,z) = \sum_{k=1}^{N(\delta)} \int_{\partial D} f(\zeta)g_k^{\delta}(\zeta)K(\zeta,z) = \sum_{k=1}^{N(\delta)} f_k(z) ,$$

where

$$f_k(z) = \int_{\partial D} f(\zeta)g_k^{\delta}(\zeta)K(\zeta,z) \qquad (k = 1,2,\cdots,N(\delta)).$$

By theorem 3.1, $f_k(z)$ belongs to the space $H(D)$ and possesses all the properties of theorem 3.1.

The Theorem is proved.

REFERENCES

[1] Bochner, S., Ann. of Math. (2) 44(1943), 652-673.

[2] Martinelli, E., Ann. di Mat., 34(1953), 277-347.

[3] Aizenberg, L. A., Yzhakov, A. P., Integraltoie Predstavleniya e Boichetoi v Mnoioternom Kompleksnom Analyze. Nauka 1979

[4] Henkin, G.M., Mat. Sb. 78(1969), 611-632.

[5] Look, C.H. and Chung, T.D., Acta Math. Sinica 7(1957), 144-165 (Chinese).

[6] Chung, T.D., Acta Math. Sinica 15(1965), 227-241 (Chinese).

[7] Gunning, R.C., Rossi, H., Analytic functions of several complex variables. Englewood Cliffs, New Jersey; Prentice Hall, 1965.

Section Five

Pseudoconvexity, Function Fields, Algebraic Varieties, Value Distribution Theory

Several Complex Variables
Proceedings of the 1981 Hangzhou Conference

SOME ASPECTS OF PSEUDOCONVEXITY THEORY IN SEVERAL COMPLEX VARIABLES

Shigeo Nakano
Research Institute for Mathematical Sciences
Kyoto University, Kyoto, Japan

The notion of pseudoconvexity goes back to very early days of the theory of functions of several complex variables. It was known to Hartogs and Levi, that the domain of existence of a holomorphic function (in $\mathbb{C}^n$) has a certain property at boundary points, the property called pseudoconvexity.

Then it was an important problem to show that a pseudoconvex domain in $\mathbb{C}^n$ is a domain of holomorphy, and the affirmative answer was one of the main contributions of K. Oka. Another important result in this direction was given by H. Grauert. He showed that a (relatively compact) strongly pseudoconvex domain on a complex manifold is holomorphically convex (Grauert [4]). He also gave examples of (weakly) pseudoconvex domains on manifolds, which have constants only as global holomorphic functions (Grauert [5]). There are also famous results on strongly pseudoconvex domains due to J. J. Kohn. There are many generalizations too. Most of them are concerned with various strong convexity properties. (For example Andreotti-Grauert [2].)

Since 1970, I and my young colleagues have made some

Received 5 October, 1981

contributions to the theory of (weak) pseudoconvexity. I shall present a review of these works.

Let me remind first that a real valued function Ψ of class C^2 on a complex manifold X is plurisubharmonic, if and only if the matrix $\left(\frac{\partial^2\Psi}{\partial z^\alpha \partial \bar{z}^\beta}\right)$ is positive semi-definite at every point x of X. Here (z^α) denotes a system of holomorphic local coordinates in a neighborhood of x.

We say X is weakly 1-complete if there exists a C^∞ plurisubharmonic function Ψ that exhausts X. This means that

$$X_c \equiv \{x \in X \mid \Psi(x) < c\}$$

is relatively compact for every $c \in \mathbb{R}$. (H. Bremermann had called a manifold X pseudoconvex if X is exhausted by a continuous plurisubharmonic function. I should have followed his terminology. But ours has been used by many authors.) We define the notion of positivity of a holomorphic vector bundle in terms of metrics along fibres and the curvature forms. In more details, we describe a holomorphic vector bundle E over X by local product representation on members of an open covering $\{U_i\}$ of X and transition matrices $\{e_{ij}\}$, then Hermitean metrics along the fibres of E are given by a system $\{h_i\}$ of positive definite Hermitean matrices h_i, with entries C^∞ functions on U_i and satisfying the relation ${}^t\bar{e}_{ij}h_i e_{ij} = h_j$ in $U_i \cap U_j$. The curvature form $\Theta = \{\Theta_i\}$ is given by $\Theta_i = \bar{\partial}(h_i^{-1}\partial h_i)$, and when we express $\Theta_i = (\Theta_i{}^\lambda{}_\mu)$, $\Theta_i{}^\lambda{}_\mu = \sum \Theta_i{}^\lambda{}_{\mu\alpha\bar{\beta}} dz^\alpha \wedge d\bar{z}^\beta$, then E is said to be positive in the strong sense if the Hermitean matrix $H = (H_{i\mu\alpha,\bar{\nu}\bar{\beta}})$ given by $H_{i\mu\alpha,\bar{\nu}\bar{\beta}} = \sum_\lambda h_{i\bar{\nu}\lambda}\Theta_i{}^\lambda{}_{\mu\alpha\bar{\beta}}$ is positive definite. In the case of a line bundle B, $\Theta_i = \sum\Theta_{\alpha\bar\beta}dz^\alpha\wedge d\bar z^\beta$ is independent of i and B is positive if $(\Theta_{\alpha\bar\beta}) > 0$.

The first results we have are:

Theorem 1 If X is weakly 1-complete and if B is a positive line bundle on X, then $H^q(X,\Omega^p(B)) = 0$ for $p+q > n = \dim X$. (Nakano [9].)

Theorem 2 If X is weakly 1-complete and if E is a holomorphic vector bundle positive in the strong sense, then $H^q(X,\Omega^n(E)) = 0$ for $q \geqq 1$ and the restriction map $H^0(X,\Omega^n(E)) \longrightarrow H^0(X_c,\Omega^n(E))$ has a dense image in the topology of uniform convergence on compact sets. (Nakano [8], Kazama [6].)

Two applications of Theorem 1 seem important.

(1) If X is weakly 1-complete and if X has a positive line bundle B, then for any $c \in \mathbb{R}$, X_c can be embedded into a projective space as a closed submanifold of an open set. Hence two points of X_c can be separated by meromorphic functions on X_c. (Analogue of Kodaira's projective embedding of Hodge manifolds. This was pointed out by Hironaka. If we have the condition $B \otimes K_X^{-1} > 0$, K_X being the canonical bundle, then two points of X can be separated by meromorphic functions on the whole X.)

(2) Application to the inverse problem of monoidal transformations. Given an n-dimensional complex manifold $\tilde X$, suppose $\tilde X$ contains a submanifold S of codimension 1, which has the structure of a $\mathbb{P}^{r-1}$-bundle over another manifold M; $\pi\colon S \longrightarrow M$, $L_a \equiv \pi^{-1}(a) \cong \mathbb{P}^{r-1}$ for all $a \in M$. If $[S]|_{La} = [e]^{-1}$, where

$[e]$ is the hyperplane bundle on $\mathbb{P}^{r-1}$, then there exist a complex manifold X containing M and a holomorphic map $\tilde{\pi}$: $\tilde{X} \longrightarrow X$ such that $\tilde{\pi}|_S = \pi$ and $(\tilde{X},\tilde{\pi})$ is the monoidal transform of X with centre M. The use of Theorem 1 lies in the fact that we can construct, for each $a \in M$, a weakly 1-complete neighborhood V of L_a in $\tilde{X}$, such that $V \cap S = \pi^{-1}(D)$, where D is a neighborhood of a on M, of the form of a ball with respect to a suitable local coordinate system around a. Our theorem allows us to extend coordinate functions on D and holomorphic cross sections of $\pi^*([e])$ on $V \cap S$ to functions and cross sections of $[S]^{-1}$ on V respectively, and these enable us to construct X. (Nakano [7].)

These applications have shown that our notion is useful in function theory. Let us try to develop the theory further! The guiding principle is "Replace strong pseudoconvexity by weak one plus positivity of bundles"! Here are some recent developments. (In the following assume X to be connected and non-compact.)

<u>Theorem 3</u> Let X be Kähler and weakly 1-complete, and let B have a metric whose curvature form is positive semi-definite and of rank $\geqq n-r+1$ everywhere, then $H^q(X,\Omega^p(B)) = 0$ for $p+q \geqq n+r$. (Girbau [3], Abdelkader [1], Takegoshi-Ohsawa [15].)

<u>Theorem 4</u> Let X be as above and let B satisfy the above condition with the possible exception of the rank condition at points of a compact subset, then $H^q(X,\Omega^n(B)) = 0$ for $q \geqq r$. (Takegoshi [14].)

Theorem 5 Let X be weakly 1-complete and B be positive outside a compact subset K, then $\dim H^q(X,\Omega^p(B)) < \infty$ for $p+q > n$ and the restriction map $H^q(X,\Omega^p(B)) \longrightarrow H^q(X_c,\Omega^p(B))$ is bijective for $p+q > n$, provided $X_c \supset K$. (Ohsawa [10],[11], Nakano-Rhai [17] and for more general results Ohsawa [13].)

Theorem 6 Let X be a weakly 1-complete surface and suppose the canonical bundle of X is negative outside a compact set, then X is holomorphically convex. (Ohsawa [12].)

Theorem 7 Let X be a weakly 1-complete surface and assume that the global holomorphic functions on X are constants only. If X has a non-constant meromorphic function, then X_c may be embedded in a projective space. If moreover X contains only a finite number of exceptional curves, then the whole X may be embedded into a projective space. (Not necessarily a proper embedding into an open subset.) (Takegoshi-Ohsawa [16].)

Finally let me mention the following question: Let X be a weakly 1-complete Kähler manifold and let γ be a (1.1)-form which is exact ($\gamma = d\varphi$ with a 1-form φ). Is there a differentiable function f on X such that $\gamma = \partial\bar\partial f$?

References

[1] O. Abdelkader: Vanishing of the cohomology of a weakly 1-complete Kähler manifold with value in a semi-positive vector bundle, C. R. Acad. Sci. Paris, 290 (1980) 75-78.

[2] A. Andreotti and H. Grauert: Théorèmes de finitude pour la cohomologies des espaces complex, Bull. Soc. Math. France, 90 (1962) 193-259.

[3] J. Girbau: Unpublished.

[4] H. Grauert: On Levi's problem and the imbedding of real analytic manifolds, Ann. of Math. 68 (1958) 460-472.

[5] H. Grauert: Bemerkenswerte pseudokonvexe Mannigfaltigkeiten, Math. Zeitschr. 81 (1963) 377-391.

[6] H. Kazama: Approximation theorem and application to Nakano's vanishing theorem for weakly 1-complete manifolds, Memoirs of Fac. Sci., Kyushu Univ., Ser. A, Math., 27 (1973) 221-240.

[7] S. Nakano: On the inverse of monoidal transformation, Publ. R. I. M. S., Kyoto Univ. 6 (1970-71) 483-502, Supplement. Ibid. 7 (1971-72) 637-644.

[8] S. Nakano: Vanishing theorems for weakly 1-complete manifolds, Number Theory, Algebraic Geometry and Commutative Algebra, in honor of Y. Akizuki, Kinokuniya, Tokyo, (1973) 169-179.

[9] S. Nakano: Vanishing theorems for weakly 1-complete manifolds II, Publ. R. I. M. S., Kyoto Univ. 10 (1974-75) 101-110.

[10] T. Ohsawa: Finiteness theorems on weakly 1-complete manifolds, Publ. R. I. M. S., 15 (1979) 853-870.

[11] T. Ohsawa: On $H^{pq}(X,B)$ of weakly 1-complete manifolds, Ibid. 17 (1981) 113-126.

[12] T. Ohsawa: Weakly 1-complete manifold and Levi problem, Ibid. 17 (1981) 153-164.

[13] T. Ohsawa: Isomorphism theorems for cohomology groups of weakly 1-complete manifolds, to appear in Publ. R. I. M. S., Kyoto Univ.

[14] K. Takegoshi: A generalization of vanishing theorems for weakly 1-complete manifolds, Publ. R. I. M. S., Kyoto Univ. 17 (1981) 311-330.

[15] K. Takegoshi and T. Ohsawa: A vanishing theorem for $H^p(X,\Omega^q(B))$ on weakly 1-complete manifold, to appear in Publ. R. I. M. S., Kyoto Univ.

[16] K. Takegoshi and T. Ohsawa: In preparation.

[17] S. Nakano and T. S. Rhai: Vector bundle version of Ohsawa's finiteness theorems, Math. Japonica 24 (1979-80) 657-664.

Several Complex Variables
Proceedings of the 1981 Hangzhou Conference

A HIGHER DIMENSIONAL ANALOGUE OF MORDELL'S CONJECTURE OVER FUNCTION FIELDS AND RELATED PROBLEMS*)

Junjiro Noguchi**)

Department of Mathematics, College of General Education
Osaka Univertsity, Toyonaka, Osaka, Japan

The aim of this talk is to present our recent results of [14] and [15], and to discuss several open problems. Let us begin with giving a generalization of de Frachis' theorem which is considered as a part of Mordell's conjecture over function fields.

Achnowledgement. The author has researched the main part of the present works during the stay at The Insitute for Advanced Study, Princeton in 1980-1981. He would like to express his sincere gratitude for the Institute.

§1. Generalization of de Franchis' theorem

Theorem (de Franchis). Let C be a complete algebraic curve over an algebraically closed field and R an algebraic variety over the same field. If the genus of C is greater than 1, then the number of separable nonconstant rational mappings of R into C is finite.

We are going to give a higher dimensional version of this simple and excellent theorem. Let V be a smooth projective variety over an algebraically closed field k with the characteristic, char $k \geq 0$, and R an algebraic variety over k. Denote by $\Xi_\mu(R, V)$ the family of separable rational mappings f of R into V of which rank $f \geq \mu$, where rank $f = \dim R - \dim_t f^{-1}f(t)$ for general $t \in R$. We say that a vector bundle E over V is negative if there is a proper birational morphism $\varphi: E \to Z$ of E onto an affine variety $Z \subset A_k^N$ such that the zero section V of E is mapped by φ to a point $0 \in Z$

---

*) These notes are an extended version of the talk at the conference.

**) Supported in part by National Science Foundation Grant MCS 77-18723 A0 4.

Received 1 December, 1981

and the restriction $\varphi|(E - V): E - V \to Z - \{0\}$ is an isomorphism.

Theorem 1.1([15]). *If the* μ-*th skew symmetric power* $\Lambda^{\mu}T(V)$ *of the tangent bundle* $T(V)$ *over* V *is negative, then* $\Xi_{\mu}(R, V)$ *is finite.*

Remark 1. In the case of dim $V = 1$, $T(V)$ is negative if and only if the genus of V is greater than 1. Therefore this is equivalent to de Franchis' theorem, when dim $V = 1$.

Remark 2. Kobayashi and Ochiai [8] for char $k = 0$, and then Martin-Deschamps and Lewin-Menegaux [10] for char $k \geq 0$, proved that if V is of general type, then $\Xi_{\dim V}(R, V)$ is finite.

Remark 3. In the case of $\mu = 1$, Urata [21] and Kalka, Shiffman and Wong [7] proved the same finiteness theorem by a different method.

In the complex analytic case ($k = \mathbf{C}$). we want to replace R by a Zariski open subset X of a compact complex space $\overline{X}$, and rational mappings by meromorphic mappings. We denote by $\mathrm{Mer}_{\mu}(X, V)$ the family of meromorphic mappings f of X into V with rank $f \geq \mu$. We need the following extension theorem, which is originally due to Carlson [1] (see also [12] and [15]).

Lemma 1.2. *Assume that* $\Lambda^{\mu}T(V)$ *is negative. Let* $f: \Delta^{*}\times\Delta^{m-1} \to V$ *be a meromorphic mapping of the product of the unit discs* $\Delta = \{z \in \mathbf{C};\ |z| < 1\}$ *and the punctured disc* $\Delta^{*} = \Delta - \{0\}$. *If rank* $f \geq \mu$, *then* f *has a meromorphic extension of* $\Delta\times\Delta^{m-1}$ *into* V.

By this lemma, we have $\mathrm{Mer}_{\mu}(X, V) = \mathrm{Mer}_{\mu}(\overline{X}, V)$. Then we can reduce $\overline{X}$ to a compact complex algebraic variety, so that we have

Theorem 1.3([15]). If $\Lambda^{\mu}T(V)$ is negative, then $\mathrm{Mer}_{\mu}(X, V)$ is finite.

Let V be a compact smooth quotient of a symmetric bounded domain D by a discrete subgroup of the automorphism group Aut(D) of D. Then the curvature tensor of the canonical metric in $\Lambda^{\mu}T(V)$ is negative if and only if μ is greater than the maximum dimension $\ell(D)$ of proper boundary components of D (see [15, §3]). Hence if $\mu > \ell(D)$, then $\Lambda^{\mu}T(V)$ is negative in the present sense. In this case, Theorem 1.3 was proved by Sunada [19] by making use of the theory of harmonic mappings.

In a special case, we can relax the rank condition on f.

Let $V = \Gamma\backslash H\times H$ be a compact smooth quotient of the product of the upper half planes H by a discrete subgroup $\Gamma\subset SL(2, \mathbf{R})\times SL(2, \mathbf{R})$. Then $\ell(H\times H) = 1$ and moreover $T(V)$ is not negative by [11].

Theorem 1.4 ([15, Proposition (4.2)]). If the projection of Γ into each component is dense, then there are only finitely many nonconstant holomorphic mappings of X into $\Gamma\backslash H\times H$.

We are naturally led to the following problem:

Problem. Find a bound of the cardinality of $\Xi_{\mu}(R, V)$ in Theorem 1.1 by some invariants.

Fujimoto [2] (cf. also [3]) obtained an interesting finiteness theorem for transcendental holomorphic mappings. Let H_i, $i = 1, \ldots, n+2$, be $n + 2$ hyperplanes in general position in the n-dimensional complex projective space $\mathbf{P}^n_{\mathbf{C}}$ and Z_i, $i = 1, \ldots, n + 2$, effective divisors on $\mathbf{C}^m$ which may be transcendental.

Theorem (Fujimoto [2]). <u>There are only finitely many linearly nondegenerate meromorphic mappings</u> $f: \mathbf{C}^m \to \mathbf{P}^n_{\mathbf{C}}$ <u>such that</u> $f^*H_i = Z_i$ <u>for all</u> i.

He proved the above theorem by using Borel's identity which follows from the second main theorem. The case of $m = 1$ would be substantial. A weak inequality of the second main theorem type which is sufficient to get Borel's identity holds in more general case. Let $D = \sum_{i=1}^{\ell} D_i$ be an effective reduced divisor on a smooth complex projective variety V and $H^0(V, \Omega^1_V(\log D))$ denote the space of logarithmic 1-forms over V with poles along D. If $H^0(V, \Omega^1_V(\log D))$ contains sufficiently many forms (see [13, Theorem 3.1]), then we have an inequality of the second main theorem type for algebraically nondegenerate holomorphic curves $f: \mathbf{C} \to V$:

$$KT_f(r) \leq N(r, f^{-1}(D)) + \text{small term},$$

where K is a positive constant independent of f (see [13, §3]).

Conjecture A. Let Z_i, $i = 1, \ldots, \ell$, be effective divisors on $\mathbf{C}$. If $H^0(V, \Omega^1_V(\log D))$ contains sufficiently many forms in the above sense, then there are only finitely many algebraically nondegenerate holomorphic curves $f: \mathbf{C} \to V$ such that $f^*D_i = Z_i$ for all i.

For equidimensional meromorphic mappings $f: \mathbf{C}^n \to V$ with rank $f =$

dim V = n, we know the second main theorem by [5] and [18].

Conjecture B. Let D be an effective reduced divisor on V with simple normal crossings such that $D + K_V$ is ample, where K_V denotes the canonical divisor. Let Z be an effective divisor on $\mathbf{C}^n$. Then there are only finitely many meromorphic mappings $f: \mathbf{C}^n \to V$ with rank f = n such that $f^*D = Z$.

This seems to be unknown even in the case of $V = \mathbf{P}^1_{\mathbf{C}}$. If we put the stronger condition, $f^*D_i = Z_i$ for all i, Conjecture B is true in the case where $V = \mathbf{P}^1_{\mathbf{C}}$ (cf. the above theorem of Fujimoto). If Z is algebraic, then f turn out to be rationl and Conjecture B is true by Tsushima [20].

§2. Mordell's conjecture over function fields

In this section we assume that the characteristic of the algebraically closed field k is zero. Let K be a function field over k. Manin [9] and Grauert [4] proved that if a curve C defined over K with genus > 1 contains infinitely many K-rational points, then there is a curve C_0 defined over k such that C is K-isomorphic to C_0; moreover, $C_0(K) - C_0(k)$ is finite, where $C_0(K)$ (resp. $C_0(k)$) denotes the set of K-rational (resp. k-rational) points of C_0. This last assertion is nothing but de Franchis' theorem in §1. Grauert also dealt with the positive characteristic case.

Theorem 2.1 ([14, Main Theorem]). Let $\mathfrak{X}$ be a smooth projective variety defined over K such that $T(\mathfrak{X})$ is negative. If the set $\mathfrak{X}(K)$ is dense, then there is a smooth projective variety $\mathfrak{X}_0$ defined over k such that $\mathfrak{X}$ is K-isomorphic to $\mathfrak{X}_0$; moreover, $\mathfrak{X}_0(K) - \mathfrak{X}_0(k)$ is finite.

The idea of the proof is due to Grauert's [4]. Take an algebraic variety R over k such that we have a proper smooth fibre space $\pi: X \to R$ over R of which generic fibre is $\mathfrak{X}$. Since $T(\mathfrak{X})$ is negative, we may assume that $T(X_t)$ is negative for all $t \in R$, where $X_t = \pi^{-1}(t)$. The set $\mathfrak{X}(K)$ corresponds to the set Γ of rational cross sections of $\pi: X \to R$. To prove Theorem 2.1, we show the following:

Theorem 2.2 ([14, Theorem (3.1)]). Let the notation be as

above. If the set $\bigcup_{s\in\Gamma} s(R)$ is dense in X, then there are a nonempty open subset R' of R and a smooth projective variety X_0 over k such that the restriction $X|R'$ of the fibre space X over R' is isomorphic to $R'\times X_0$ as fibre space; moreover, all $s\in\Gamma$ except for a finite number of $s\in\Gamma$ reduce to constant ones.

The proof is divided into two parts: The first is to show the infinitesimal triviality of the fibre space $\pi: X \to R$ which is the crucial part, and the second is to show the global triviality over some nonempty open subset of R.

The following example shows that the denseness condition for Γ can not be replaced by the infiniteness of Γ.

Example. Let M be any smooth projective variety of dimension $m \geqq 3$ such that T(M) is negative. For instance, M is a smooth compact quotient of the unit ball B^m of $\mathbb{C}^m$. Let $M \subset \mathbb{P}^N_{\mathbb{C}}$ be an embedding such that no linear subspace contains M. Take hyperplanes $H_1, \ldots, H_{m-1}$ in $\mathbb{P}^N_{\mathbb{C}}$ such that $H_i \cap M$ are smooth and $C = H_1\cap\ldots\cap H_{m-1}\cap M$ is a curve. Put $R = \{\{H\} \in \mathbb{P}^{N*}_{\mathbb{C}};\ H\cap M$ is smooth and $H \supset C\}$ and

$$X = \bigcup_{\{H\}\in R} \{H\}\times(H\cap M) \subset R\times M$$

with the natural projection $\pi: X \to R$. Then $\dim X_t = m - 1$ and by Kalka [6] or by Theorem 1.1 the fibre space $\pi: X \to R$ is not trivial over any nonempty open subset of R even in the sense of differential topology. By definition the trivial fibre space $\pi|(R\times C): R\times C \to R$ is contained in $\pi: X \to R$. Therefore Γ is infinite.

Riebesehl [16] recently obtained, independently, the following related result:

Theorem (Riebesehl [16]). Let R be a compact Riemann surface, $X \subset R \times \mathbb{P}^N_{\mathbb{C}}$ a complex suvariety which may be singular and $\pi: X \to R$ denote the natural projection. Assume that the Zariski tangent space $T(X_t)$ of each fibre X_t carries a Finsler metric of which curvature is strictly negative. If there are infinitely many holomorphic cross sections of $\pi: X \to R$, then the fibre space $\pi: X \to R$ contains a subfamily which is birationally trivial.

He first proved that the family of holomorphic cross sections of the fibre space forms a normal family and then by making use of

Grauert's theorem [4] he deduced the existence of such a subfamily of curves.

Conjecture C. Let $\pi: X \to R$ be a proper smooth fibre space such that the canonical line bundle K_{X_t} of X_t are ample or more generally X_t are of general type. If $\bigcup_{s\in\Gamma} s(R)$ is dense in X, then there are a nonempty open subset R' and a smooth projective variety X_0 such that $X|R'$ is isomorphic to $R'\times X_0$ as fibre space.

This is an analogue over function fields of the following question in Bombieri's lecture at Chicago University in 1980:

Let V be a projective variety of general type defined over a number field L. Then is V(L) not Zariski dense in V?

Sampson [17, p. 227] is posing some related question.

References

[1] J. Carlson, "Some degeneracy theorem for entire functions with values in an algebraic variety", Trans. Amer. Math. Soc., 168 (1972), 273-301.

[2] H. Fujimoto, "Remarks to the uniqueness problem of meromorphic maps into $\mathbf{P}^N(\mathbb{C})$, IV", Nagoya Math. J., 83 (1981), 153-181.

[3] ———, "On meromorphic maps into a compact complex manifold", preprint.

[4] H. Grauert, "Mordells Vermutung über rationale Punkte auf algebraischen Kurven und Funktionenköper", Publ. Math. I.H.E.S., 25 (1965), 131-149.

[5] P. Griffiths and J. King, "Nevanlinna theory and holomorphic mappings between algebraic varieties", Acta Math., 130 (1973), 145-220.

[6] M. Kalka, "Deformation of submanifolds of strongly negatively curved manifolds", Math. Ann., 251 (1980), 243-248.

[7] ———, B. Shiffman and B. Wong, "Finiteness and rigidity theorems for holomorphic mappings", Michigan Math. J., 28 (1981), 289-295.

[8] S. Kobayashi and T. Ochiai, "Meromorphic mappings onto compact complex spaces of general type", Invent. Math., 31 (1975), 7-16.

[9] Ju. Manin, "Rational points of algebraic curves over function fields", Izvestija Akad. Nauk. SSSR. Mat., 27 (1963), 1395-1440.

[10] M. Martin-Deschamps and R. Lewin-Menegaux, "Applications rationelles séparables dominantes sur une variété de type générale", Bull. Soc. Math. France, 105 (1978), 279-287.

[11] Y. Matsushima and G. Shimura, "On the cohomology groups attached to certain vector valued differential forms on the product of the upper half planes", Ann. Math., 78 (1963), 417-449.

[12] J. Noguchi, "Meromorhic mappings into a compact complex space", Hiroshima Math. J., 7 (1977), 411-425.

[13] ———, "Lemma on logarithmic derivatives and holomorphic curves in algebraic varieties", Nagoya Math. J., 83 (1981), 213-233.

[14] ———, "A higher dimensional analogue of Mordell's conjecture over function fields", Math. Ann. 258 (1981),207-212.

[15] ——— and T. Sunada, "Finiteness of the family of rational and meromorphic mappings into algebraic varieties", Amer. J. Math., 104 (1982), 887-900.

[16] D. Riebesehl, "Hyperbolische komplexe Räume und die Vermutung von Mordell", Math. Ann., 257 (1981), 99-110.

[17] J. Sampson, "Some properties and applications of harmonic mappings", Ann. Scie. École Norm. Sup., 11 (1978), 211-228.

[18] B. Shiffman, "Nevanlinna defect relations for singular divisors", Invent. Math., 31 (1975), 155-182.

[19] T. Sunada, "Holomorphic mappings into a compact quotient of symmetric bounded domain", Nagoya Math. J., 64 (1976), 159-175.

[20] R. Tsushima, "Rational maps to varieties of hyperbolic type", Proc. Japan Acad., 55 (1979), 95-100.

[21] T. Urata, "Holomorphic mappings onto a certain compact complex analytic space", Tohoku Math. J., 33 (1981), 573-585.

The present address:

Department of Mathematics
Tokyo Institute of Technology
Ookayama, Meguro, Tokyo 152
Japan.

Several Complex Variables
Proceedings of the 1981 Hangzhou Conference

Rank-complete function fields

K. Stein

Let X be a reduced irreducible complex space and $K(X)$ be the field of meromorphic functions on X. A subfield A of $K(X)$ is called rank-complete or analytically closed in $K(X)$ if it has the following property: Let $\{f_1,..,f_k\}$ be a system of elements of A and $f \in K(X)$ a meromorphic function analytically dependent on $\{f_1,..,f_k\}$, then $f \in A$. Rank-complete subfields $A \subset K(X)$ are intimately related with maximal meromorphic mappings (as to the notations concerning meromorphic mappings see [2]). A meromorphic mapping $F_m: X \longrightarrow Y$ is called m-maximal iff (i) F_m is surjective and (ii) F_m majorizes every meromorphic mapping dependent on F_m. If F_m is m-maximal, then $F_m^* K(Y)$ is a rank-complete subfield of $K(X)$. It is an open problem whether every rank-complete subfield of $K(X)$ can be obtained in this manner by means of a suitable m-maximal meromorphic mapping F_m. This is possible at least if the rank $\mathrm{rk}A$ of A equals 0, 1 or $\dim X$. Generally one has the following proposition: Let $A \subset K(X)$ be rank-complete, let $\{f_1,..,f_l\}$ be a system of meromorphic functions in A with $\mathrm{rk}\{f_1,..,f_l\} = \mathrm{rk}A$. Consider the meromorphic junction

$$\phi = [f_1,..,f_l] : X \longrightarrow \mathbb{P}_1^l ,$$

assume that there is a m-maximal meromorphic mapping $\phi_m: X \longrightarrow Z$

Received 25 March, 1983

related to ϕ (i.e. ϕ_m is dependent on ϕ , and ϕ is dependent on ϕ_m ; the pair (ϕ_m, Z) is then called a complex m-base with respect to ϕ); then $\phi_m^* K(Z) = A$. It is unknown whether a meromorphic mapping always admits a complex m-base, but some sufficient conditions are known (see [1], [2], [3]). In special cases one can survey the possible rank-complete subfields of $K(X)$. As an example the case

$$X = \{(z_1, z_2) \in \mathbb{C}^2 : \frac{1}{2} < |z_j| < 1 (j = 1,2)\}$$

was discussed.

References

[1] K. Stein, Maximale holomorphe und meromorphe Abbildungen, II. Amer. Journ. of Math. 86 (1964), 823-868.

[2] ————, Dependence of meromorphic mappings. Ann. Polonici Math. 33 (1976), 107-115.

[3] ————, Topological properties of holomorphic and meromorphic mappings. In: Variêtés analytiques compactes, Lecture notes in Mathematics, Springer Verlag, Vol. 683 (1978), 203-216.

Several Complex Variables
Proceedings of the 1981 Hangzhou Conference

Chern classes on algebraic varieties with arbitrary singularities

Wu Wen-tsun

(Institute of Systems-Science, Academia Sinica)

In [2] the author introduced the notion of Chern classes for projective algebraic varieties with arbitrary singularities. Unlike the intricate method due to MacPherson et al (e.g. [1]), our method is simple and direct and may be briefly described as follows.

Let V_d be an irreducible algebraic variety in the projective space S_n on $\underline{C}$. Take a generic point P of V_d with tangent space L_p. The pair (P, L_p) will determine a subvariety $\tilde{V}_d$ of the composite Grassmannian $\tilde{\Omega}^n_{o,d}$ of pairs $\{S_o, S_d\}$ with $S_o \subset S_d \subset S_n$. Let $A^*(M) = \sum A^r(M)$ be the group of algebraic equivalence classes for an arbitrary variety M with r=codimension. In the case of $M = \tilde{\Omega}^n_{o,d}$ which has no singularity, A* is a ring under intersections and the basis in A are in correspondence with the Ehresmann symbols

$$E = \begin{bmatrix} n-a_i & & \\ n-a_d, \ldots, & n-a_i, \ldots, & n-a_o \end{bmatrix}$$

with

$$0 \leq a_0 < \cdots < a_i < \cdots < a_d \leq n, \quad r = \sum_{j=0}^{d} (a_j - j) + i \ .$$

Received 30 April 1983

To each such element $E \in A^r$ the intersection with V_d will give an element $\tilde{E} \in A^r(\tilde{V}_d)$ and thus an element $E(V_d) \in A^r(V_d)$, to be defined as the <u>(generalized) characteristic class</u> of V_d corresponding to the symbol E. Of particular interest are the elements

$$c^s(V_d) = \sum_{t=0}^{s} (-1)^t \binom{d-t-1}{d-s-1} E_t^s(V_d) ,$$

in which $E_t^s = \begin{bmatrix} n-s+t \\ n-d-1,\dots,n-d-2+t,n-d+t,\dots,n \end{bmatrix}$.

Let

$$h\colon A^r(V_d) \longrightarrow H_{2d-2r}(V_d,\underline{C})$$

be the natural morphism and in the case of non-singular V_d let

$$D\colon H_{2d-2r}(V_d,\underline{C}) \longrightarrow H^{2r}(V_d,\underline{C})$$

be the Poincaré duality, then by Gamkrelidze, $Dhc^s(V_d)$ are just the usual Chern classes c_s of V_d.

For s = 0 the classes reduce to numbers which will be called <u>(generalized) Chern numbers</u> of V_d. These are just the enumerative characters of V_d in the sense of Severi. Under certain assumptions we have:

<u>The Hilbert polynomial of an arbitrary algebraic variety is completely determined by its generalized Chern numbers</u>.

The explicit expressions can then be determined in an elementary manner which generalizes the Hirzebruch formula for arithmetic genera in the non-singular case.

References

[1] R.D. MacPherson. Chern classes for singular algebraic varieties. Ann. of Math. 100 (1974), 423-432.

[2] W.-t. Wu. Shuxue Jinzhan 8 (1965), 395-409.

Several Complex Variables
Proceedings of the 1981 Hangzhou Conference

A GENERAL CRITERION

Yang Lo

(Inst. of Math., Academia Sinica, Beijing)

In this talk, we will give a general criterion for normality which includes the criteria due to Miranda, Valiron, Chuang and Ku respectively (cf. [1,4]).

Theorem. Let k be a positive integer, $\mathcal{F}$ be a family of meromorphic functions in a region D and $\alpha_j(z)$ $(j = 0,1,2,\cdots,k-1)$ be holomorphic functions there. If, for every $f(z) \in \mathcal{F}$, $f(z) \neq 0$ and $f^{(k)}(z) + \sum_{j=0}^{k-1} \alpha_j(z) f^{(j)}(z) \neq 1$, then $\mathcal{F}$ is normal in D.

It is worthy to note that the corresponding theorem of Picard-Liouville type has not been verified, except a special case in which $\alpha_{k-1}(z) \equiv 0$. Perhaps this is the first time that a criterion for normality is proved before the corresponding theorem of Picard-Liouville type. (Cf. [1,3])

An outline of its proof can be shown by formulating a series of lemmas.

Let k be a positive integer.

Lemma 1. Suppose that f(z) is meromorphic and $\alpha_j(z)$ $(j = 0,1,2,\cdots,k)$ are holomorphic in $|z| < R$ $(0 < R < \infty)$ and that $\alpha_k(z)$ has no zero there. If

$$f_k(z) = \sum_{j=0}^{k} \alpha_j(z) f^{(j)}(z);$$

$f(0) \neq 0,\infty$; $f_k(0) \neq 1$; $f_k'(0) \neq 0$, then we have

Received 1 Dec. 1981

$$T(r,f) < \overline{N}(r,f) + N(r,\frac{1}{f}) + \overline{N}(r,\frac{1}{f_k-1}) - N_0(r,\frac{1}{f_k'}) + S(r,f)$$

for $0 < r < R$, where

$$S(r,f) = m(r,\frac{f_k}{f}) + m(r,\frac{f_k'}{f}) + m(r,\frac{f_k'}{f_k-1})$$

$$+ \log\left|\frac{f(0)(f_k(0)-1)}{f_k'(0)}\right| + \log 2 ,$$

and in $N_0(r,\frac{1}{f_k'})$ only zeros of $f_k'(z)$, which are not zeros of $f_k(z)-1$, are to be considered.

<u>Lemma 2</u>. Suppose that $f(z)$ satisfies the assumptions of Lemma 1 and that in addition $\alpha_{k-1}(z) \equiv 0$. Then we have

$$N_{1)}(r,f) \le \overline{N}_{(2}(r,f) + \overline{N}(r,\frac{1}{f_k-1}) + N_0(r,\frac{1}{f_k'})$$

$$+ m(r,\frac{g'}{g}) + \log\left|\frac{g(0)}{g'(0)}\right| ,$$

where $N_{1)}(r,f)$ and $N_{(2}(r,f)$ denote the counting functions with respect to the simple and multiple poles of $f(z)$ respectively, each pole being counted only once and

$$g(z) = \frac{(f_k'(z))^{k+1}}{(f_k(z)-1)^{k+2}}$$

(cf. [2]).

<u>Lemma 3</u>. Under the same hypotheses of Lemma 2, we have

$$\overline{N}(r,f) \le \frac{2}{3}T(r,f) + \frac{1}{3}\{\overline{N}(r,\frac{1}{f_k-1}) + N_0(r,\frac{1}{f_k'})$$

$$+ m(r,\frac{g'}{g}) + \log\left|\frac{g(0)}{g'(0)}\right|\}.$$

Lemma 4. Under the same hypotheses of Lemma 2, if

$$(k+1)f_k''(0)(f_k(0)-1) - (k+2)f_k'(0)^2 \neq 0,$$

then we have

$$T(r,f) < 3N(r,\frac{1}{f}) + 4\bar{N}(r,\frac{1}{f_k-1}) - 2N_0(r,\frac{1}{f_k'}) + S_1(r,f),$$

where

$$S_1(r,f) = 3m(r,\frac{f_k}{f}) + 3m(r,\frac{f_k'}{f}) + 4m(r,\frac{f_k'}{f_k-1}) + m(r,\frac{f_k''}{f_k'})$$

$$+4+\log(k+2)+3\log\left|\frac{f(0)(f_k(0)-1)}{f_k'(0)}\right| +\log\left|\frac{f_k'(0)(f_k(0)-1)}{(k+1)f_k''(0)(f_k(0)-1)-(k+2)f_k'(0)^2}\right|$$

Lemma 5. Suppose that $f(z)$ satisfies the assumptions of Lemma 4 and that in addition $f(z) \neq 0$ and $f_k(z) \neq 1$ in $|z| < R$ $(<\infty)$. Then we have

$$\log M(r,\frac{1}{f}) < C\frac{R}{R-r}\{1 + B + \log\frac{R}{R-r}\}$$

for $0 < r < R$, where

$$B = \log^+ R + \log^+\frac{1}{R} + \sum_{j=0}^{k} m(R,\alpha_j) + \sum_{j=0}^{k} m(R,\alpha_j')$$

$$+ \log^+|f(0)| + \log^+|f_k(0)| + \log^+\frac{1}{|f_k'(0)|}$$

$$+ \log^+\frac{1}{|(k+1)\ f_k''(0)(f_k(0)-1)-(k+2)f_k'(0)^2|}.$$

Lemma 6. Let $f(z)$, $\alpha_j(z)$ $(j = 0,1,2,\cdots,k)$ be holomorphic in a neighborhood of a segment $\overline{z_1z_2}$, $\alpha_{k-1}(z) \equiv 0$ and $f_k(z) = \sum_{j=0}^{k} \alpha_j(z) f^{(j)}(z)$. Suppose there is a positive number A such that

$$A > 2, \qquad \min_{z\in\overline{z_1z_2}} |\alpha_k(z)| > A^{-1}$$

and $|z_1 - z_2| < \frac{1}{2A^2}$. If

$$\max_{z\in\overline{z_1z_2}} \left|f_k'(z)\right| < \frac{1}{2} \quad \text{and} \quad \sum_{j=0}^{k} |f^{(j)}(z_2)| \leq \frac{1}{4},$$

then we have $|f(z_1)| < \frac{1}{2}$.

Lemma 7. Let $f(z)$ be meromorphic and $\alpha_j(z)(j = 0,1,2,\cdots,k)$ be holomorphic in $|z| < 1$. Suppose that $\alpha_k(z)$ has no zero and $\alpha_{k-1}(z) \equiv 0$ there. If $f(z) \neq 0$ and $f_k(z) = \sum_{j=0}^{k} \alpha_j(z) f^{(j)}(z) \neq 1$ in $|z| < 1$ and

$$A = \max\left\{2, \frac{1}{\min_{|z|\leq\frac{1}{2}} |\alpha_k(z)|}, \max_{\substack{|z|\leq\frac{1}{2}\\ 0\leq j\leq k}} |\alpha_j(z)|, \max_{\substack{|z|\leq\frac{1}{2}\\ 0\leq j\leq k}} |\alpha_j'(z)|\right\},$$

then either $|f(z)| < 1$ or $|f(z)| > \frac{C}{e^{C(1+A)}}$ uniformly in $|z| < \frac{1}{16A^2}$, where C is a positive constant depending only on k.

<u>Lemma 8</u>. Suppose that $\mathfrak{F}$ is a family of meromorphic functions in $|z| < 1$ and that $\alpha_j(z)$ $(j = 0,1,2,\cdots,k-1)$ are holomorphic there. If, for every $f(z) \in \mathfrak{F}$, $f(z) \neq 0$ and $f^{(k)}(z) + \sum_{j=0}^{k-1} \alpha_j(z)f^{(j)}(z) \neq 1$ in $|z| < 1$, then $\mathfrak{F}$ is normal in a neighborhood of the origin.

In the Theorem the condition $f^{(k)}(z) + \sum_{j=0}^{k-1} \alpha_j(z)f^{(j)}(z) \neq 1$ can be replaced by the condition that all the zeros of $f^{(k)}(z) + \sum_{j=0}^{k-1} \alpha_j(z)f^{(j)}(z) - 1$ are of multiplicity $> 3k+4$ in D (cf. [6]).

References

[1] Drasin, D., Normal families and the Nevalinna theory, Acta Math., 122 (1969), 231-263.

[2] Hayman, W.K., Picard's values of meromorphic functions and their derivatives, Ann. of Math., 70(1959), 9-42.

[3] ____________, Research Problems in Function Theory, London, 1967.

[4] Ku Yung-hsing, Un critère de normalité des familles de fonctions meromorphes, Sci. Sinica, special issue (1), 1979, 267-274.

[5] Yang Lo, Meromorphic functions and their derivatives, J. London Math. Soc., (to appear).

[6] _______, A fundamental inequality and its application, Preprint.

Several Complex Variables
Proceedings of the 1981 Hangzhou Conference

RIEMANN-ROCH THEOREM FOR STRONGLY PSEUDOCONVEX MANIFOLDS OF DIMENSION THREE

Paul C.-P. Yang and Stephen S.-T. Yau

It is generally expected that an analogous formula of Riemann-Roch holds for strongly psudoconvex manifolds of arbitrary dimensions. In dimension two such a formula for integral divisors was derived by Kato ([1]). In this short note, we shall extend this formula to three dimensions.

Let M be a complex manifold. A real valued $\mathcal{C}^\infty$ function ϕ defined on M is strongly plurisubharmonic if and only if the hermitian form

$$\sum_{\alpha,\beta} \frac{\partial^2 \phi}{\partial z^\alpha \partial \bar{z}^\beta} dz^\alpha d\bar{z}^\beta$$

is positive definite with respect to any system of local coordinates $(z^1,\ldots,z^n)$. M is then said to be strongly pseudoconvex if there is a $\mathcal{C}^\infty$ exhaustion function ϕ on M which is strongly plurisubharmonic outside a compact set K of M. It is well known that such manifolds are modification of a Stein space at a finite number of points. Let A denote the maximal compact analytic set in M. According to Laufer ([2]), the following sequence is exact:

$$o \to \Gamma(M, \mathcal{O}(F)) \to \Gamma_\infty(M, \mathcal{O}(F)) \to H^1_*(M, \mathcal{O}(F)) \to \ldots$$

where F is a line bundle on M, $H^1_*(M, \mathcal{O}(F))$ is the cohomogy with support at infinity. Since any section of F defined near the boundary has an analytic continuation to M-A (Siu [3],p.374),

Received 18 April, 1983

$\Gamma_\infty(M, \mathcal{O}(F))) \to \Gamma(M-A, \mathcal{O}(F))$ is an isomorphism; and thus $H^1_*(M, \mathcal{O}(F)) \approx H^1(M, \mathcal{O}(K-F))$ is finite dimensional. Because of the inequality.

$$\dim[\Gamma(M-A, \mathcal{O}(f))/\Gamma(M, \mathcal{O}(F))] \leq \dim H^1_*(M, \mathcal{O}(F)) = \dim H^1(M, \mathcal{O}(K-F)) < \infty,$$

it is permissible to define

$$\chi(M,F) = \dim \Gamma(M-A, \mathcal{O}(F))/\Gamma(M, \mathcal{O}(F)) - \sum_{q=1}^{n-1}(-1)^q \dim H^q(M, \mathcal{O}(F)).$$

Let $c_1(F)$, $c_1(D)$, $c_{i,M}$ denote respectively the chern classes of the line bundle F, the divisor D, and the manifold M, as curvature forms.

<u>Theorem</u> Let M^3 be a strongly pseudo convex manifold, with exceptional set A. F be a line bundle on M, and D an integral divisor on M then

$$\chi(M,F+[D]) - \chi(M,F) = -\int_D[\tfrac{1}{6}c_1^2(D) + \tfrac{1}{4}c_{1,M}c_1(D) + \tfrac{1}{12}(c_{1,M}^2 + c_{2,M})]$$
$$-\tfrac{1}{2}\int_D[c_1^2(F) + c_1(F)c_1(D) + c_{1,M}c_1(F)]$$

<u>Corollary 1</u>

$$\chi(M,[D]) = -\int_D[\tfrac{1}{6}c_1^2(D) + \tfrac{1}{4}c_{1,M}c_1(D) + \tfrac{1}{12}(c_{1,M}^2 + c_{2,M})] + (M, \mathcal{O}).$$

<u>Corollary 2</u> Suppose that the isolated singularities obtained by blowing down the exceptional set A are complete intersection, then

$$\mathcal{X}(M,[D]) = -\int_D[\frac{1}{6}c_1^2(D) + \frac{1}{4}c_{1,M}c_1(D) + \frac{1}{12}(c_{1,M}^2 + c_{2,M})]$$

$$-\frac{1}{24}\int_K c_{2,M}$$

where K is the canonical divisor of M.

Remark: Let $\pi : M \to V$ blows down A to $x \in V$, with V defined locally by equations $f_1,\ldots,f_m$ in C^{m+3}. Then K in corollary 2 is described by $\pi^*\omega$ where $\omega = dx_1 \wedge dx_2 \wedge dx_3/(\frac{\partial(f_1,\ldots,f_m)}{\partial(x_4,\ldots,x_{m+3})})$

Proof of theorem:

Let $D = \sum_{i=1} n_i X_i$, $n_i \in Z$, where we may without loss of generality assume that X_i's are smooth and have normal crossings. Let X be a compact complex non-singular surface in M. Consider the exact sequence:

$$o \to \mathcal{O}(F-[X]) \to \mathcal{O}(F) \to \mathcal{O}_X(F) \to o.$$

Passing to the long exact sequence, by a standard argument,

(1) $\mathcal{X}(M,F-[X]) - \mathcal{X}(M,F)$

$$= \dim \Gamma(M,\mathcal{O}_X(F)) - \dim H^1(M,\mathcal{O}_X(F)) + \dim H^2(M,\mathcal{O}_X(F))$$

$$= \frac{1}{2}\int_X[c_1^2(F) + c_1(F)c_{1,X}] + \frac{1}{12}\int_X[c_{1,X}^2 + c_{2,X}]$$

where we have applied the Hirzebruch-Riemann-Roch formula.

Let N_X be the normal bundle of X in M. We have the exact sequence:

$$0 \to T_X \to T_M|_X \to N_X \to 0$$

Hence $T_M|_X \simeq T_X \oplus N_X$ as $\mathcal{C}^\infty$-bundle and

(2) $$c(T_M|_X) = c(T_X) \cdot c(N_X)$$

where $c(E) = \sum_{i \geq 0} c_i(E)$ is the total chern class of the vector bundle E. Suppose X is given locally by the functions $f_\alpha \in \mathcal{O}(U_\alpha)$, then the line bundle [X] on M is described by transition functions $\{g_{\alpha\beta} = f_\alpha / f_\beta\}$.

$$df_\alpha = d(f_\beta g_{\alpha\beta})$$

$$= df_\beta g_{\alpha\beta} + f_\beta dg_{\alpha\beta}$$

(3) $$= df_\beta \cdot g_{\alpha\beta} \qquad \text{on } U_\alpha \cap U_\beta \cap X.$$

Since $f_\alpha \equiv 0$ on $X \cap U_\alpha$, the differential df_α is a section of the conormal bundle N_X^*. As X is smooth, df_α is nowhere zero; and (3) shows $\{df_\alpha\}$ is a non-zero global section of $N_X^* \oplus [X]$, therefore $N_X^* = [-X]|_X$ and

(4) $$c(T_M|_X) = c(T_X) \cdot c([X]|_X)$$

(1) and (4) gives

(5) $$\mathcal{X}(M,F-[X]) - \mathcal{X}(M,F) = \frac{1}{2}\int_X [c_1^2(F) + c_1(F)(c_{1,M}-c_1(X))$$

$$+\frac{1}{12}\int_X [(c_{1,M}-c_1(X))^2 + c_{2,M}-c_1(X)(c_{1,M}-c_1(X))].$$

Telescoping (5) and regrouping terms

(6) $\mathcal{X}(M,F-n[X]) - \mathcal{X}(M,F)$

$$= \frac{1}{2}\int_X (c_1^2(F) + c_1^2(F-[X]) + \ldots + c_1^2(F-(n-1)[X])]$$

$$+\frac{1}{2}\int_X [c_1(F) + c_1(F-[X]) + \ldots + c_1(F-(n-1)[X])]\cdot(c_{1,M}-c_1(X))$$

$$+\frac{n}{12}\int_X [(c_{1,M}-c_1(X))^2 + c_{2,M}-c_1(X)\cdot(c_{1,M}-c_1(X))]$$

$$= \frac{n}{2}\int_X c_1^2(F) - \frac{n(n-1)}{2}\int_X c_1(F)c_1(X) + \frac{1}{2}\,\frac{n(n-1)(2n-1)}{6}\int_X c_1^2(X)$$

$$-\frac{n}{2}\int_X c_1(F)c_1(X) - \frac{n(n-1)}{4}\int_X c_{1,M}c_1(X) + \frac{n}{2}\int_X c_1(F)c_{1,M}$$

$$+\frac{n(n-1)}{4}\int_X c_1^2(X) + \frac{n}{12}\int_X c_{1,M}^2 - \frac{n}{4}\int_X c_{1,M}c_1(X) + \frac{n}{6}\int_X c_1^2(X)$$

$$+\frac{n}{12}\int_X c_{2,M}$$

$$= \int_X \frac{n^2}{6}\, c_1^2(X) - \int_X \frac{n^2}{4}\, c_{1,M}c_1(X) - \int_X \frac{n^2}{2}\, c_1(F)c_1(X)$$

$$+ \int_X \frac{n}{2}\, c_1^2(F) + \int_X \frac{n}{2}\, c_{1,M}c_1(F) + \int_X \frac{n}{12}\,(c_{1,M}^2 + c_{2,M})$$

$$=-\int_{nX}[\frac{1}{6}\, c_1^2(-nX) + \frac{1}{4}\, c_{1,M}c_1(-nX) + \frac{1}{12}\,(c_{1,M}^2 + c_{2,M})]$$

$$-\int_{nX}[\frac{1}{2}\, c_1^2(F) + \frac{1}{2}\, c_1(F)c_1(-nX) + \frac{1}{2}\, c_{1,M}c_1(F)].$$

Replacing F by F + [nX] in (b), we obtain after regrouping,

$$\mathcal{X}(M,F) - \mathcal{X}(M,F+n[x]) = \int_{nX} \tfrac{1}{6}c_1^2(nX) - \int_{nX} \tfrac{1}{4} c_{1,M}c_1(nX) + \int_{nX} \tfrac{1}{12} (c_{1,M}^2 + c_{2,M}$$

$$+ \int_{nX}[\tfrac{1}{2} c_1^2(F) - \tfrac{1}{2} c_1(F) \cdot c_1(nX) + \tfrac{1}{2} c_{1,M}c_1(F)]$$

$$+ \int_{nX} c_1(F)c_1(nX) + \int_{nX} \tfrac{1}{2} c_{1,M}c_1(nX)$$

This implies that

(7) $$\mathcal{X}(M,F + n[X]) - \mathcal{X}(M,F) = - \int_{nX}[\tfrac{1}{6} c_1^2(nX) + \tfrac{1}{4} c_{1M} c_1(nX) + \tfrac{1}{12} (c_{1,M}^2+c_{2,M})] - \int_{nX}[\tfrac{1}{2} c_1^2(F) + \tfrac{1}{2} c_1(F) c_1(nX) + \tfrac{1}{2} c_{1,M} c_1(F)].$$

We prove the theorem by induction on r, where $D = \sum_{i=1}^{r} n_i X_i$.

For r = 1, the theorem reduces to the formula (7). Suppose it is true for r-1. Let $D' = \sum_{i=1}^{r-1} n_i X_i$. By (6) and (7) we find

(8) $$\mathcal{X}(M,F+[D]) - \mathcal{X}(M,F+[D']) = - \int_{n_rX_r} [\tfrac{1}{6} c_1^2(n_rX_r) + \tfrac{1}{4} c_{1,M} c_1(n_rX_r) + \tfrac{1}{12} (c_{1,M}^2 + c_{2,M})] - \int_{n_rX_r} [\tfrac{1}{2} c_1^2(F+[D']) + \tfrac{1}{2}c_1(F+[D'])c_1(n_rX_r) + \tfrac{1}{2} c_{1,M} c_1(F+[D'])]$$

Using the induction hypothesis:

(9) $\mathcal{X}(M,F+[D]) - \mathcal{X}(M,F)$

$$= - \int_{D'} [\tfrac{1}{6} c_1^2(D') + \tfrac{1}{4} c_{1,M} c_1(D') + \tfrac{1}{12} (c_{1,M}^2 + c_{2,M})]$$

$$- \tfrac{1}{2} \int_{D'} [c_1^2(F) + c_1(F)c_1(D') + c_{1,M} c_1(F)]$$

$$- \int_{n_r X_r} [\tfrac{1}{6} c_1^2(n_r X_r) + \tfrac{1}{4} c_{1,M} c_1(n_r X_r) + \tfrac{1}{12} (c_{1,M}^2 + c_{2,M})]$$

$$- \tfrac{1}{2} \int_{n_r X_r} [c_1^2(F+[D']) + c_1(F+[D'])c_1(n_r X_r) + c_{1,M} c_1(F+[D'])].$$

(10) $- \int_D [\tfrac{1}{6} c_1^2(D) + \tfrac{1}{4} c_{1,M} c_1(D) + \tfrac{1}{12} (c_{1,M}^2 + c_{2,M})]$

$$= - \int_{D'} [\tfrac{1}{6} c_1^2(D') + \tfrac{1}{3} c_1(D') c_1(n_r X_r) + \tfrac{1}{6} c_1^2(n_r X_r) + \tfrac{1}{4} c_{1,M} c_1(D')$$

$$+ \tfrac{1}{4} c_{1,M} c_1(n_r X_r) + \tfrac{1}{12} (c_{1,M}^2 + c_{2,M})]$$

$$- \int_{n_r X_r} [\tfrac{1}{6} c_1^2(D') + \tfrac{1}{3} c_1(D') c_1(n_r X_r) + \tfrac{1}{6} c_1^2(n_r X_r)$$

$$+ \tfrac{1}{4} c_{1,M} c_1(D') + \tfrac{1}{4} c_{1,M} c_1(n_r X_r) + \tfrac{1}{12} (c_{1,M}^2 + c_{2,M})]$$

$$= - \int_{D'} [\tfrac{1}{6} c_1^2(D') + \tfrac{1}{4} c_{1,M} c_1(D') + \tfrac{1}{12} (c_{1,M}^2 + c_{2,M})]$$

$$- \int_{n_r X_r} [\tfrac{1}{6} c_1^2(n_r X_r) + \tfrac{1}{4} c_{1,M} c_1(n_r X_r) + \tfrac{1}{12} (c_{1,M}^2 + c_{2,M})]$$

$$- \int_{D'} \tfrac{1}{3} c_1(D') c_1(n_r X_r) - \int_{D'} \tfrac{1}{4} c_{1,M} c_1(n_r X_r) - \int_{D'} \tfrac{1}{6} c_1^2(n_r X_r)$$

$$- \int_{n_r X_r} \tfrac{1}{3} c_1^2(D') - \int_{n_r X_r} \tfrac{1}{4} c_1(D') c_1(n_r X_r) - \int_{n_r X_r} \tfrac{1}{4} c_{1,M} c_1(D')$$

And expanding

(11) $\quad -\frac{1}{2} \int_D [c_1^2(F) + c_1(F)c_1(D) + c_{1,M}c_1(F)]$

$$= -\frac{1}{2} \int_{D'} [c_1^2(F) + c_1(F)c_1(D') + c_{1,M}c_1(F)] - \frac{1}{2} \int_{D'} c_1(F)c_1(n_r X_r)$$

$$-\frac{1}{2} \int_{n_r X_r} [c_1^2(F) + c_1(F)c_1(D') + c_1(F)c_1(n_r X_r) + c_{1,M}c_1(F)].$$

$$= -\frac{1}{2} \int_{D'} [c_1^2(F) + c_1(F)c_1(D') + c_{1,M}c_1(F)]$$

$$-\frac{1}{2} \int_{n_r X_r} [c_1^2(F+[D'] + c_1(F+[D'])c_1(n_r X_r) + c_{1,M}c_1(F+[D'])]$$

$$-\frac{1}{2} \int_{D'} c_1(F)c_1(n_r X_r) + \frac{1}{2} \int_{n_r X_r} c_1(F)c_1(D')$$

$$+\frac{1}{2} \int_{n_r X_r} [c_1^2(D') + c_1(D')c_1(n_r X_r) + c_{1,M}c_1(D')]$$

Lemma $\int_{X_i} c_1(F)c_1(X_j) = \int_{X_j} c_1(F)c_1(X_i).$

Proof Let $X_i \cdot X_j = \sum_k Y_k$ where Y_k are nonsingular curves. We claim that $\int_{X_i} c_1(F)c_1(X_j) = \sum_k \int_{Y_k} c_1(F|_{Y_k}).$

Recall that $\int_{X_i} c_1(F)c_1(X_j) = \int_{X_i} c_1(F|_{X_i})c_1([X_j]|_{X_i})$. If we denote the homology class in X_i which correspond by Poincare duality to $c_1(F|_{X_i})$ by $F|_{X_i}$; the homology class $F|_{X_i} \cdot Y_k$ in Y_k is the Poincare dual to $c_1(F|_{Y_k})$ in Y_k. On the other hand, it is well known that the homology class $X_i \cdot X_j$ is the Poincare dual to $c_1([X_j]|_{X_i})$ in X_i. Therefore

$$\int_{X_i} c_1(F)c_1(X_j) = \Sigma(F|_{X_i}) \cdot (X_j \cdot X_k)$$

$$= \Sigma(F|_{X_i}) \cdot Y_k$$

$$= \Sigma_k \int_{Y_k} c_1(F|_{Y_k})$$

Interchanging the role of i and j, we obtain

$$\int_{X_j} c_1(F)c_1(X_i) = \Sigma_k \int_{Y_k} c_1(F|_{Y_k}).$$ The lemma is proved.

We finish the proof of the theorem. According to the lemma, (10) and (11) become

$$(12) \qquad - \int_{D'}[\tfrac{1}{6} c_1^2(D') + \tfrac{1}{4} c_{1,M}c_1(D') + \tfrac{1}{12} (c_{1,M}^2 + c_{2,M})]$$

$$- \int_{n_rX_r}[\tfrac{1}{6} c_1^2(n_rX_r) + \tfrac{1}{4} c_{1,M}c_1(n_rX_r) + \tfrac{1}{12} (c_{2,M})]$$

$$= - \int_D[\tfrac{1}{6} c_1^2(D) + \tfrac{1}{4} c_{1,M}c_1(D) + \tfrac{1}{12} (c_{1,M}^2 + c_{2,M})]$$

$$+ \tfrac{1}{2} \int_{D'} [c_1(D')c_1(n_rX_r) + c_{1,M}c_1(n_rX_r) + c_1^2(n_rX_r)]$$

$$(13) \qquad - \tfrac{1}{2} \int_{D'} [c_1^2(F) + c_1(F)c_1(D') + c_{1,M}c_1(F)]$$

$$- \tfrac{1}{2} \int_{n_rX_r} [c_1^2(F+[D']) + c_1(F+[D'])c_{1,M}c_1(F+[D'])]$$

$$= - \tfrac{1}{2} \int_D[c_1^2(F) + c_1(F)c_1(D) + c_{1,M}c_1(F)]$$

$$- \frac{1}{2} \int_{n_r X_r} [c_1^2(D') + c_1(D')c_1(n_r X_r) + c_{1,M}c_1(D')].$$

put (12) (13) into (9), we obtain the statement of the theorem.

q.e.d.

REFERENCES

1. Kato, M., Riemann-Roch theorem for strongly pseudoconvex manifolds of dimensions 2., Math. Ann. 222, 243-250 (1976).

2. Laufer, H., On rational singularities. Amer. J. Math. 94, 597-608 (1972).

3. Siu, Y.-T., Absolute gap-sheaves and extensions of coherent analytic sheaves. Trans. Amer. Math. Soc. 141, 361-376 (1969).